The Essential
NOËL COWARD
COMPENDIUM

ALSO BY NOËL COWARD

The Essential
NOËL COWARD
COMPENDIUM

THE VERY BEST OF HIS WORK
LIFE AND TIMES

EDITED BY BARRY DAY

Methuen Drama

METHUEN DRAMA

1 3 5 7 9 10 8 6 4 2

Methuen Drama
A & C Black Publishers Limited
36 Soho Square, London W1D 3QY
www.methuendrama.com

ISBN: 978 1 408 10869 7

A CIP catalogue record for this book is available from the British Library

Typeset by Country Setting, Kingsdown, Kent CT14 8ES
Printed in Great Britain by CPI Cox and Wyman, Reading RG1 8EX

CONTENTS

PREFACE

'There are probably greater painters than Noël, greater novelists than Noël, greater librettists, greater composers of music, greater singers, greater dancers, greater comedians, greater tragedians, greater stage producers, greater film directors, greater cabaret artists, greater TV stars . . . If there are, they are fourteen different people. Only *one* man combined all fourteen different talents – The Master. Noël Coward.'

LORD LOUIS MOUNTBATTEN
at a party for Noël's seventieth birthday,
December 1969

INTRODUCTION

'There will always be a few people . . . in every generation
who will find my work entertaining and true.'

Diaries, 23 April 1951

When Noël Coward was 'rediscovered' in the early 1960s, he gleefully called
it 'Dad's Renaissance'. Now, forty years later, it can safely be reckoned 'Dad's
Restoration'.

He has never been better known or more respected. Revivals of his plays
are staged at an increasing rate all over the world and in languages which one
can hardly believe catch the subtlety of 'Very flat, Norfolk' or 'This haddock's
disgusting'. But presumably do.

When they know you are connected with Coward and his work, the most
unlikely people will declare a lifelong addiction and quote extended passages
from scene or song. They often do so in a very, *very* clipped tone – but one
can't have everything.

Even more interesting is the appearance of more and more young people
who have just seen or read something by The Master. 'What *else* did he write?'
'I thought he was old-fashioned but this man's talking to *me*.' And so the
wheel turns.

For the man who thought 'it would be nice to have a little niche in
posterity' but was genuinely afraid that he would be forgotten, it must be
pleasing to sit back in those Elysian Fields and wag a finger at Shaw,
Maugham and the rest.

The Essential Noël Coward Compendium is for those who know their Coward
but would like 'the best of Noël' in one handy volume. It's also for those
who *don't* know their Coward but would like to discover him without having
to pick their way through his formidable output. That will come later.

It is also an attempt – a personal one, admittedly – to show the range of
the man's work across so many of the artistic worlds Mountbatten mentions

him conquering – plays, song, verse, fiction, film. Although the book is divided into those general sections, I have not felt myself bound by them. If a song is part of the context of a play, or a piece of verse complements a lyric, that's where you will find it.

I have drawn from the plays, the lyrics, the verse, the diaries, the films, the fiction, the letters and the *bons mots*. I've also tried to provide some necessary context for the material and the occasional anecdote, usually in Noël's own words.

And that word 'Essential' needs a little redefinition. There remains a lot of Noël's work that you have never seen and probably never will. An unfinished or unproduced play, a fragment of verse or lyric. And yet they are often vintage Coward. A few of them are here.

It's been an interesting journey, made next to impossible by one man who never left my side and kept insisting – 'You haven't put in anything from . . .' '*Surely* you're going to . . . ?' Sometimes he made me so mad I couldn't look him in the eye for days. Except in the shaving mirror. And then we'd both smile.

BARRY DAY

2009

TO DANY

who now carries the torch

CHRONOLOGY

1899   16 December, Noël Peirce Coward born in Teddington, Middlesex, eldest surviving son of Arthur Coward, piano salesman and Violet (*née* Veitch). A 'brazen, odious little prodigy', his early circumstances were of refined suburban poverty.

1907   First public appearances in school and community concerts.

1908   Family moved to Battersea and took in lodgers.

1911   First professional appearance as Prince Mussel in *The Goldfish*, produced by Lila Field at the Little Theatre, and revived in same year at Crystal Palace and Royal Court Theatre. Cannard the page-boy in *The Great Name* at the Prince of Wales Theatre, and William in *Where the Rainbow Ends* with Charles Hawtrey's Company at the Savoy Theatre.

1912   Directed *The Daisy Chain* and stage-managed *The Prince's Bride* at Savoy in series of matinées featuring the work of the children of the *Rainbow* cast. Mushroom in *An Autumn Idyll*, ballet, Savoy.

1913   An angel (Gertrude Lawrence was another) in Basil Dean's production of *Hannele*. Slightly in *Peter Pan*, Duke of York's.

1914   Toured in *Peter Pan*. Collaborated with fellow performer Esmé Wynne on songs, sketches, and short stories – 'beastly little whimsies'.

1915   Admitted to sanatorium for tuberculosis.

1916   Five-month tour as Charley in *Charley's Aunt*. Walk-on in *The Best of Luck*, Drury Lane. Wrote first full-length song, 'Forbidden Fruit'. Basil Pycroft in *The Light Blues*, produced by Robert Courtneidge, with daughter Cicely also in cast, Shaftesbury. Short spell as dancer at Elysée Restaurant (subsequendy the Café de Paris). Jack Morrison in *The Happy Family*, Prince of Wales.

1917   'Boy pushing barrow' in D. W. Griffith's film *Hearts of the World*. Co-author with Esmé Wynne of one-acter *Ida Collaborates*, Theatre Royal, Aldershot. Ripley Guildford in *The Saving Grace*, with Charles

Hawtrey, 'who . . . taught me many points of comedy acting', Garrick. Family moved to Pimlico and reopened boarding house.

1918   Called up for army. Medical discharge after nine months. Wrote unpublished novels *Cats and Dogs* (loosely based on Shaw's *You Never Can Tell*) and the unfinished *Cherry Pan* ('dealing in a whimsical vein with the adventures of a daughter of Pan'), and lyrics for Darewski and Joel, including 'When You Come Home on Leave' and 'Peter Pan'. Also composed 'Tamarisk Town'. Sold short stories to magazines. Wrote plays *The Rat Trap*, *The Last Trick* (unproduced) and *The Impossible Wife* (unproduced). Courtenay Borner in *Scandal*, Strand. *Woman and Whiskey* (co-author Esmé Wynne) produced at Wimbledon Theatre.

1919   Ralph in *The Knight of the Burning Pestle*, Birmingham Repertory, played with 'a stubborn Mayfair distinction' demonstrating a 'total lack of understanding of the play'. Collaborated on *Crissa*, an opera, with Esmé Wynne and Max Darewski (unproduced). Wrote *I'll Leave It to You*.

1920   Bobbie Dermott in *I'll Leave It to You*, New Theatre. Wrote play *Barriers Down* (unproduced). *I'll Leave It to You* published, London.

1921   On holiday in Alassio, met Gladys Calthrop for the first time. Clay Collins in American farce *Polly with a Past*: during the run 'songs, sketches, and plays were bursting out of me'. Wrote *The Young Idea*, *Sirocco* and *The Better Half*. First visit to New York, and sold parts of *A Withered Nosegay* to *Vanity Fair* and short-story adaptation of *I'll Leave It to You* to *Metropolitan*. House guest of Laurette Taylor and Hartley Manners, whose family rows inspired the Bliss household in *Hay Fever*.

1922   *Bottles and Bones* (sketch) produced in benefit for Newspaper Press Fund, Drury Lane. *The Better Half* produced in 'grand guignol' season, Little Theatre. Started work on songs and sketches for *London Calling!* Adapted Louis Verneuil's *Pour avoir Adrienne* (unproduced). Wrote *The Queen Was in the Parlour* and *Mild Oats*.

1923   Sholto Brent in *The Young Idea*, Savoy. Juvenile lead in *London Calling!* Wrote *Weatherwise*, *Fallen Angels* and *The Vortex*.

1924   Wrote *Hay Fever* (which Marie Tempest at first refused to do, feeling it was 'too light and plotless and generally lacking in action') and *Easy Virtue*. Nicky Lancaster in *The Vortex*, produced at Everyman by Norman MacDermot.

1925 Established as a social and theatrical celebrity. Wrote *On with the Dance* with London opening in spring followed by *Fallen Angels* and *Hay Fever*. *Hay Fever* and *Easy Virtue* produced, New York. Wrote silent screen titles for Gainsborough Films.

1926 Toured USA in *The Vortex*. Wrote *This Was a Man*, refused a licence by Lord Chamberlain but produced in New York (1926), Berlin (1927) and Paris (1928). *Easy Virtue*, *The Queen Was in the Parlour* and *The Rat Trap* produced, London. Played Lewis Dodd in *The Constant Nymph*, directed by Basil Dean. Wrote *Semi-Monde* and *The Marquise*. Bought Goldenhurst Farm, Kent, as country home. Sailed for Hong Kong on holiday but trip broken in Honolulu by nervous breakdown.

1927 *The Marquise* opened in London while Coward was still in Hawaii, and *The Marquise* and *Fallen Angels* produced, New York. Finished writing *Home Chat*. *Sirocco* revised after discussions with Basil Dean and produced, London.

1928 Clark Storey in Behrman's *The Second Man*, directed by Dean. Gainsborough Films productions of *The Queen Was in the Parlour*, *The Vortex* (starring Ivor Novello) and *Easy Virtue* (directed by Alfred Hitchcock) released – but only the latter, freely adapted, a success. *This Year of Grace!* produced, London, and with Coward directing and in cast, New York. Made first recording, featuring numbers from this show. Wrote *Concerto* for Gainsborough Films, intended for Ivor Novello, but never produced. Started writing *Bitter-Sweet*.

1929 Played in *This Year of Grace!* (USA) until spring. Directed *Bitter-Sweet*, London and New York. Set off on travelling holiday in Far East.

1930 On travels wrote *Private Lives* (1929) and song 'Mad Dogs and Englishmen', the latter on the road from Hanoi to Saigon. In Singapore joined the Quaints, company of strolling English players, as Stanhope for three performances of *Journey's End*. On voyage home wrote *Post-Mortem*, which was 'similar to my performance as Stanhope: confused, under-rehearsed and hysterical'. Directed and played Elyot Chase in *Private Lives*, London, and Fred in *Some Other Private Lives*. Started writing *Cavalcade* and unfinished novel *Julian Kane*.

1931 Elyot Chase in New York production of *Private Lives*. Directed *Cavalcade*, London. Film of *Private Lives* produced by MGM. Set off on trip to South America.

1932   On travels wrote *Design for Living* (hearing that Alfred Lunt and Lynn Fontanne finally free to work with him) and material for new revue including songs 'Mad about the Boy', 'Children of the Ritz' and 'The Party's Over Now'. Produced in London as *Words and Music*, with book, music and lyrics exclusively by Coward and directed by him. The short-lived Noël Coward Company, independent company which enjoyed his support, toured UK with *Private Lives*, *Hay Fever*, *Fallen Angels* and *The Vortex*.

1933   Directed *Design for Living*, New York, and played Leo. Films of *Cavalcade*, *To-Night Is Ours* (remake of *The Queen Was in the Parlour*), and *Bitter-Sweet* released. Directed London revival of *Hay Fever*. Wrote *Conversation Piece* as vehicle for Yvonne Printemps, and hit song 'Mrs Worthington'.

1934   Directed *Conversation Piece* in London and played Paul. Cut links with C.B. Cochran and formed own management in partnership with John C. Wilson and the Lunts. Appointed President of the Actors' Orphanage, in which he invested great personal commitment until resignation in 1956. Directed Kaufman and Ferber's *Theatre Royal*, Lyric, and Behrman's *Biography*, Globe. Film of *Design for Living* released, London. *Conversation Piece* opened, New York. Started writing autobiography, *Present Indicative*. Wrote *Point Valaine*.

1935   Directed *Point Valaine*, New York. Played lead in film *The Scoundrel* (Astoria Studios, New York). Wrote *Tonight at 8:30*.

1936   Directed and played in *Tonight at 8:30*, London and New York. Directed *Mademoiselle* by Jacques Deval, Wyndham's.

1937   Played in *Tonight at 8:30*, New York, until second breakdown in health in March. Directed (and subsequendy disowned) Gerald Savory's *George and Margaret*, New York. Wrote *Operette*, with hit song 'The Stately Homes of England'. *Present Indicative* published, London and New York.

1938   Directed *Operette*, London. *Words and Music* revised for American production as *Set to Music*. Appointed adviser to newly formed Royal Naval Film Corporation.

1939   Directed New York production of *Set to Music*. Visited Soviet Union and Scandinavia. Wrote *Present Laughter* and *This Happy Breed*: rehearsals stopped by declaration of war. Wrote for revue *All Clear*, London. Appointed to head Bureau of Propaganda in Paris, to liaise with French Ministry of Information, headed by Jean Giraudoux and André Maurois. This posting prompted speculative attacks in the press, prevented by wartime secrecy from getting a clear statement of the exact nature of his work. Troop concert in Arras with Maurice Chevalier. *To Step Aside* (short story collection) published.

1940 Increasingly 'oppressed and irritated by the Paris routine'. Visits USA to report on American isolationism and attitudes to war in Europe. Return to Paris prevented by German invasion. Returned to USA to do propaganda work for Ministry of Information. Propaganda tour of Australia and New Zealand, and fund-raising for war charities. Wrote play *Time Remembered* (unproduced).

1941 Mounting press attacks in England because of time spent allegedly avoiding danger and discomfort of Home Front. Wrote *Blithe Spirit*, produced in London (with Coward directing) and New York. MGM film of *Bitter-Sweet* (which Coward found 'vulgar' and 'lacking in taste') released, London. Wrote screenplay for *In Which We Serve*, based on the sinking of HMS *Kelly*. Wrote songs including 'London Pride', 'Could You Please Oblige Us with a Bren Gun?', and 'Imagine the Duchess's Feelings'.

1942 Produced and co-directed (with David Lean) *In Which We Serve*, and appeared as Captain Kinross (Coward considered the film 'an accurate and sincere tribute to the Royal Navy'). Played in countrywide tour of *Blithe Spirit*, *Present Laughter* and *This Happy Breed*, and gave hospital and factory concerts. MGM film of *We Were Dancing* released.

1943 Played Garry Essendine in London production of *Present Laughter* and Frank Gibbons in *This Happy Breed*. Produced *This Happy Breed* for Two Cities Films. Wrote 'Don't Let's Be Beastly to the Germans', first sung on BBC Radio (then banned on grounds of lines 'that Goebbels might twist'). Four-month tour of Middle East to entertain troops.

1944 February–September, toured South Africa, Burma, India and Ceylon. Troop concerts in France and 'Stage Door Canteen Concert' in London. Screenplay of *Still Life*, as *Brief Encounter*. *Middle East Diary*, an account of his 1943 tour, published, London and New York – where a reference to 'mournful little boys from Brooklyn' inspired formation of a lobby for the 'Prevention of Noël Coward Re-entering America'.

1945 *Sigh No More*, with hit song 'Matelot', completed and produced, London. Started work on *Pacific 1860*. Film of *Brief Encounter* released.

1946 Started writing *'Peace in Our Time'*. Directed *Pacific 1860*, London.

1947 Garry Essendine in London revival of *Present Laughter*. Supervised production of *'Peace in Our Time'*. *Point Valaine* produced, London.

Directed American revival of *Tonight at 8:30*. Wrote *Long Island Sound*.

1948 Replaced Graham Payn briefly in American tour of *Tonight at 8:30*, his last stage appearance with Gertrude Lawrence. Wrote screenplay for Gainsborough film of *The Astonished Heart*. Max Aramont in *Joyeux Chagrins* (French production of *Present Laughter*). Built house at Blue Harbour, Jamaica.

1949 Christian Faber in film of *The Astonished Heart*, Wrote *Ace of Clubs* and *Home and Colonial* (produced as *Island Fling* in USA and *South Sea Bubble* in UK).

1950 Directed *Ace of Clubs*, London. Wrote *Star Quality* (short stories) and *Relative Values*.

1951 Deaths of Ivor Novello and C.B. Cochran. Paintings included in charity exhibition in London. Wrote *Quadrille*. One-night concert at Theatre Royal, Brighton, followed by season at Café de Paris, London, and beginning of new career as leading cabaret entertainer. Directed *Relative Values*, London, which restored his reputation as a playwright after run of post-war flops. *Island Fling* produced, USA.

1952 Charity cabaret with Mary Martin at Café de Paris for Actors' Orphanage. June cabaret season at Café de Paris. Directed *Quadrille*, London. 'Red Peppers', *Fumed Oak* and *Ways and Means* (from *Tonight at 8:30*) filmed as *Meet Me Tonight*. September, death of Gertrude Lawrence: 'no one I have ever known, however brilliant . . . has contributed quite what she contributed to my work.'

1953 Completed second volume of autobiography, *Future Indefinite*. King Magnus in Shaw's *The Apple Cart*. Cabaret at Café de Paris, again 'a triumphant success'. Wrote *After the Ball*.

1954 *After the Ball* produced, UK. July, mother died. September, cabaret season at Café de Paris. November, Royal Command Performance, London Palladium. Wrote *Nude With Violin*.

1955 June, opened in cabaret for season at Desert Inn, Las Vegas, and enjoyed 'one of the most sensational successes of my career'. Played Hesketh-Baggott in film of *Around the World in Eighty Days*, for which he wrote own dialogue. October, directed and appeared with Mary Martin in TV spectacular *Together with Music* for CBS, New York. Revised *South Sea Bubble*.

1956 Charles Condomine in television production of *Blithe Spirit*, for CBS, Hollywood. For tax reasons took up Bermuda residency. Resigned from presidency of the Actors' Orphanage. *South Sea*

Bubble produced, London. Directed and played part of Frank Gibbons in television production of *This Happy Breed* for CBS, New York. Co-directed *Nude With Violin* with John Gielgud (Eire and UK), opening to press attacks on Coward's decision to live abroad. Wrote play *Volcano* (unproduced).

1957   Directed and played Sebastien in *Nude With Violin*, New York. *Nude With Violin* published, London.

1958   Played Gary Essendine in *Present Laughter* alternating with *Nude With Violin* on US West Coast tour. Wrote ballet *London Morning* for London Festival Ballet. Wrote *Look After Lulu!*

1959   *Look After Lulu!* produced, New York, and by English Stage Company at Royal Court, London. Film roles of Hawthorne in *Our Man in Havana* and ex-King of Anatolia in *Surprise Package*. *London Morning* produced by London Festival Ballet. Sold home in Bermuda and took up Swiss residency. Wrote *Waiting in the Wings*.

1960   *Waiting in the Wings* produced, Eire and UK. *Pomp and Circumstance* (novel) published, London and New York.

1961   Directed American production of *Sail Away*. *Waiting in the Wings* published, New York.

1962   Wrote music and lyrics for *The Girl Who Came to Supper* (adaptation of Rattigan's *The Sleeping Prince*, previously filmed as *The Prince and the Showgirl*). *Sail Away* produced, UK.

1963   *The Girl Who Came to Supper* produced, USA. Revival of *Private Lives* at Hampstead signals renewal of interest in his work.

1964   Directed New York production of *High Spirits*, musical adaptation of *Blithe Spirit*, and later 'supervised' London production at Savoy. Introduced Granada TV's 'A Choice of Coward' series, which included *Present Laughter*, *Blithe Spirit*, *The Vortex* and *Design for Living*. Directed *Hay Fever* for National Theatre, first living playwright to direct his own work there. *Pretty Polly Barlow* (short story collection) published.

1965   Played the landlord in film, *Bunny Lake is Missing*. Wrote *Suite in Three Keys*. Badly weakened by attack of amoebic dysentery contracted in Seychelles.

1966   Played in *Suite in Three Keys*, London, which taxed his health further. Started adapting his short story *Star Quality* for the stage.

1967   Caesar in TV musical version of *Androcles and the Lion* (score by Richard Rodgers), New York. Witch of Capri in film *Boom*, adaptation of Tennessee Williams's play *The Milk Train Doesn't Stop*

Here Any More. Lorn Loraine, Coward's manager, and friend for many years, died, London. Worked on new volume of autobiography, *Past Conditional*. *Bon Voyage* (short story collection) published.

1968   Played Mr Bridger, the criminal mastermind, in *The Italian Job.*

1970   Awarded knighthood in New Year's Honours List.

1971   Tony Award, USA, for Distinguished Achievement in the Theatre.

1973   26 March, died peacefully at his home in Firefly, Jamaica. Buried on Firefly Hill.

The Man They Called
'THE MASTER'

Coward . . . on Coward

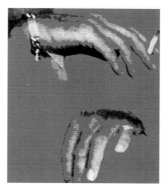

'He had long, delicate hands
of which he was very proud.'

Joan Hirst, his last secretary

PERSONAL REMINISCENCE

I cannot remember
I cannot remember
The house where I was born
But I know it was in Waldegrave Road
Teddington, Middlesex
Not far from the border of Surrey
An unpretentious abode
Which, I believe,
Economy forced us to leave
In rather a hurry.
But I *can* remember my grandmother's Indian shawl
Which, although exotic to behold,
Felt cold.
Then there was a framed photograph in the hall
Of my father wearing a Norfolk jacket,
Holding a bicycle and a tennis racquet
And leaning against a wall
Looking tenacious and distinctly grim
As though he feared they'd be whisked away from him.
I can also remember with repulsive clarity
Appearing at a concert in aid of charity
At which I sang, not the 'Green Hill Far Away' that you know
But the one by Gounod.
I remember a paper-weight made of quartz.
And a sombre Gustave Doré engraving
Illustrating the 'Book of Revelations'
Which, I am told, upset my vibrations.
I remember, too, a most peculiar craving
For 'Liquorice All-Sorts'.
Then there was a song, 'Oh that we two were Maying'
And my uncle, who later took to the bottle, playing
And playing very well
An organ called the 'Mustel'
I remember the smell of rotting leaves
In the Autumn quietness of suburban roads
And seeing the Winter river – flooding

And swirling over the tow-path by the lock.
I remember my cousin Doris in a party frock
With 'broderie anglaise' at the neck and sleeves
And being allowed to stir the Christmas pudding
On long ago, enchanted Christmas Eves.
All this took place in Teddington, Middlesex
Not far from the Surrey border
But none of these little episodes
None of the things I call to mind
None of the memories I find
Are in chronological order
Is in chronological order.

I was truculent apparently about being born and made, with my usual theatrical acumen, a delayed entrance.

Diaries, 1954

★

Oh, how fortunate I was to be born poor. If mother had been able to afford to send me to private school, Eton and Oxford or Cambridge, it would probably have set me back years.

Diaries, 1967

★

I have always distrusted too much education and intellectualism; it seems to me that they are always dead wrong about things that really matter.

Diaries, 1967

★

My good fortune was to have a bright, acquisitive, but not, *not* an intellectual mind, and to have been impelled by circumstances to get out and earn my living.'

Diaries, 1969

And so he became . . .

THE BOY ACTOR

I can remember. I can remember.
The months of November and December
    Were filled for me with peculiar joys
So different from those of other boys
    For other boys would be counting the days
Until end of term and holiday times
    But I was acting in Christmas plays
While they were taken to pantomimes.
    I didn't envy their Eton suits,
Their children's dances and Christmas trees.
    My life had wonderful substitutes
For such conventional treats as these.
    I didn't envy their country larks,
Their organized games in panelled halls:
    While they made snowmen in stately parks
I was counting the curtain calls.

    I remember the auditions, the nerve-racking auditions:
    Darkened auditorium and empty, dusty stage,
    Little girls in ballet dresses practising 'positions'
    Gentlemen with pince-nez asking you your age.
    Hopefulness and nervousness struggling within you,
    Dreading that familiar phrase, 'Thank you dear, no more.'
    Straining every muscle, every tendon, every sinew
    To do your dance much better than you'd ever done before.
    Think of your performance. Never mind the others,
    Never mind the pianist, talent must prevail.
    Never mind the baleful eyes of other children's mothers
    Glaring from the corners and willing you to fail.

I can remember. I can remember.
The months of November and December
    Were more significant to me
Than other months could ever be
    For they were the months of high romance

When destiny waited on tip-toe,
    When every boy actor stood a chance
Of getting into a Christmas show,
    Not for me the dubious heaven
Of being some prefect's protégé!
    Not for me the Second Eleven.
For me, two performances a day.

    Ah those first rehearsals! Only very few lines:
    Rushing home to mother, learning them by heart,
    'Enter Left through window' – Dots to mark the cue lines:
    'Exit with the others' – Still it *was* a part.
    Opening performance; legs a bit unsteady,
    Dedicated tension, shivers down my spine,
    Powder, grease and eye-black, sticks of make-up ready
    Leichner number three and number five and number nine.
    World of strange enchantment, magic for a small boy
    Dreaming of the future, reaching for the crown,
    Rigid in the dressing room, listening for the call-boy
    'Overture Beginners – Everybody Down!'

I can remember. I can remember.
The months of November and December,
    Although climatically cold and damp,
Meant more to me than Aladdin's lamp;
    I see myself, having got a job,
Walking on wings along the Strand,
    Uncertain whether to laugh or sob
And clutching tightly my mother's hand,
    I never cared who scored the goal
Or which side won the silver cup,
    I never learned to bat or bowl
But I heard the curtain going up.

★

'I was, I believe, one of the worst boy actors ever inflicted on a paying public.

'I was a brazen, odious little prodigy, over-pleased with myself and precocious to a degree.

'I am certain that, could my adult self have been present . . . he would have crept out, at the first coy gurgle, and been mercifully sick outside.'

Present Indicative, 1937

After a 'nervous breakdown' in the early 1920s his doctor advised Noël to sit down and conduct an honest self-analysis of his strengths and weaknesses. He did so and called it a 'Mental Purge' . . .

DEFECTS	ASSETS
Over-emotional and hysterical	An excellent knowledge of psychology when unaffected by emotion
Over-anxiety to attain popularity	
Jealousy fostered by over introspection	Strong sense of humour
Intolerance	Facility in conversation
Lack of restraint – particularly emotionally	Power of demanding and holding affection
Self-pitying	Loyalty to friends and personal standards
Predatory	
Sentimental	Generosity and kindness of heart
Almost complete ignorance upon many subjects that I should know thoroughly, and a facility for faking knowledge	Power of concentration
	Several talents
	Moral courage
Physical cowardice	Strength of will when unaffected by emotion
Histrionic in private life	
Given to mental gymnastics at cost of other people's peace of mind	Common sense
	Personality
Domineering	
Over-emphatic in argument and practically everything	

With 1913 came a booking to appear in Manchester and Liverpool in a turgid German drama in which he was an angel. On the train he met a fellow child actor,

'to whom I took an instant fancy. She wore a black satin coat and a black velvet military hat with a peak. Her face was far from pretty, but tremendously alive. She was very *mondaine*, carried a handbag with a powder-puff and frequently dabbed her generously turned-up nose. She confided to me that her name was Gertrude Lawrence, but that I was to call her Gert because everybody else did, that she was fourteen . . . She then gave me an orange and told me a few mildly dirty stories, and I loved her from then onwards.'

From there he graduated to regular appearances in two pieces that became integral to the Christmas theatrical season – Where the Rainbow Ends *and* Peter Pan. *In the latter he specialized in the part of Slightly, one of the Lost Boys, causing the critic Kenneth Tynan to say of the mature Noël: 'Forty years ago he was Slightly in* Peter Pan *and you might say that he has been wholly in* Peter Pan *ever since.'*

And somewhere beyond that rainbow he knew that there was a New World to be conquered . . .

★

Of all the things that delighted him on the first poverty-stricken visit to New York in the summer of 1921 the most delightful was his instant and lasting friendship with Alfred Lunt and Lynn Fontanne, two other actors beginning to make their name on Broadway and living in close proximity in a West Side boarding house.

'We projected ourselves into future eminence. We discussed, the three of us, over delicatessen potato salad and dill pickles, our most secret dreams of success. Lynn and Alfred were to be married. That was the first plan. They were to become definitely idols of the public. That was the second plan. Then, all of this being successfully accomplished, they were to act exclusively together. This was the third plan. It remained for me to supply the fourth, which was that when all three of us had become stars of sufficient magnitude to be able to count upon an individual following of each other, then, poised serenely upon that enviable plane of achievement, we would meet and act triumphantly together.'

Which, of course, is precisely what they did in the 1933 Design for Living, *which Noël wrote specifically for the three of them.*

★

Broadway in the early 1920s was a revelation . . .

'The theatre here is something to wonder at . . . The *speed*! Everybody seems to say their lines at such a rate you'd think you wouldn't understand a word – but you do! And then it suddenly struck me – that's the way people actually *talk*. Wait till I get back to Shaftesbury Avenue!!'

'I remembered the beauty of New York at night, viewed not from a smart penthouse on Park Avenue, but from a crowded seat in Washington Square. And it seemed, in spite of its hardness and irritating, noisy efficiency, a great and exciting place.'

★

After several plays, which attracted little attention – other than the fact that they were written by a young man in his early twenties – Noël seized public attention in 1924 with The Vortex *in which he also starred. Or, rather, public attention seized him . . .*

'Success took me to her bosom like a maternal boa constrictor.

'No Press interviewer, photographer, or gossip-writer had to fight in order to see me. I was wide open to them all, smiling and burbling bright witticisms, giving my views on this and that, discussing such problems as whether or not the modern girl would make a good mother. I was photographed in every conceivable position.

'I was unwise enough to be photographed in bed wearing a Chinese dressing gown and an expression of advanced degeneracy. This last was accidental and was caused by blinking at the flashlight, but it emblazoned my unquestionable decadence firmly in the minds of all who saw it. It even brought forth a letter of indignant protest from a retired Brigadier-General in Gloucestershire.'

Noël grew confident enough to tease his questioners . . .

'I really have a frightfully depraved mind. I am never out of opium dens, cocaine dens and other evil places. My mind is a mass of corruption.'

★

'The legend of my modesty grew. I became extraordinarily unspoiled by my great success. As a matter of fact, I still am.'

'I was in an enviable position. Everyone except Somerset Maugham said I was the second Somerset Maugham, with the exception of a few who preferred to describe me as a second Sacha Guitry.'

Noël took The Vortex *to Broadway, where it enjoyed even greater success. On the short US tour that followed, it was in Chicago where reality hit.*

'They seemed unappreciative of the comedy in the first act, but we struggled manfully across the damp patches where the laughs should have been, deciding in our minds that they were a dramatic audience rather than a comedy one.'

But by the end of the second act Chicagoans had decided they had got the hang of the thing and started to unleash their belly laughs.

'The last act was worse than I could ever have imagined it to be. The sight of me in pyjamas and dressing gown started them off happily, and from then onwards they laughed without ceasing . . . The curtain fell to considerable applause and I even had to make a speech, which, remembering that I was English, was a model of grateful restraint.'

'Before leaving . . . I wrote on the wall of my dressing room in indelible pencil, "Noël Coward died here", and when I visited Clifton Webb in the same room years later, I was delighted to see that the inscription was still there.'

★

But then a pattern began to emerge that was to be repeated several times in his career – a roller-coaster ride from success to failure and back again.

'I opened my arms a little too wide to everything that came, and enjoyed it. Later on, just a little while later – three years, to be exact – circumstances showed me that my acceptance had been a thought too credulous. The "darling" of the London Theatre received what can only be described as a sharp kick in the pants.'

When asked in later years what was his single biggest regret, his answer –

'Not having taken more trouble with some of my work.'

★

'Seated one day at the organ,
I was weary and ill at ease
And my fingers wandered idly
Over the noisy keys.'

Adelaide Ann Procter
'A Lost Chord' (1858)

*In 1928 the pendulum began to swing
back decisively in Noël's favour. His revue
for impresario Charles Cochran,* This
Year of Grace!, *was rapturously received
by the same critics who had written him
off a year earlier and the idea for what
was to be his most successful musical came
to him.*

*At the end of a weekend visit to mutual
friends with his designer, Gladys Calthrop,
they were listening to an orchestral
recording of* Die Fledermaus . . .

'Immediately a confused picture
of uniforms, bustles, chandeliers
and gas-lit cafés formed in my
mind and later, when we were
driving over Wimbledon
Common, we drew the car
to a standstill by the roadside,
and in the shade of a giant
horse-chestnut tree mapped
out roughly the story of
Sari Linden.'

*Bitter-Sweet was produced
the following year in both
London and New York —
and was a triumphant
success in both.*

He now took off on a lengthy trip to the Far East, a trip that yielded far more than the exotic sights along the way.

Private Lives *was conceived in the Imperial Hotel, Tokyo, and delivered in the Cathay Hotel, Shanghai. While on a long car ride in what was then French Indo-China he composed the complex lyric of 'Mad Dogs and Englishmen' and managed to remember every word until he had pen and paper to hand.*

Later he would reflect on his lifelong passion for travelling . . .

'My body has certainly wandered a good deal, but I have an uneasy suspicion that my mind has not wandered nearly enough. It is a well-trained mind, disciplined to observe, record and store up impressions without any particular wear and tear or exhaustive effort. It is capable of functioning quickly, and making rapid and usually intelligent decisions. It is at its best when dealing with people and at its worst when dealing with the inanimate.'

★

By 1930, another Coward annus mirabilis, again he seemed able to do no wrong. Private Lives *was an enormous hit, with Coward playing Elyot to Gertrude Lawrence's Amanda. As he later came to realize, the parts 'are practically synonymous' and Noël and Gertie were 'Noël&Gertie' from then on.*

That same year he felt the urge to write a big spectacular show and – just as Private Lives *had appeared to him in Tokyo – there was another epiphany waiting in the wings . . .*

'One day I happened to buy at Foyle's in the Charing Cross Road, some ancient bound volumes of *Black and White* and the *Illustrated London News*. This was chance, and extremely happy chance. In the first volume I opened there was a full-page picture of a troopship leaving for the Boer War, and the moment I saw it I knew that I had found what I wanted. I can't explain why it rang the bell so sharply, I only know that it did. The tunes came into my mind first, tunes belonging to my very earliest childhood . . .

'The emotional basis of *Cavalcade* (the show's eventual title) was undoubtedly music. The whole story was threaded on to a string of popular melodies . . . Popular tunes probe the memory more swiftly than anything else, and *Cavalcade*, whatever else it did, certainly awakened many echoes.'

For many people it remained his signature work. At one of those cocktail parties at which a guest has to balance plate and teacup a waiter hurried up to Noël with a fork. The lady standing next to him, who had not been similarly indulged, asked him, 'How come you get a fork?' 'Well,' Noël replied, 'I did write Cavalcade, *you know.'*

'I travel alone . . . '

★

The 1930s rushed by for him. Words and Music (*1932*) *another successful revue, was followed by* Design for Living (*1933*) *with the Lunts ('in which we all three gave the worst performances of our careers every night for months and managed to be very good indeed') and* Conversation Piece (*1934*). *'I am now giving an exquisite performance as a syphilitic French duke,' he wrote to Alexander Woollcott.*

The high point came in 1936 with Tonight at 8:30 *— a sequence of nine one-act plays with Noël&Gertie taking the leading parts in all of them. To Woollcott again:*

'They are all brilliantly written, exquisitely directed and I am bewitching in all of them.'

★

That same year brought a piece of theatre even Noël could not have dreamed up —
a letter from GRETA GARBO, *no less, proposing marriage.*

'And it's Tuesday.

Dear Little Coward,

Received your very loved, small and tiny letter. Dear person, it almost makes
me wish the newspapers in this country was right. I am so dreadfully fond
of you, that I wish I could forget you. Can't think of anything more terrific
than to fall in love with you. Eternally occupied as you are and in need of
absolutely no one and looking forward to splendid loneliness completely
immune to any female charm!!! Well, this might be an English lesson.
Anyhow, I take the opportunity to ask if you will be my little bride (it's
Leap Year, you know). Don't accept, please, I would have to come and get
you right away. How you must dislike my writing this way — but — that
fluttering, tired and sad heart of mine has been in such a peculiar state
since a few weeks ago, but I don't suppose I know you well enough to go
into that too much.

I have a very humbling wish that you would write a story for me (us),
if you ever have time from the theatre. I can't beg you any harder, as you
will do as fits you anyhow — naturally. Besides that I would like, horribly
I think, to go on dusty roads with you and tell you little fairy tales —
beautiful ones about solitary figures living in white castles on top of
moonlit mountains (permanent moonlight). And as finish I must tell you
that what I really would like to tell you I haven't told — Darling, you are
so flippantly serious.'

Noël claimed he was tempted to accept — but he just knew Garbo would demand
top billing!

★

As the 1930s were ending, a new and sombre drama was taking shape. Noël had no
hand in writing it but he was to play a part in acting it out.

In 1938 he was recruited by Sir Robert Vansittart at the Foreign Office to join an
unofficial team of businessmen and other prominent men whose daily business took
them to Europe. Clearly, World War II was imminent — at least in the minds of
those who took the trouble to see — and the Vansittart faction needed 'intelligence'
to make the case for Britain to rearm. Noël and the others were asked to report back
on the attitude they found in the places they visited.

NOEL COWARD   **MAKES HIS OWN**   **CONTRIBUTION**

TO THE PROBLEM   **OF HOW TO**   **TREAT GERMAN**

Noël performs his satirical wartime song, 'Don't Let's Be Beastly to the Germans'.
The BBC banned it as treasonable but Churchill personally resurrected it.

'We have nothing to worry about but the destruction of civilization,' he wrote to
Woollcott, as he went off to be 'Noël Coward, singing my little songs and being
a bit of a silly ass'. Innocent as he may have thought he appeared, he managed to
wind up on the Nazi blacklist that came to light after the war. Rebecca West, who
was also on the list, cabled him: 'MY DEAR THE PEOPLE WE SHOULD HAVE
BEEN SEEN DEAD WITH.'

When war was finally declared, Noël was sent to Paris to set up a Bureau of Information or propaganda and then to America to gauge opinion. As someone working for the British Government in what was still a neutral country, he was technically now a spy. He was recruited by William ('Little Bill') Stephenson – 'A Man Called Intrepid' – the US-based intelligence link between Roosevelt and Churchill, to be one of 'Little Bill's boys', a group that included Leslie Howard, David Niven, Alexander Korda, Cary Grant and Ian Fleming.

'He saw where my celebrity value would be useful and he seemed to think I ought to be as flamboyant as possible, which was very smart of him. My disguise would be my own reputation as a bit of an idiot . . . a merry playboy. It was very disarming. Very clever of him . . .

'In talking to people I ridiculed the whole business of intelligence, because that's the best way to get on with it – ridicule and belittle ourselves, and say what an awful lot of duffers we are, can't get the facts straight and all that sort of thing. I was awfully bewildered. I thought it would be more Mata Hari – and then I told myself, "Well, hardly that. I couldn't wear a jewel in my navel, which I believe she was given to doing . . . " I was never much good as a spy, really . . . So many career intelligence officers went around looking terribly mysterious – long black boots and sinister smiles. Nobody ever issued me with a false beard. In fact, the hush–hush side of it was frankly disappointing. I never had to do any disguises.

'Except occasionally I had to look rather idiotic – but that wasn't all that difficult. I'm a *splendid* actor.'

★

The rest of Noël's War was a mixed bag. Tours – goodwill, government-backed tours to Australia, New Zealand and South Africa – earned him vilification in the British press for apparently avoiding the war at home. And he toured, too, to the Middle East, the Far East and every remote part of the British Isles to entertain the fighting forces.

Along the way he managed to write Blithe Spirit *and tour two plays –* This Happy Breed *and* Present Laughter. *These had been in rehearsal when the war began but had to be abandoned when London theatres were temporarily closed.*

And then in 1942 there was the film In Which We Serve, *inspired by the story of his friend Mountbatten. It was opposed by countless Whitehall mandarins before the decisive support of King George VI tipped the scales, and was the wartime achievement of which Noël was proudest.*

Noël as 'Captain D' in *In Which We Serve* (1942).

Tributes poured in from all sides but few can have pleased him more than this from his crusty colleague, Aleck Woollcott:

'My dear Noël, this job you have done seems to me a really perfect thing. There was no moment of it from which I drew back or dissented. I went away marvelling at its sure-footedness and realizing that all the ups and downs of your life (in particular the downs) had taught you to be unerring for your great occasion. All your years were a kind of preparation for this. If you had done nothing else and were never again to do anything else they would have been well spent.

'Of course, I have thought of all these things afterwards. At the time I just sat and cried quietly. For, after all, this picture is of courage all compact and courage is the only thing that brings the honourable moisture to these eyes.'

There was to be only one jarring note and the cause of it was not decisively proved until official files were opened years later. There had been talk of a knighthood for Noël as early as Cavalcade *(1931) but the honour was considered premature. There was plenty of time. In fact, there turned out to be forty years of it.*

After the reception of In Which We Serve, *Mountbatten argued the case to his cousin, King George VI. Noël was sounded out. Should there be such an offer . . . ? Noël would be honoured to accept. But the offer never came and a letter from Churchill, dated 29 December 1942, reveals why . . .*

'With considerable personal reluctance I have therefore come to the conclusion that I could not advise Your Majesty to proceed with this proposal on the present occasion.

> With my humble duty, I remain
> Your Majesty's faithful subject and servant
> WINSTON S. CHURCHILL'

Although he always suspected that this was the case, Noël did his best not to bear a grudge. The relationship between the two men was always wary but the admiration was mutual.

★

On 3 May 1945 the war in Europe was finally over but, as Noël reflected, 'There was still the future to be fought.'

'I wish I had more feeling about it. My mind seems unable to take it in. It has all been too long and too stupid and cruel. We shall see how the sweet face of peace looks. I cannot help visualizing an insane, vacuous grin.'

Diary, 10 August 1945

'The very deep feelings I had during the war and have since, almost deliberately, been in danger of losing. If I forget these feelings or allow them to be obscured, because they are uncomfortable, I shall be lost . . . I must hang on to those moments or I shall not have survived the war.'

20 January 1946

★

The immediate post-war years did not treat Noël kindly. Austerity Britain with its new Labour Government could see no possible merit in an effete playwright who only seemed to write about duchesses and people who did nothing for a living. His time was clearly past. For the next decade – with rare exceptions – everything he did was dismissed by the critics.

But not quite everything. October the following year turned out to be significant in a way no one could have anticipated. He was invited to appear in cabaret – a form of entertainment he had only tried once before – in 1916, when he had appeared as part of a duo with a young lady called Eileen Dennis at the Elysée Restaurant, which later became the Café de Paris. He was not a marked success. Attempting a solo number, he forgot the words and had to make an undignified exit murmuring 'La-la-la' to the bewilderment of the patrons.

Noël and accompanist
Norman Hackforth
in cabaret at the Café
de Paris.

This time things were very different but only at the very last minute:

'In the afternoon rehearsal at the Café de Paris – everything perfect except
my voice, which is failing fast . . . This is the cruelest luck. I feel fine, the
microphone is perfect, all London fighting to get in to see me – and now
this happens. I am heart-broken.'   *Diary*, 26 October 1951

Enter Noël's throat specialist, and on the following Monday . . .

'Went to the Café feeling slightly tremulous. Really triumphant success –
tore the place up.'

It was to be the start of a whole new career.

★

*The twin symbolic masks of tragedy and comedy appeared to be ever present in
Noël's life. From his diary for 6 September 1952:*

'A day that started gaily and ended in misery. The happy part was going
to the Folkestone races with Cole [his secretary] and Gladys. I backed
several winners and it was great fun. Just as I was leaving, Coley told me
it was in the Stop Press – Gertie Lawrence was dead . . .

'Poor, darling old Gertie – a lifelong friend. With all her over-actings and silliness I never knew her do a mean or unkind thing. I am terribly, terribly unhappy to think that I shall never see her again.

'No one I have ever known, however brilliant and however gifted, has contributed what she contributed to my work.'

★

It was in 1955 that the real breakthrough came. One evening the previous November at the Café de Paris he had a visitor . . .

'A character called Joe Glaser flew in from New York to sign me up for Las Vegas. A typical shrewd, decent, sharp agent-type. The discussion was satisfactory financially, everything being contingent on whether or not I like Las Vegas, so he is escorting me there for a couple of days so that I can case the joint and decide which room I prefer to appear in, if any. Joe Glaser watched my performance at the Café and was obviously bewildered as to why the audience liked it so much. We are getting together in New York.'

The tax-free fee soon swept aside any reservations Noël might have had and June 1955 found him the king of the 'fabulous madhouse'.

'I have never had such an ovation in my life . . . also I have never known such generosity. Judy Garland was in tears and told me that she and Frank Sinatra decided that I was better than anyone they had ever seen and could give them lessons, which couldn't have been more comforting or more sweet. If you note a slight egocentric strain in this letter you will have to forgive it because it was a rather dangerous challenge and has turned out to be successful beyond my wildest dreams.'

America continued to restore his fortunes – both professional and financial. CBS offered him $450,000 for three live TV specials which turned out to be Together with Music *with Mary Martin,* Blithe Spirit *and* This Happy Breed. *Noël starred in all of them. The amount of money involved caused him to have a serious reappraisal of his circumstances, as well as to determine – after endless interviews – that 'television is for appearing on not looking at'.*

Reluctantly, he concluded it would be foolish to continue to be domiciled in England with its penal tax system. He was already in debt and the prospect of living from overdraft to overdraft from his mid-fifties into old age – about to start 'next Tuesday', as he put it – did not appeal. There was a brief sojourn in Bermuda, which proved to be too British suburban. Then Jamaica proved to be 'where my heart is'.

JAMAICA

Jamaica's an island surrounded by sea
(Like Corsica, Guam and Tasmania)
The tourist does not need to wear a topee
Or other macabre miscellanea.
Remember that this is a tropical place
Where violent hues are abundant
And bright coloured clothes with a bright yellow face
Look, frankly, a trifle redundant.
A simple ensemble of trousers and shirt
Becomes both the saint and the sinner
And if a head waiter looks bitterly hurt
You *can* wear a jacket for dinner.

Jamaica's an island surrounded by sea
(It shares this distinction with Elba)
It's easy to order a goat fricassee
But madness to ask for Pêche Melba.
You'll find (to the best of this writer's belief)
That if you want rice you can get it
But visitors ordering mutton or beef
Will certainly live to regret it.
There's seldom a shortage of ackees and yams
Or lobsters, if anyone's caught them
But if you've a passion for imported hams
You'd bloody well better import them.

Jamaica's an island surrounded by sea
(It has this in common with Cuba)
Its national tunes, to a certain degree,
Are founded on boop-boop-a-duba;
'Neath tropical palms under tropical skies
Where equally tropical stars are
The vocal Jamaicans betray no surprise
However off-key their guitars are.
The native calypsos which seem to be based
On hot-air-conditioned reflexes

Conclusively prove that to people of taste
There's nothing so funny as sex is.

Jamaica's an island surrounded by sea
(Like Alderney, Guernsey and Sark are)
It's wise not to dive with exuberant glee
Where large barracuda and shark are.
The reefs are entrancing, the water is clear,
The colouring couldn't be dreamier
But one coral scratch and you may spend a year
In bed with acute septicemia.
The leading hotels are extremely well run
The service both cheerful and dextrous
But even the blisters you get from the sun
Are firmly included as extras.

Jamaica's an island surrounded by sea
(*Unlike* Ecuador or Guiana)
The tourist may not have a 'Fromage de Brie'
But always can have a banana.
He also can have, if he has enough cash,
A pleasantly rum-sodden liver
And cure his rheumatic complaints in a flash
By shooting himself at Milk river.
In fact every tourist who visits these shores
Can thank his benevolent Maker
For taking time off from the rest of His chores
To fashion the Isle of Jamaica.

*From his house by the water (Blue Harbour) he could also retreat, for complete
privacy, to a newly built bungalow (Firefly) on the top of the mountain.*

'Last night we took a thermos full of cocktails up . . . and sat and watched
the sun set and the lights come up over the town and it really was magical.
The sky changed from deep blue to yellow and pale green and then all the
colour went and out came the stars and the fireflies . . . The view is really
staggering, particularly when the light begins to go and the far mountains
become purple against a pale lemon sky.

'There is a very sweet white owl who comes and hoots at us every evening.
I don't think he does it in any spirit of criticism but just to be friendly.'

When he, Graham, and Coley were there together, painting became a shared passion.

'We are all painting away like crazy. Little Lad [Graham Payn], as usual, is at work upon a very large ruined cathedral. I can't think why he has such a penchant for hysterical Gothic. Perhaps he was assaulted in childhood by a South African nun. Coley is bashing away at a lot of thin people by a river while I, swifter than the eye can follow, have finished a group of negroes and I am now busy with a crowded fairground with swings and roundabouts and what should be a Ferris wheel but looks like a steel ovary. The trouble with me is that I don't know the meaning of the word *peur*.

'Little Lad has done a sort of "Rose Red City", which looks a bit like Golders Green. The effect is dashing but the architecture is a bit dodgy. I keep on doing lots of people walking about and I'm sick to death of them.'

'Little Lad is painting a large picture of a Priest and an Acolyte in acid moonlight. He suddenly changed the Priest into a lady in a red dress, which is better really but perhaps not better enough. She is very tall and the Acolyte is crouching. It is all a great worry.'

★

'The plumbing has proved to be a trifle eccentric and my lavatory hiccups and sprays my behind with cold water every now and then which is all very gay and sanitary.

'When it decides to rain here there are no half measures about it. It comes down in a deluge and there is already some valuable Penicillin growing in all my shoes!

'There are no dangerous insects or animals here but I have just found a beetle the size of a saucer nestling among a lot of three-halfpenny stamps. It seems fairly amiable but its expression does not inspire confidence. I have now thrown it over the verandah and I *think* it went into Graham's bedroom window.

'I rather enjoy my morning shopping trips into Port Maria. Everyone is very amiable and their colours are graded from deep ebony to pale *café au lait*.

'Mr Philpot in the General Store is coal black with far more teeth than are usual and he always wrings my hand like a pump handle and we make little jokes. Then, of course, there is Madame Cecilia Chung, my Chinese groceress. She, having read in some obscure Chinese newspaper that I was renowned for being witty, goes into gales of oriental laughter when I ask quite ordinarily for Colman's mustard or Worcester sauce!

'The girls in the Post Office start giggling with anticipatory delight before I get out of my car, so you do see that there is never a dull moment for anybody!

'Oh la la! As I always say, having acted so prettily in the French language.'

★

But he increasingly felt the need for a European base, too, and a Swiss search began in earnest. Shangri-la turned out to be Les Avants, high in the mountains behind Montreux. He flirted with the idea of calling it Shilly Chalet, but the locals decided for him. Chalet Covair (their approximation of Coward) they called it – and still do. Far from being an architectural gem – there was a touch of Eastbourne about it, Cecil Beaton's friends told him, though Rebecca West favoured Margate or Folkestone and thought its white wooden balconies should have been hung with drying bathing dresses. Nonetheless, it was 'home' and 'it worked'.

'It is eight o'clock in the morning and I am sitting up comfortably in bed in my own house at last. Outside it is still blue-dark but the sun is preparing to come up from behind the Rochers de Naye. The mountains are beginning to turn pink and the visible world is white with snow. The house is really beautiful, much more so than I would have believed . . .'

Diary, 21 December 1959

★

Although it wasn't immediately obvious 'Dad's Renaissance' had quietly begun.

In late 1963 there was a little-heralded revival of Private Lives *at the new Hampstead Theatre Club in London. Critics – many of whom were too young to have seen it before – found it 'the funniest play to have adorned the English theatre in this century'. Noël found it particularly satisfying that this should have happened in Hampstead, the scene of his first major success almost forty years before.*

Early the next year Sir Laurence Olivier, now running the new National Theatre, invited him to direct a revival of Hay Fever *with a cast 'that could have played the Albanian telephone directory'. It was the first time a living playwright had been so honoured. 'So you've been nationalized at last,' Terence Rattigan wrote to him and the critic Ronald Bryden dubbed him 'demonstrably the greatest living English playwright'. Noël noted:*

Remembered laughter . . .

'Such (almost) unanimous praise has not been lavished upon me for many a long year and to pretend that I am not delighted by it would be the height of affectation.'

★

There was to be one last hurrah: Suite in Three Keys — *a full-length and two one-act plays, all set in a Swiss hotel, the play fittingly called* A Song at Twilight. *Noël intended to play them in London in 1965 and subsequently on Broadway, but things did not work out that way. A travelling-alone vacation in the Seychelles left him with a severe case of amoebic dysentery.*

The following April the plays were finally staged and Noël the actor did more than justice to Noël the playwright, but there were worrying signs. He, who valued word

'You'd better call me *Sir* Noelie now!' The Investiture, 1970.

perfection above almost every other acting attribute, found himself forgetting lines that he had written himself. 'Time's wingèd chariot,' as he put it, 'is beginning to goose me.' His triumph was indisputable but the message was clear. There would be no Broadway production — at least not during his lifetime.

There would be another couple of film roles — a sideline that had become a significant source of income — and that would be that. Our last view of him is as Mr Bridger, the master criminal, accepting the acclaim of his fellow prisoners on the successful completion of The Italian Job *(1968). It was a fitting public exit.*

★

The critical praise and the honours flowed unabated, culminating in the long-delayed knighthood in the 1970 New Year's Honours List. There was nothing left to do. Noël even stopped writing his Diary.

He made his last public appearance in New York at a special performance of the revue, Oh! Coward. *Graham and Coley were there with him. Marlene was on his arm, though it was not entirely clear who was supporting whom.*

Had he enjoyed the show? 'One does not laugh at one's own jokes.' But then he relented. 'But I did leave humming the songs.'

A few weeks later in his Jamaican eyrie overlooking the Spanish Main he died peacefully. The marvellous party was finally over.

When asked what he would like as an epitaph, Noël had replied:

'He was much loved because he made people laugh and cry.'

A song at twilight. Noël at Chalet Coward not long before he died.

Noël's grave at Firefly, overlooking the Spanish Main.

THE PLAYS

'The theatre must be treated with respect.
It is a house of strange enchantment, a temple of dreams.'

Noël Coward

'It's all a question of masks, really, brittle, painted masks.
We all wear them as a form of protection, modern life forces us to.
We must have some means of shielding our timid, shrinking souls
from the glare of civilization.'

Gilda in *Design for Living* (1932)

'It seems to me that a professional writer should be animated
by no other motive than the desire to write and, by doing so,
to earn his living.'

Introduction to *Play Parade* (1934)

JOANNA: I expect it's because you're an actor. They're always
apt to be a bit *papier mâché*.
GARRY: Just puppets, Joanna, dear, creatures of tinsel and
sawdust, how clever of you to have noticed it.

Present Laughter (1939)

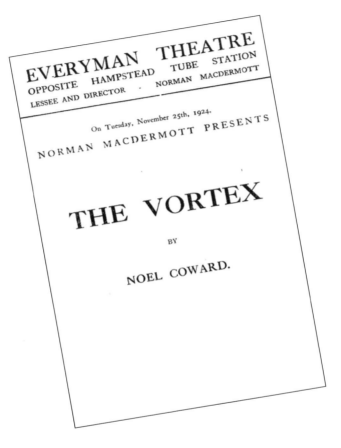

EVERYMAN THEATRE
OPPOSITE HAMPSTEAD TUBE STATION
LESSEE AND DIRECTOR · NORMAN MACDERMOTT

On Tuesday, November 25th, 1924.

NORMAN MACDERMOTT PRESENTS

THE VORTEX

BY

NOEL COWARD.

By the time he was twenty Noël had already written a number of plays and by his mid-twenties two of them – I'll Leave It to You (1920) and The Young Idea (1922) – had been produced in the West End of London.

But it was on the night of 25 November 1924 at Hampstead's Everyman Theatre that the breakthrough occurred – though it took Shakespeare to get it past the censor. The Lord Chamberlain's Office was all for banning it altogether, until one of their inspectors pointed out ruefully, 'If we ban this, we shall have to ban Hamlet.'

THE VORTEX

(1924)

FLORENCE LANCASTER   Lilian Braithwaite
NICKY LANCASTER   Noël Coward

Directed by Noël Coward
Everyman Theatre, Hampstead, 25 November 1924

The Vortex *was the story of a mother, Florence Lancaster, clinging desperately to the illusion of youth by having affairs with men young enough to be her son. Her own son, Nicky, has taken to drugs. In the last act – like Hamlet with Gertrude – he confronts her with the truth about both of them . . .*

The door opens and NICKY *enters. He is in dressing gown and pyjamas. His face looks strained and white.*

FLORENCE: Nicky!

NICKY: Helen, I want to talk to mother, please.

HELEN: All right, Nicky.

FLORENCE: What is it?

NICKY: I couldn't sleep.

HELEN: Florence dear – goodnight.

FLORENCE: No – no, Helen – don't go yet –

HELEN: I must.

FLORENCE: Helen – stay with me.

NICKY: Please go.

HELEN: I can't stay, Florence – it's quite impossible.

She goes out.

FLORENCE: I don't know what you mean – by coming here and ordering Helen out of my room.

NICKY: I'm sorry, mother. I felt I had to talk to you alone.

FLORENCE: At this hour of the night – you're mad!

NICKY: No, I'm not, I think. I'm probably more unhappy than I've ever been in my life.

FLORENCE: You're young – you'll get over it.

NICKY: I hope so.

FLORENCE: I knew the first moment I saw her – what sort of a girl she was.

NICKY: Oh, mother!

FLORENCE: It's true. I had an *instinct* about her.

NICKY: It's all been rather a shock, you know –

FLORENCE (*becoming motherly*): Yes, dear – I know – I know – but you mustn't be miserable about her – she isn't worth it. (*She goes to kiss him.*)

NICKY (*gently pushing her away*): Don't, mother!

FLORENCE: Listen, Nicky – go back to bed now – there's a dear – my head's splitting.

NICKY: I can't yet.

FLORENCE: Take some aspirin – that'll calm your nerves.

NICKY: I'm afraid I'm a little beyond aspirin.

FLORENCE: I don't want you to think I don't sympathize with you, darling – my heart *aches* for you – I know so well what you're going through.

NICKY: Do you?

FLORENCE: It's agony – absolute agony – but, you see – it will wear off – it always does in time.

NICKY *doesn't answer.*

Nicky, please go now!

NICKY: I want to talk to you.

FLORENCE: Tomorrow – we'll talk tomorrow.

NICKY: No, now – *now*!

FLORENCE: You're inconsiderate and cruel – I've told you my head's bursting.

NICKY: I want to sympathize with you, too – and try to understand everything – as well as I can –

FLORENCE: Understand everything?

NICKY: Yes, please.

FLORENCE: I don't know what you mean —

NICKY: Will you tell me things — as though I were somebody quite different?

FLORENCE: What kind of things?

NICKY: Things about you — your life.

FLORENCE: Really, Nicky — you're ridiculous — asking me to tell you stories at this hour!

NICKY (*with dead vehemence*): Mother — sit down quietly. I'm not going out of this room until I've got everything straight in my mind.

FLORENCE (*sinking down — almost hypnotized*): Nicky — please — I —

NICKY: Tom Veryan has been your lover, hasn't he?

FLORENCE (*almost shrieking*): Nicky — how dare you!

NICKY: Keep calm — it's our only chance — keep calm.

FLORENCE (*bursting into tears*): How dare you speak to me like that — suggest such a thing — I —

NICKY: It's true, isn't it?

FLORENCE: Go away — go away!

NICKY: It's true, isn't it?

FLORENCE: No — no!

NICKY: It's true, isn't it?

FLORENCE: No — I tell you — no — no — no!

NICKY: You're lying to me, mother. What's the use of that?

FLORENCE: You're mad — mad —

NICKY: Does father know?

FLORENCE: Go away!

NICKY: Does father know?

FLORENCE: Your father knows nothing — he doesn't understand me any more than you do.

NICKY: Then it's between us alone.

FLORENCE: I tell you I don't know what you're talking about.

NICKY: Mother — don't go on like that, it's useless — we've arrived at a crisis, wherever we go — whatever we do we can't escape from it. I know we're neither of us very strong-minded or capable, and we haven't much hope of coming through successfully — but let's try — it's no good pretending any more – our lives are built up of pretences all the time. For years – ever since I began to think at all, I've been bolstering up my illusions about you. People have made remarks not realizing that I was your son, and I've pretended that they were inspired by cattiness and jealousy. I've noticed things – trivial incriminating little incidents, and I've brushed them aside and not thought any more about them because you were my mother – clever and beautiful and successful – and naturally people *would* slander you *because* you were so beautiful – and now I *know* – they were right!

FLORENCE: Nicky – I implore you – go away now – leave me alone.

NICKY: No, I can't.

FLORENCE: You're cruel – cruel to torment me –

NICKY: I don't want to be cruel –

FLORENCE: Go to bed then, and we'll talk everything over quietly another time.

NICKY: It is true about Tom Veryan, isn't it?

FLORENCE: No. No –

NICKY: We're on awfully dangerous ground – I'm straining every nerve to keep myself under control. If you lie to me and try to evade me any more – I won't be answerable for what might happen.

FLORENCE (*dropping her voice – terrified*): What do you mean?

NICKY: I don't know – I'm frightened.

FLORENCE: Nicky – darling Nicky – I –

She approaches him.

NICKY: Don't touch me, please.

FLORENCE: Have a little pity for me.

NICKY: Was Tom Veryan your lover?

FLORENCE (*in a whisper*): Yes.

NICKY: I want to understand why –

FLORENCE: He loved me.

NICKY: But you – did you love him?

FLORENCE: Yes.

NICKY: It was something you couldn't help, wasn't it – something that's always been the same in you since you were quite, quite young – ?

FLORENCE: Yes, Nicky – yes –

Noël Coward and Lilian Braithwaite in *The Vortex*.

NICKY: And there have been others, too, haven't there?

FLORENCE (*with her face in her hands*): I won't be cross-questioned any more — I won't — I won't —

NICKY: I wish you'd understand I'm not blaming you — I'm trying to help you — to help us both —

FLORENCE: What good can all this possibly do?

NICKY: Clear things up, of course. I can't go on any more half knowing —

FLORENCE: Why should that side of my life be any concern of yours?

NICKY: But, mother!

FLORENCE: I'm different from other women — completely different — and you expect me to be the same — why can't you realize that with a temperament like mine it's impossible to live an ordinary humdrum life — you're not a boy any longer — you're a man — and —

NICKY: I'm nothing – I've grown up all wrong.

FLORENCE: It's not my fault.

NICKY: Of course it's your fault, mother – who else's fault *could* it be?

FLORENCE: Your friends – the people you mix with –

NICKY: It wouldn't matter *who* I mixed with if only I had a background.

FLORENCE: You've got as much money as you want – you've got your home –

NICKY (*bitterly*): Home! That's almost funny – there's no peace anywhere – nothing but the ceaseless din of trying to be amused –

FLORENCE: David never complains.

NICKY: I don't suppose you've looked at father during the last few years – or you wouldn't say that.

FLORENCE: He's perfectly happy because he's sensible – he lives his own life and doesn't try to interfere with mine.

NICKY: It must be your vanity that makes you so dreadfully blind – and foolish.

FLORENCE: Understand once and for all, I *won't* be spoken to like this –

NICKY: You've had other lovers besides Tom Veryan – haven't you?

FLORENCE: Yes, I have – I have. Now then!

NICKY: Well, anyhow – that's the truth – at last –

He rises, turns his back on her and stands looking out of the window.

FLORENCE (*after a pause – going to him*): Nicky – don't be angry – please don't be angry with me.

NICKY: I'm not angry a bit – I realize that I'm living in a world where things like this happen – and they've got to be faced and given the right value. If only I'd had the courage to realize everything before – it wouldn't be so bad now – it's the sudden shock that's thrown the whole thing out of focus for me – but I mean to get it right – please help me!

FLORENCE (*dully*): I don't know what to do.

NICKY: It's your life, and you've lived it as you've wanted to live it – that's fair –

FLORENCE: Yes – yes.

NICKY: You've wanted love always – passionate love, because you were made like that – it's not your fault – it's the fault of circumstances and civilization — civilization makes rottenness so much easier — we're utterly rotten — both of us —

FLORENCE: Nicky — don't — don't —

NICKY: How can we help ourselves? — We swirl about in a vortex of beastliness — this is a chance — don't you see — to realize the truth — our only chance.

FLORENCE: Oh, Nicky, do stop — go away!

NICKY: Don't keep on telling me to stop when our only hope is to hammer it out.

FLORENCE: You're overwrought — it isn't as bad as you think.

NICKY: Isn't it?

FLORENCE: No, no. Of course it isn't. Tomorrow morning you'll see things quite differently.

NICKY: You haven't understood.

FLORENCE: Yes, I have — I have.

NICKY: You haven't understood. Oh, my God, you haven't understood! You're building up silly defences in your mind. I'm overwrought. Tomorrow morning I shall see things quite differently. That's true — that's the tragedy of it, and you won't see — Tomorrow morning I *shall* see things differently. All this will seem unreal — a nightmare — the machinery of our lives will go on again and gloss over the truth as it always does — and our chance will be gone for ever.

FLORENCE: Chance — chance? What are you talking about — what chance?

NICKY: I must make you see somehow.

FLORENCE: You're driving me mad.

NICKY: Have patience with me — please — please —

FLORENCE (*wildly*): How can I have patience with you? — You exaggerate everything.

NICKY: No I don't — I wish I did.

FLORENCE: Listen — let me explain something to you.

NICKY: Very well — go on.

FLORENCE: You're setting yourself up in judgement on me — your own mother.

NICKY: No, I'm not.

FLORENCE: You are – you are – let me speak – you don't understand my temperament in the least – nobody does – I –

NICKY: You're deceiving yourself – your temperament's no different from thousands of other women, but you've been weak and selfish and given way all along the line –

FLORENCE: Let me speak, I tell you – !

NICKY: What's the use – you're still pretending – you're building up barriers between us instead of helping me to break them down.

FLORENCE: What are you accusing me of having done?

NICKY: Can't you see yet?

FLORENCE: No, I can't. If you're preaching morality you've no right to – that's my affair – I've never done any harm to anyone.

NICKY: Look at me.

FLORENCE: Why – what do you mean?

NICKY: You've given me *nothing* all my life – nothing that counts.

FLORENCE: Now you're pitying yourself.

NICKY: Yes, with every reason.

FLORENCE: You're neurotic and ridiculous – just because Bunty broke off your engagement you come and say wicked, cruel things to me –

NICKY: You forget what I've seen tonight, mother.

FLORENCE: I don't care what you've seen.

NICKY: I've seen you make a vulgar, disgusting scene in your own house, and on top of that humiliate yourself before a boy half your age. The misery of losing Bunty faded away when that happened – everything is comparative after all.

FLORENCE: I didn't humiliate myself –

NICKY: You ran after him up the stairs because your vanity wouldn't let you lose him – it isn't that you love him – that would be easier – you never love anyone, you only love them loving you – all your so-called passion and temperament is false – your whole existence had degenerated into an endless empty craving for admiration and flattery – and then you say you've done no harm to anybody. Father used to be a clever man, with a strong will and a capacity for enjoying everything – I can remember him like that, and now he's nothing – a complete nonentity because his spirit's crushed. How could it be otherwise? You've let him down consistently for years – and God knows I'm nothing for him to look forward to – but I might have been if it hadn't been for you –

FLORENCE: Don't talk like that. Don't – don't – it can't be such a crime being loved – it can't be such a crime being happy – .

NICKY: You're not happy – you're never happy – you're fighting – fighting all the time to keep your youth and your looks – because you can't bear the thought of living without them – as though they mattered in the end.

FLORENCE (*hysterically*): What does anything matter – ever?

NICKY: That's what I'm trying to find out.

FLORENCE: I'm still young inside – I'm still beautiful – why shouldn't I live my life as I choose?

NICKY: You're not young or beautiful; I'm seeing for the first time how old you are – it's horrible – your silly fair hair – and your face all plastered and painted –

FLORENCE: Nicky – Nicky – stop – stop – stop!

She flings herself face downwards on the bed. NICKY *goes over to her.*

NICKY: Mother!

FLORENCE: Go away – go away – I hate you – go away –

NICKY: Mother – sit up –

FLORENCE (*pulling herself together*): Go out of my room –

NICKY: Mother –

FLORENCE: I don't ever want to see you again – you're insane – you've said wicked, wicked things to me – you've talked to me as though I were a woman off the streets. I can't bear any more – I can't bear any more!

NICKY: I have a slight confession to make –

FLORENCE: Confession?

NICKY: Yes.

FLORENCE: Go away – go away –

NICKY (*taking a small gold box from his pocket*): Look –

FLORENCE: What do you mean – what is it – ?

NICKY: Don't you know?

FLORENCE *takes the box with trembling fingers and opens it. She stares at it for a moment. When she speaks again her voice is quite dead.*

FLORENCE: Nicky, it isn't – you haven't – ?

NICKY: Why do you look so shocked?

FLORENCE (*dully*): Oh, my God!

NICKY: What does it matter?

FLORENCE *suddenly rises and hurls the box out of the window.*

That doesn't make it any better.

FLORENCE (*flinging herself on her knees beside him*): Nicky, promise me, oh, promise you'll never do it again – never in your life – it's frightful – horrible –

NICKY: It's only just the beginning.

FLORENCE: What can I say to you – what can I say to you?

NICKY: Nothing – under the circumstances.

FLORENCE: What do you mean?

NICKY: It can't possibly matter – now.

FLORENCE: Matter – but it's the finish of everything – you're young, you're just starting on your life – you must stop – you must swear never to touch it again – swear to me on your oath, Nicky – I'll help you – I'll help you –

NICKY: You!

He turns away.

FLORENCE (*burying her face in her hands and moaning*): Oh – oh – oh!

NICKY: How could you possibly help me?

FLORENCE (*clutching him*): Nicky!

NICKY (*almost losing control*): Shut up – shut up – don't touch me –

FLORENCE (*trying to take him in her arms*): Nicky – Nicky –

NICKY: I'm trying to control myself, but you won't let me – you're an awfully rotten woman, really.

FLORENCE: Nicky – stop – stop – stop –

She beats him with her fists.

NICKY: Leave go of me!

He breaks away from her, and going up to the dressing table he sweeps everything off on to the floor with his arm.

FLORENCE (*screaming*): Oh – oh – Nicky – !

NICKY: Now then! Now then! You're not to have any more lovers; you're not going to be beautiful and successful ever again – you're going to be my mother for once – it's about time I had one to help me, before I go over the edge altogether –

FLORENCE: Nicky – Nicky –

NICKY: Promise me to be different – you've got to promise me!

FLORENCE (*sinking on to the end of couch, facing audience*): Yes – yes – I promise – (*The tears are running down her face.*)

NICKY: I love you, really – that's why it's so awful.

He falls on his knees by her side and buries his face in her lap.

FLORENCE: No. No, not awful – don't say that – I love you, too.

NICKY (*sobbing hopelessly*): Oh, mother – !

FLORENCE (*staring in front of her*): I wish I were dead!

NICKY: It doesn't matter about death, but it matters terribly about life.

FLORENCE: I know –

NICKY (*desperately*): Promise me you'll be different – promise me you'll be different –

FLORENCE: Yes, yes – I'll try –

NICKY: We'll both try.

FLORENCE: Yes, dear – Oh, my dear – !

She sits quite still, staring in front of her – the tears are rolling down her cheeks, and she is stroking NICKY*'s hair mechanically in an effort to calm him.*

Curtain

American impresario, Gilbert Miller

'gave me some useful pieces of advice on the art of play-writing. He said among other things, that although my dialogue was nearly always good, my construction was "lousy" . . . the construction of a play was as important as the foundations of a house, whereas dialogue, however good, could only, at best, be considered as interior decoration. This I recognized as being authentic wisdom.

'I will never again embark on so much as a revue sketch that is not carefully and meticulously constructed beforehand.'

PRIVATE LIVES

an intimate comedy

(1930)

ELYOT CHASE	Noël Coward
AMANDA PRYNNE	Gertrude Lawrence
VICTOR PRYNNE	Laurence Olivier
SYBIL CHASE	Adrianne Allen

Directed by Noël Coward
Phoenix Theatre, London, 24 September 1930

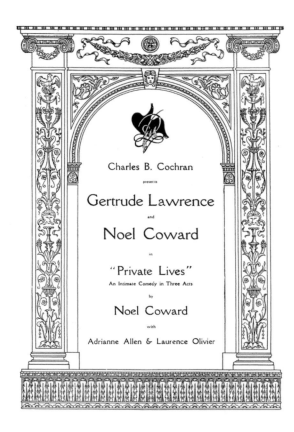

Charles B. Cochran

presents

Gertrude Lawrence

and

Noel Coward

in

"Private Lives"

An Intimate Comedy in Three Acts

by

Noel Coward

with

Adrianne Allen & Laurence Olivier

Noël wrote this — his most famous play — on a trip to the Far East. He intended it as a vehicle for himself and Gertrude Lawrence.

He recalled in his first autobiography, Present Indicative (*1937*):

'The Imperial Hotel, Tokyo was grand and comfortable and was renowned for having stood firm during the big earthquake. A wire was handed me from Jeffrey [*Amherst, his travelling companion*] saying that he had missed a boat in Shanghai and wouldn't be with me for three days which, although disappointing, was a relief, as I had begun to think I was never going to hear from him at all.

'The night before he arrived I went to bed early as I wanted to greet him as brightly as possible at seven in the morning, but the moment I switched out the lights, Gertrude appeared in a white Molyneux dress on a terrace in the South of France and refused to go again until four a.m., by which time *Private Lives*, title and all had constructed itself.

'In 1923 the play would have been written and typed within a few days of my thinking of it, but in 1929 I had learned the wisdom of not welcoming a new idea too ardently, so I forced it into the back of my mind, trusting to its own integrity to emerge again later on, when it had become sufficiently set and matured.

'A bout of influenza laid me low in Shanghai, and I lay, sweating gloomily, in my bedroom in the Cathay Hotel for several days. The ensuing convalescence, however, was productive, for I utilized it by writing *Private Lives*. The idea by now seemed ripe enough to have a shot at, so I started it, propped up in bed with a writing-block and an Eversharp pencil, and completed it, roughly, in four days. It came easily, and with the exception of a few of the usual "blood and tears" moments, I enjoyed writing it. I thought it a shrewd and witty comedy, well constructed on the whole, but psychologically unstable; however, its entertainment value seemed obvious enough, and its acting opportunities for Gertie and me admirable, so I cabled to her immediately in New York . . .

' "HAVE WRITTEN DELIGHTFUL NEW COMEDY STOP GOOD PART FOR YOU STOP WONDERFUL ONE FOR ME STOP KEEP YOURSELF FREE FOR AUTUMN PRODUCTION."

'To which the lady replied . . .

'"HAVE READ NEW PLAY STOP NOTHING WRONG THAT CAN'T BE FIXED STOP GERTIE."'

Noël's response was sharp and to the point . . .

'THE ONLY THING THAT WILL NEED TO BE FIXED IS YOUR PERFORMANCE STOP NOËL.'

★

The play opened at London's new Phoenix Theatre on 24 September 1930 and they became 'Noël&Gertie' overnight and for ever after.

'I am deeply attached to it. It has been enthusiastically and profitably patronized by the public wherever and in whatever language it has been played.'

Elyot Chase and Amanda had been married to each other then divorced. Now they have both remarried – Elyot to Sibyl and Amanda to Victor Prynne. In a coincidence permitted only to playwrights both couples find themselves staying on their wedding night not only at the same hotel in France but in adjoining terrace rooms – a fact they discover in suitably dramatic fashion.

While their partners are dressing for dinner, Elyot and Amanda emerge on their respective terraces . . .

ELYOT *saunters down to the balustrade. He looks casually over on to the next terrace, and then out at the view. He looks up at the moon and sighs, then he sits down in a chair with his back towards the line of tubs, and lights a cigarette.* AMANDA *steps gingerly on to her terrace carrying a tray with two champagne cocktails on it. She is wearing a charmingly simple evening gown, her cloak is flung over her right shoulder. She places the tray carefully on the table, puts her cloak over the back of a chair, and sits down with her back towards* ELYOT. *She takes a small mirror from her handbag, and scrutinizes her face in it. The orchestra downstairs strikes up a new melody. Both* ELYOT *and* AMANDA *give a little start. After a moment,* ELYOT *pensively begins to hum the tune the band is playing. It is a sentimental, romantic little tune* ['Some Day I'll Find You']. AMANDA *hears him, and clutches at her throat suddenly as though she were suffocating. Then she jumps up noiselessly, and peers over the line of tubs.* ELYOT, *with his back to her, continues to sing obliviously. She sits down again, relaxing with a gesture almost of despair.*

Then she looks anxiously over her shoulder at the window in case VICTOR *should be listening, and then, with a little smile, she takes up the melody herself, clearly.* ELYOT *stops dead and gives a gasp, then he jumps up, and stands looking at her. She continues to sing, pretending not to know that he is there. At the end of the song, she turns slowly, and faces him.*

AMANDA: Thoughtful of them to play that, wasn't it?

ELYOT (*in a stifled choke*): What are you doing here?

AMANDA: I'm on honeymoon.

ELYOT: How interesting, so am I.

AMANDA: I hope you're enjoying it.

ELYOT: It hasn't started yet.

AMANDA: Neither has mine.

ELYOT: Oh, my God!

AMANDA: I can't help feeling that this is a little unfortunate.

ELYOT: Are you happy?

AMANDA: Perfectly.

ELYOT: Good. That's all right, then, isn't it?

AMANDA: Are you?

ELYOT: Ecstatically.

AMANDA: I'm delighted to hear it. We shall probably meet again sometime. Au revoir! (*She turns.*)

ELYOT (*firmly*): Goodbye.

She goes indoors without looking back. He stands gazing after her with an expression of horror on his face.

The shock of their meeting causes Elyot to have a row with Sibyl and Amanda with Victor. The new spouses storm off and Elyot and Amanda retreat to the terrace . . .

ELYOT *stamps down to the balustrade and lights a cigarette, obviously trying to control his nerves.* AMANDA *sees him, and comes down too.*

AMANDA: Give me one for God's sake.

ELYOT (*hands her his case laconically*): Here.

AMANDA (*taking a cigarette*): I'm in such a rage.

ELYOT (*lighting up*): So am I.

AMANDA: What are we to do?

ELYOT: I don't know.

AMANDA: Whose yacht is that?

ELYOT: The Duke of Westminster's I expect. It always is.

AMANDA: I wish I were on it.

ELYOT: I wish you were too.

AMANDA: There's no need to be nasty.

ELYOT: Yes there is, every need. I've never in my life felt a greater urge to be nasty.

AMANDA: And you've had some urges in your time, haven't you?

ELYOT: If you start bickering with me, Amanda, I swear I'll throw you over the edge.

AMANDA: Try it, that's all, just try it.

ELYOT: You've upset everything, as usual.

AMANDA: I've upset everything! What about you?

ELYOT: Ever since the first moment I was unlucky enough to set eyes on you, my life has been insupportable.

AMANDA: Oh do shut up, there's no sense in going on like that.

ELYOT: Nothing's any use. There's no escape, ever.

AMANDA: Don't be melodramatic.

ELYOT: Do you want a cocktail? There are two here.

AMANDA: There are two over here as well.

ELYOT: We'll have my two first.

AMANDA crosses over into ELYOT*'s part of the terrace. He gives her one, and keeps one himself.*

AMANDA: Shall we get roaring screaming drunk?

ELYOT: I don't think that would help, we did it once before and it was a dismal failure.

AMANDA: It was lovely at the beginning.

ELYOT: You have an immoral memory Amanda. Here's to you.

They raise their glasses solemnly and drink.

AMANDA: I tried to get away the moment after I'd seen you, but he wouldn't budge.

ELYOT: What's his name?

AMANDA: Victor, Victor Prynne.

ELYOT (*toasting*): Mr and Mrs Victor Prynne. (*He drinks.*) Mine wouldn't budge either.

AMANDA: What's her name?

ELYOT: Sibyl.

AMANDA (*toasting*): Mr and Mrs Elyot Chase. (*She drinks.*) God pity the poor girl.

ELYOT: Are you in love with him?

AMANDA: Of course.

ELYOT: How funny.

AMANDA: I don't see anything particularly funny about it, you're in love with yours, aren't you?

ELYOT: Certainly.

AMANDA: There you are then.

ELYOT: There we both are then.

AMANDA: What's she like?

ELYOT: Fair, very pretty, plays the piano beautifully.

AMANDA: Very comforting.

ELYOT: How's yours?

AMANDA: I don't want to discuss him.

ELYOT: Well, it doesn't matter, he'll probably come popping out in a minute and I shall see for myself. Does he know I'm here?

AMANDA: Yes, I told him.

ELYOT (*with sarcasm*): That's going to make things a whole lot easier.

AMANDA: You needn't be frightened, he won't hurt you.

ELYOT: If he comes near me I'll scream the place down.

AMANDA: Does Sibyl know I'm here?

ELYOT: No, I pretended I'd had a presentiment. I tried terribly hard to persuade her to leave for Paris.

AMANDA: I tried too, it's lucky we didn't both succeed, isn't it? Otherwise we should probably all have joined up in Rouen or somewhere.

ELYOT (*laughing*): In some frowsy little hotel.

AMANDA (*laughing too*): Oh dear, it would have been much, much worse.

ELYOT: I can see us all sailing down in the morning for an early start.

AMANDA (*weakly*): Lovely, oh lovely.

ELYOT: Glorious!

They both laugh helplessly.

AMANDA: What's happened to yours?

ELYOT: Didn't you hear her screaming? She's downstairs in the dining room I think.

AMANDA: Mine is being grand, in the bar.

ELYOT: It really is awfully difficult.

AMANDA: Have you known her long?

ELYOT: About four months, we met in a house party in Norfolk.

AMANDA: Very flat, Norfolk.

ELYOT: How old is dear Victor?

AMANDA: Thirty-four, or five; and Sibyl?

ELYOT: I blush to tell you, only twenty-three.

AMANDA: You've gone a mucker all right.

ELYOT: I shall reserve my opinion of your choice until I've met dear Victor.

AMANDA: I wish you wouldn't go on calling him 'Dear Victor'. It's extremely irritating.

ELYOT: That's how I see him. Dumpy, and fair, and very considerate, with glasses. Dear Victor.

AMANDA: As I said before I would rather not discuss him. At least I have good taste enough to refrain from making cheap gibes at Sibyl.

ELYOT: You said Norfolk was flat.

AMANDA: That was no reflection on her, unless she made it flatter.

ELYOT: Your voice takes on an acid quality whenever you mention her name.

AMANDA: I'll never mention it again.

ELYOT: Good, and I'll keep off Victor.

AMANDA (*with dignity*): Thank you.

There is silence for a moment. The orchestra starts playing the same tune that they were singing previously.

ELYOT: That orchestra has a remarkably small repertoire.

AMANDA: They don't seem to know anything but this, do they?

She sits down on the balustrade, and sings it, softly. Her eyes are looking out to sea, and her mind is far away. [Amanda sings.]

SOME DAY I'LL FIND YOU

When one is lonely the days are long;
You seem so near
But never appear.
Each night I sing you a lover's song;
Please try, try to hear,
My dear, my dear.

Can't you remember the fun we had?
Time is so fleet,
Why shouldn't we meet
When you're away from me days are sad;
Life's not complete,
My sweet, my sweet.

Some day I'll find you,
Moonlight behind you,
True to the dream I am dreaming
As I draw near you
You'll smile a little smile;
For a little while
We shall stand
Hand in hand.
I'll leave you never,
Love you for ever,
All our past sorrow redeeming,
Try to make it true,
Say you love me too.
Some day I'll find you again.

ELYOT *watches her while she sings. When she turns to him at the end, there are tears in her eyes. He looks away awkwardly and lights another cigarette.*

ELYOT: You always had a sweet voice, Amanda.

AMANDA (*a little huskily*): Thank you.

ELYOT: I'm awfully sorry about all this, really I am. I wouldn't have had it happen for the world.

AMANDA: I know. I'm sorry too. It's just rotten luck.

ELYOT: I'll go away tomorrow whatever happens, so don't you worry.

AMANDA: That's nice of you.

ELYOT: I hope everything turns out splendidly for you, and that you'll be very happy.

AMANDA: I hope the same for you, too.

The music, which has been playing continually through this little scene, returns persistently to the refrain. They both look at one another and laugh.

ELYOT: Nasty insistent little tune.

AMANDA: Extraordinary how potent cheap music is.

ELYOT: What exactly were you remembering at that moment?

AMANDA: The Palace Hotel Skating Rink in the morning, bright strong sunlight, and everybody whirling round in vivid colours, and you kneeling down to put on my skates for me.

ELYOT: You'd fallen on your fanny a few moments before.

AMANDA: It was beastly of you to laugh like that, I felt so humiliated.

ELYOT: Poor darling.

AMANDA: Do you remember waking up in the morning, and standing on the balcony, looking out across the valley?

ELYOT: Blue shadows on white snow, cleanness beyond belief, high above everything in the world. How beautiful it was.

AMANDA: It's nice to think we had a few marvellous moments.

ELYOT: A few! We had heaps really, only they slip away into the background, and one only remembers the bad ones.

AMANDA: Yes. What fools we were to ruin it all. What utter, utter fools.

ELYOT: You feel like that too, do you?

AMANDA (*wearily*): Of course.

AMANDA: Why did we?

AMANDA: The whole business was too much for us.

ELYOT: We were so ridiculously over in love.

AMANDA: Funny wasn't it?

ELYOT (*sadly*): Horribly funny.

AMANDA: Selfishness, cruelty, hatred, possessiveness, petty jealousy. All those qualities came out in us just because we loved each other.

ELYOT: Perhaps they were there anyhow.

AMANDA: No, it's love that does it. To hell with love.

ELYOT: To hell with love.

AMANDA: And yet here we are starting afresh with two quite different people. In love all over again, aren't we? (ELYOT *doesn't answer.*) Aren't we?

ELYOT: No.

AMANDA: Elyot.

ELYOT: We're not in love all over again, and you know it. Goodnight, Amanda.

He turns abruptly, and goes towards the French windows.

AMANDA: Elyot — don't be silly — come back.

ELYOT: I must go and find Sibyl.

AMANDA: I must go and find Victor.

ELYOT (*savagely*): Well, why don't you?

AMANDA: I don't want to.

ELYOT: It's shameful, shameful of us.

AMANDA: Don't: I feel terrible. Don't leave me for a minute, I shall go mad if you do. We won't talk about ourselves any more, we'll talk about outside things, anything you like, only just don't leave me until I've pulled myself together.

ELYOT: Very well.

There is a dead silence.

AMANDA: What have you been doing lately? During these last years?

ELYOT: Travelling about. I went round the world you know after —

AMANDA (*hurriedly*): Yes, yes, I know. How was it?

ELYOT: The world?

AMANDA: Yes.

ELYOT: Oh, highly enjoyable.

AMANDA: China must be very interesting.

ELYOT: Very big, China.

AMANDA: And Japan —

ELYOT: Very small.

AMANDA: Did you eat sharks' fins, and take your shoes off, and use chopsticks and everything?

ELYOT: Practically everything.

AMANDA: And India, the burning Ghars, or Ghats, or whatever they are, and the Taj Mahal. How *was* the Taj Mahal?

ELYOT (*looking at her*): Unbelievable, a sort of dream.

AMANDA: That was the moonlight I expect, you must have seen it in the moonlight.

ELYOT (*never taking his eyes off her face*): Yes, moonlight is cruelly deceptive.

AMANDA: And it didn't look like a biscuit box, did it? I've always felt that it might.

ELYOT (*quietly*): Darling, darling, I love you so.

AMANDA: And I do hope you met a sacred elephant. They're lint white, I believe, and very, very sweet.

ELYOT: I've never loved anyone else for an instant.

AMANDA (*raising her hand feebly in protest*): No, no, you mustn't – Elyot – stop.

ELYOT: You love me, too, don't you? There's no doubt about it anywhere, is there?

AMANDA: No, no doubt anywhere.

ELYOT: You're looking very lovely you know, in this damned moonlight. Your skin is clear and cool, and your eyes are shining, and you're growing lovelier and lovelier every second as I look at you. You don't hold any mystery for me, darling, do you mind? There isn't a particle of you that I don't know, remember, and want.

AMANDA (*softly*): I'm glad, my sweet.

ELYOT: More than any desire anywhere, deep down in my deepest heart I want you back again – please –

AMANDA (*putting her hand over his mouth*): Don't say any more, you're making me cry so dreadfully.

He pulls her gently into his arms and they stand silently, completely oblivious to everything but the moment, and each other. When, finally, they separate, they sit down, rather breathlessly, on the balustrade.

AMANDA: What now? Oh darling, what now?

ELYOT: I don't know, I'm lost, utterly.

AMANDA: We must think quickly, oh quickly –

ELYOT: Escape?

AMANDA: Together?

ELYOT: Yes, of course, now, now.

AMANDA: We can't, we can't, you know we can't.

ELYOT: We must.

AMANDA: It would break Victor's heart.

ELYOT: And Sibyl's too probably, but they're bound to suffer anyhow. Think of the hell we'd lead them into if we stayed. Infinitely worse than any cruelty in the world, pretending to love them, and loving each other, so desperately.

AMANDA: We must tell them.

ELYOT: What?

AMANDA: Call them, and tell them.

ELYOT: Oh no, no, that's impossible.

AMANDA: It's honest.

ELYOT: I can't help how honest it is, it's too horrible to think of. How should we start? What should we say?

AMANDA: We should have to trust to the inspiration of the moment.

ELYOT: It would be a moment completely devoid of inspiration. The most appalling moment imaginable. No, no, we can't, you must see that, we simply can't.

AMANDA: What do you propose to do then? As it is they might appear at any moment.

ELYOT: We've got to decide instantly one way or another. Go away together now, or stay with them, and never see one another again, ever.

AMANDA: Don't be silly, what choice is there?

ELYOT: No choice at all, come – (*He takes her hand.*)

AMANDA: No, wait. This is sheer raving madness, something's happened to us, we're not sane.

ELYOT: We never were.

AMANDA: Where can we go?

ELYOT: Paris first, my car's in the garage, all ready.

AMANDA: They'll follow us.

ELYOT: That doesn't matter, once the thing's done.

AMANDA: I've got a flat in Paris.

ELYOT: Good.

AMANDA: It's in the Avenue Montaigne. I let it to Freda Lawson, but she's in Biarritz, so it's empty.

ELYOT: Does Victor know?

AMANDA: No, he knows I have one but he hasn't the faintest idea where.

ELYOT: Better and better.

AMANDA: We're being so bad, so terribly bad, we'll suffer for this, I know we shall.

ELYOT: Can't be helped.

AMANDA: Starting all those awful rows all over again.

ELYOT: No, no, we're older and wiser now.

AMANDA: What difference does that make? The first moment either of us gets a bit nervy, off we'll go again.

ELYOT: Stop shilly-shallying, Amanda.

AMANDA: I'm trying to be sensible.

ELYOT: You're only succeeding in being completely idiotic.

AMANDA: Idiotic indeed! What about you?

ELYOT: Now look here Amanda –

AMANDA (*stricken*): Oh my God!

ELYOT (*rushing to her and kissing her*): Darling, darling, I didn't mean it –

AMANDA: I won't move from here unless we have a compact, a sacred, sacred compact never to quarrel again.

ELYOT: Easy to make but difficult to keep.

AMANDA: No, no, it's the bickering that always starts it. The moment we notice we're bickering, either of us, we must promise on our honour to stop dead. We'll invent some phrase or catchword which when either of us says it, automatically cuts off all conversation for at least five minutes.

ELYOT: Two minutes dear, with an option of renewal.

AMANDA: Very well, what shall it be?

ELYOT (*hurriedly*): Solomon Isaacs.

AMANDA: All right, that'll do.

ELYOT: Come on, come on.

AMANDA: What shall we do if we meet either of them on the way downstairs?

ELYOT: Run like stags.

AMANDA: What about clothes?

ELYOT: I've got a couple of bags I haven't unpacked yet.

AMANDA: I've got a small trunk.

ELYOT: Send the porter up for it.

AMANDA: Oh this is terrible – terrible –

ELYOT: Come on, come on, don't waste time.

AMANDA: Oughtn't we to leave notes or something?

ELYOT: No, no, no, we'll telegraph from somewhere on the road.

AMANDA: Darling, I daren't, it's too wicked of us, I simply daren't.

ELYOT (*seizing her in his arms and kissing her violently*): Now will you behave?

AMANDA: Yes, but Elyot darling –

ELYOT: Solomon Isaacs!

> *They rush off together through* ELYOT'*s suite. After a moment or so,* VICTOR
> *steps out on to the terrace and looks round anxiously. Then he goes back indoors
> again, and can be heard calling 'Mandy'. Finally he again comes out on to the*

Tea for two – times two. Victor (Laurence Olivier), Sybil (Adrianne Allen),
Elyot (Noël Coward) and Amanda (Gertrude Lawrence) in *Private Lives*.

terrace and comes despondently down to the balustrade. He hears SIBYL's *voice calling 'Elli' and looks round as she comes out of the French windows. She jumps slightly upon seeing him.*

VICTOR: Good evening.

SIBYL (*rather flustered*): Good evening – I was – er – looking for my husband.

VICTOR: Really, that's funny. I was looking for my wife.

SIBYL: Quite a coincidence. (*She laughs nervously.*)

VICTOR (*after a pause*): It's very nice here isn't it?

SIBYL: Lovely.

VICTOR: Have you been here long?

SIBYL: No, we only arrived today.

VICTOR: Another coincidence. So did we.

SIBYL: How awfully funny.

VICTOR: Would you care for a cocktail?

SIBYL: Oh no thank you – really –

VICTOR: There are two here on the table.

SIBYL *glances at the two empty glasses on the balustrade, and tosses her head defiantly.*

SIBYL: Thanks very much, I'd love one.

VICTOR: Good, here you are.

SIBYL *comes over to* VICTOR's *side of the terrace. He hands her one and takes one himself.*

SIBYL: Thank you.

VICTOR (*with rather forced gaiety*): To absent friends. (*He raises his glass.*)

SIBYL (*raising hers*): To absent friends.

They both laugh rather mirthlessly and then sit down on the balustrade, pensively sipping their cocktails and looking at the view.

It's awfully pretty isn't it? The moonlight, and the lights of that yacht reflected in the water –

VICTOR: I wonder who it belongs to.

The curtain slowly falls.

Noël was pleased to note in his Introduction to the first volume of Play
Parade *that the critics variously described the play as 'tenuous', 'thin',
'brittle', 'gossamer', 'iridescent' and 'delightfully daring'.*

'All of which connoted, to the public mind, "cocktails", "evening
dress", "repartee", and irreverent allusions to copulation, thereby
causing a gratifying number of respectable people to queue up
at the box office . . .

'There is actually more to the play than this . . . but on the whole
not very much. It is a reasonably well-constructed duologue for
two experienced performers, with a couple of extra puppets
thrown in to assist the plot and to provide contrast.'

*In this he misses a good part of his own point. For most productions
over the years the 'thin' and 'brittle' wit has been the keynote and
another clue that Noël himself seemed to pass over has been picked up
only recently by directors coming to the text with a fresh eye.*

AMANDA: Selfishness, cruelty, hatred, possessiveness, petty jealousy.
All those qualities came out in us just because we loved each
other.

*On an anything-but-superficial level it can be claimed that the play is
really about the impossibility of sustaining love. The wit is merely the
surface coating to conceal the hurt.*

★

'I will accept anything in the theatre . . . provided it amuses or
moves me. But if it does neither, I want to go home.

'Consider the public. Treat it with tact and courtesy. It will
accept much from you if you are clever enough to win it to
your side. Never fear it or despise it. Coax it, charm it, interest
it, stimulate it, shock it now and then if you must, make it
laugh, make it cry and make it think, but above all . . . never,
never, never bore the living hell out of it.'

Sunday Times, 1961

HAY FEVER

(1925)

JUDITH BLISS	Marie Tempest
SOREL BLISS	Helen Spencer
SIMON BLISS	Robert Andrews
RICHARD GREATHAM	Athole Stewart

Directed by Noël Coward
Ambassadors Theatre, London, 17 September 1925

*Hay Fever was based upon Noël's experience in the somewhat frenzied
New York home of American actress, Laurette Taylor. When Taylor
realized that she was the model for the heroine, she refused to speak to
Noël for several years before friendly relations were finally resumed.
Today – thanks to the play – the character is better remembered than
the original. But that's show business . . .*

'When I tapped out this little comedy so exuberantly on to my
typewriter in the year 1924, I would indeed have been astonished
if anyone had told me that it was destined to emerge, fresh and
blooming, forty years later. One of the reasons it was hailed so
warmly in 1925 was that there happened to be at that time an
ardent journalistic campaign being conducted against "sex" plays,
and *Hay Fever*, as I remarked in my first night speech, was, whether
good, bad or indifferent, at least it was clean as a whistle.

'I enjoyed writing it and producing it, and I have frequently
enjoyed watching it.

'The idea came to me suddenly in the garden and I finished it
in about three days, a feat which later on when I had become
news value, seemed to excite gossip-writers inordinately,
although why the public would care whether a play takes three
days or three years to write I shall never understand. Perhaps
they don't. However, when I had finished it and had it neatly
typed and bound up, I read it through and was rather unimpressed
with it. This was an odd sensation for me, as in those days I was
almost always enchanted with everything I wrote. I knew certain
scenes were good, especially the breakfast scene in the last act
and the dialogue between the giggling flapper and the diplomat
in the first act, but apart from these it seemed to me a little
tedious. I think the reason for this was that I was passing through
a transition stage as a writer; my dialogue was becoming more
natural and less elaborate and I was beginning to concentrate
more on the comedy values of situation rather than the comedy
values of actual lines. I expect that when I read through *Hay
Fever* that first time, I was subconsciously bemoaning its lack of
snappy epigrams.'

*In her day Judith Bliss was a resplendent star on the London stage –
the grande dame of the matinée tea trays. Though reluctantly retired from
the stage when the play opens, the actress in her will not be denied – as
her family and guests find to their cost.*

*On one particular weekend she, her husband David, son Simon and
daughter Sorel have each – unbeknownst to the rest of the family –
invited a guest. They then proceed to ignore them and a degree of social
chaos ensues. Before the guests arrive Judith confides to her children . . .*

JUDITH: I made a great decision this morning.

SIMON: What kind of decision?

JUDITH: It's a secret.

SOREL: Aren't you going to tell us?

JUDITH: Of course. I meant it was a secret from your father.

SIMON: What is it?

JUDITH *goes up C. and looks off L. to make sure no one is listening, then returns
to C.*

JUDITH: I'm going back to the stage.

SIMON: I knew it! (*Drops on to form below piano.*)

JUDITH: I'm stagnating here. I won't stagnate as long as there's breath left
in my body.

SOREL: Do you think it's wise? You retired so very finally last year. What
excuse will you give for returning so soon?

JUDITH: My public, dear – letters from my public!

SIMON: Have you had any?

JUDITH: One or two. That's what decided me, really – I ought to have had
hundreds.

SOREL (*kneels on R. corner of sofa*): We'll write some lovely ones, and you
can publish them in the papers.

JUDITH: Of course.

SOREL: You will be dignified about it all, won't you, darling?

JUDITH: I'm much more dignified on the stage than in the country – it's
my *milieu*. I've tried terribly hard to be 'landed gentry', but without any
real success. (*Moves up C. with outstretched arms.*) I long for excitement
and glamour. (*Comes down to R. corner of sofa.*) Think of the thrill of a first

night; all those ardent playgoers willing one to succeed; the critics all leaning forward with glowing faces, receptive and exultant – emitting queer little inarticulate noises as some witty line tickles their fancy. The satisfied grunt of the *Daily Mail*, the abandoned gurgle of the *Sunday Times*, and the shrill, enthusiastic scream of the *Daily Express*! I can distinguish them all –

SIMON: Have you got a play?

JUDITH: I think I shall revive *Love's Whirlwind*.

SOREL (*collapsing on to sofa*): Oh, Mother! (*She giggles with laughter.*)

SIMON (*weakly*): Father will be furious.

JUDITH: I can't help that.

SOREL: It's such a fearful play.

JUDITH: It's a marvellous part.

SOREL *opens her mouth to speak.*

You mustn't say too much against it, Sorel. I'm willing to laugh at it a little myself, but, after all, it *was* one of my greatest successes.

SIMON: Oh, it's appalling – but I love it. It makes me laugh.

JUDITH: The public love it too, and it doesn't make them laugh – much. (*Moves to C. and very dramatically she recites.*) 'You are a fool, a blind pitiable fool. You think because you have bought my body that you have bought my soul!' (*Turning to* SIMON.) You must say that's dramatic – 'I've dreamed of love like this, but I never realized, I never knew how beautiful it could be in reality!' (*Wipes away imaginary tears.*) That line always brought a tear to my eye.

SIMON: The second act *is* the best, there's no doubt about that.

JUDITH (*turning to* SOREL): From the moment Victor comes in it's strong – tremendously strong . . . Be Victor a minute, Sorel –

SOREL (*rising*): Do you mean when he comes in at the end of the act?

JUDITH: Yes. You know – 'Is this a game?'

SOREL (*going to* JUDITH *and speaking in a very dramatic voice*): 'Is this a game?'

JUDITH (*with spirit*): 'Yes – and a game that must be played to the finish.'

SIMON (*rising and moving to* JUDITH, *and speaking in deep dramatic voice*): 'Zara, what does this mean?'

JUDITH: 'So many illusions shattered – so many dreams trodden in the dust!'

SOREL (*runs behind* JUDITH *and in front of* SIMON *to down* R.): I'm George now – 'I don't understand! You and Victor – My God!' (*Strikes dramatic pose.*)

JUDITH (*moving a little to L. – listening*): 'Shhh! Isn't that little Pam crying?'

SIMON (*savagely*): 'She'll cry more, poor mite, when she realizes her mother is a – '

The front-door bell rings.

JUDITH: Damn! There's the bell!

When the guests arrive Judith finds herself alone with Sorel's guest, the rather stuffy civil servant, Richard Greatham. The opportunity for a little improvisational 'performance' is a temptation too strong to resist . . .

JUDITH: You'll get used to us in time, and then you'll feel cosier. Why don't you sit down? (*She sits on sofa.*)

RICHARD (*sits beside her*): I'm enjoying myself very much.

JUDITH: It's very sweet of you to say so, but I don't see how you can be.

RICHARD (*laughing suddenly*): But I am!

JUDITH: There now, that was quite a genuine laugh! We're getting on. Are you in love with Sorel?

RICHARD (*surprised and embarrassed*): In love with Sorel?

JUDITH (*repentantly*): Now I've killed it – I've murdered the little tender feeling of comfort that was stealing over you, by sheer tactlessness! Will you teach me to be tactful?

RICHARD: Did you really think I was in love with Sorel? .

JUDITH: It's so difficult to tell, isn't it? – I mean, you might not know yourself. She's very attractive.

RICHARD: Yes, she is – very.

JUDITH: Have you heard her sing?

RICHARD: No, not yet.

JUDITH: She sings beautifully. Are you susceptible to music?

RICHARD: I'm afraid I don't know very much about it.

JUDITH: You probably are, then. I'll sing you something.

RICHARD: Please do.

JUDITH (*rises and crosses to piano; he rises and stands C.*): It's awfully sad for a woman of my temperament to have a grown-up daughter, you know. I have to put my pride in my pocket and develop in her all the charming little feminine tricks which will eventually cut me out altogether.

RICHARD: That wouldn't be possible.

JUDITH: I do hope you meant that, because it was a sweet remark. (*She is at the piano, turning over music.*)

RICHARD (*crosses to piano*): Of course I meant it.

JUDITH: Will you lean on the piano in an attentive attitude? It's such a help.

RICHARD (*leaning on piano*): You're an extraordinary person.

JUDITH (*beginning to play*): In what way extraordinary?

RICHARD: When I first met Sorel, I guessed what you'd be like.

JUDITH: Did you, now? And am I?

RICHARD (*smiling*): Exactly.

JUDITH: Oh, well! . . .

She plays and sings a little French song. There is a slight pause when it is finished.

RICHARD (*with feeling*): Thank you.

JUDITH (*rising from the piano*): It's pretty, isn't it?

RICHARD: Perfectly enchanting.

JUDITH (*crosses to sofa*): Shall we sit down again? (*She re-seats herself on sofa.*)

RICHARD (*moving over to her*): Won't you sing any more?

JUDITH: No, no more – I want you to talk to me and tell me all about yourself, and the things you've done.

RICHARD (*sits beside her*): I've done nothing.

JUDITH: What a shame! Why not?

RICHARD: I never realize how *dead* I am until I meet people like you. It's depressing, you know.

JUDITH: What nonsense! You're not a bit dead.

RICHARD: Do you always live here?

JUDITH: I'm going to, from now onwards. I intend to sink into a very beautiful old age. When the children marry, I shall wear a cap.

RICHARD (*smiling*): How absurd!

JUDITH: I don't mean a funny cap.

RICHARD: You're far too full of vitality to sink into anything.

JUDITH: It's entirely spurious vitality. If you troubled to look below the
surface, you'd find a very wistful and weary spirit. I've been battling
with life for a long time.

RICHARD: Surely such successful battles as yours have been are not
wearying?

JUDITH: Yes, they are – frightfully. I've reached an age now when I just
want to sit back and let things go on around me – and they do.

RICHARD: I should like to know exactly what you're thinking about –
really.

JUDITH: I was thinking of calling you Richard. It's such a nice
uncompromising name.

RICHARD: I should be very flattered if you would.

JUDITH: I won't suggest you calling me Judith until you feel really
comfortable about me.

RICHARD: But I do – Judith.

JUDITH: I'm awfully glad. Will you give me a cigarette?

RICHARD (*producing case*): Certainly.

JUDITH (*taking one*): Oh, what a divine case!

RICHARD: It was given to me in Japan three years ago. All those little
designs mean things.

JUDITH (*bending over it*): What sort of things?

He lights her cigarette.

RICHARD: Charms for happiness, luck, and – love.

JUDITH: Which is the charm for love?

RICHARD: That one.

JUDITH: What a dear!

RICHARD *kisses her gently on the neck. She sits upright, with a scream.*
Richard!

RICHARD (*stammering*): I'm afraid I couldn't help it.

JUDITH (*dramatically*): What are we to do? What are we to do?

RICHARD: I don't know.

JUDITH (*rises, thrusts the case in his hand and crosses to R.C.*): David must be
told – everything!

RICHARD (*alarmed*): Everything?

JUDITH (*enjoying herself*): Yes, yes. There come moments in life when it is necessary to be honest – absolutely honest. I've trained myself always to shun the underhand methods other women so often employ – the truth must be faced fair and square –

RICHARD (*extremely alarmed*): The truth? I don't quite understand. (*He rises.*)

JUDITH: Dear Richard, you want to spare me, I know – you're so chivalrous; but it's no use. After all, as I said before, David has been a good husband to me, according to his lights. This may, of course, break him up rather, but it can't be helped. I wonder – oh, I wonder how he'll take it! They say suffering's good for writers, it strengthens their psychology. Oh, my poor, poor David! Never mind. You'd better go out into the garden and wait –

RICHARD (*flustered*): Wait? What for? (*Moves to C.*)

JUDITH: For me, Richard, for me. I will come to you later. Wait in the summer-house. I had begun to think that Romance was dead, that I should never know it again. Before, of course, I had my work and my life in the theatre, but now, nothing – nothing! Everything is empty and hollow, like a broken shell.

She sinks on to form below piano, and looks up at RICHARD *with a tragic smile, then looks quickly away.*

RICHARD: Look here, Judith, I apologize for what I did just now. I –

JUDITH (*ignoring all interruption, she rises and crosses to L.C.*): But now you have come, and it's all changed – it's magic! I'm under a spell that I never thought to recapture again. Go along –

She pushes him towards the garden.

RICHARD (*protesting*): But, Judith –

JUDITH (*pushing him firmly until he is off*): Don't – don't make it any harder for me. I am quite resolved – and it's the only possible way. Go, go!

She pushes him into the garden and waves to him bravely with her handkerchief; then she comes back into the room and powders her nose before the glass and pats her hair into place.

★

If Judith Bliss had lived to be a hundred, she would still have been acting and incorporating the advancing years seamlessly into the character she was playing. In Noël's experience, not every senior female thespian was so resilient . . .

EPITAPH FOR AN ELDERLY ACTRESS

She got in a rage
About age
And retired, in a huff, from the stage.
Which, taken all round, was a pity
Because she was still fairly pretty
But she got in a rage
About age.

She burst into tears
It appears
When the rude, inconsiderate years
Undermined her once flawless complexion
And whenever she saw her reflection
In a mirror, she burst into tears
It appears.

She got in a state
About weight
And resented each morsel she ate.
Her colon she constantly sluiced
And reduced and reduced and reduced
And, at quite an incredible rate,
Put on weight.

She got in a rage
About age
But she still could have played Mistress Page
And she certainly could have done worse
Than *Hay Fever* or Juliet's Nurse
But she got in a terrible rage
About age.

And she moaned and she wept and she wailed
And she roared and she ranted and railed
And retired, very heavily veiled,
From the stage.

'God preserve me in future from female stars. I don't suppose
He will.'

*And, indeed — fortunately — He didn't. Most of them trod the boards
but there were those whose legend was enshrined on the silver screen.
Like Marlene Dietrich — or Louisa.*

LOUISA

Louisa was a movie queen.
Before she'd achieved the age of sweet sixteen,
Long before Cagney threw those girls about,
Little Louisa tossed her curls about.
Later when the talkies came
The whole world
Resounded with her fame,
Each time she married
Every daily paper carried
Headlines blazing her name.
Not only headlines
But photographs and interviews,
Everything she did was news
That held the world in thrall.

Some said she read lines
Better than Marlene could,
No other entertainer could
Compare with her at all.
But regardless of the fact
That she could sing and dance and act
And owned furniture that wasn't 'Little Rockery',
And regardless of her gems,
Which were hers, not MGM's,
Her life was one long mockery.

Louisa was terribly lonely,
Success brought her naught but despair.
She derived little fun from the Oscars she'd won
And none from her home in Bel Air.

She declared she was weary of living
On a bestial terrestrial plane.
When friends came to visit their hands she would clutch,
Crying, 'Tell me, why is it I suffer so much?
If only, if only, if only,
My life wasn't quite such a strain.'
And soon after that she was terribly lonely,
All over again.

Louisa was terribly lonely.
Louisa was terribly sad.
It appears that the cheers that had rung in her ears
For years had been driving her mad.
She sobbed when men offered her sables
And moaned when they gave her champagne.
She remarked to her groom on their honeymoon night
As he tenderly kissed her and turned out the light,
'If only, if only, if only
I'd thrown myself out of the plane . . .'
The very next day she was terribly lonely,
All over again.

Louisa was terribly lonely
(The girl had no fun),
Louisa was tired of it all
(Not a call from anyone),
She gazed like a dazed belated Sphinx
At her hundred and eight mutated minks
And she wrung her hands and she beat her breast,
Crying, 'My, my, my, I'm so depressed.'
Nobody knew the trouble she'd seen,
Nobody knew but you know who

The tribulations of a movie queen.
So farewell to lovely Louisa
(Who just let life tease her),
Let's leave her seeking in vain
(To find someone to explain)
Why destiny should single her out to be only lonely,
Over and over again!

COWARD ON ACTING

'I think the most dangerous theory advanced in modern days is that you have to feel what you do for eight performances a week. It's out of the question. And also, acting is not a state of being. Acting is acting . . . It's giving an *impression* of feeling. If it's real feeling, then you're very liable to lose your performance and lose the attention of the audience, because if you lose yourself, you're liable to lose them.'

'Great Acting', BBC Television interview, 1966

★

'Acting is an instinct. A gift that is often given to people who are very silly as people. But as they come on to the stage, up goes the temperature.'

★

'When you've learned the words, analyse the part. Find out what it's about. When he goes out on that stage, an actor should forget himself and remember the part . . . Remember the other actors who are sharing the stage with you. Look at them. Not at their foreheads. Not at their ears. But at their eyes. Then learn to laugh and cry – without feeling happy or sad.'

DESIGN FOR LIVING

ALFRED LUNT, NOEL COWARD AND LYNN FONTANNE

ETHEL BARRYMORE
THEATRE

DESIGN FOR LIVING

(1933)

GILDA	Lynn Fontanne
OTTO	Alfred Lunt
LEO	Noël Coward

Directed by Noël Coward
Ethel Barrymore Theatre, New York, 24 January 1933

Noël often referred to Design for Living *as his favourite play. It had its origins in that first visit to New York in the summer of 1921 where he met Alfred Lunt and Lynn Fontanne – not yet 'The Lunts'.*

He wrote to Violet . . .

'Darling,

Do you remember Lynn Fontanne? She played some small parts in London and came to New York. Well, she's had a huge success in a play called *Dulcy* (she's Dulcy). I went to see her opening night with her fiancé, an actor called Alfred Lunt, and, my dear, a star was born. Well, *two* stars, actually, as Alfred is also making a name for himself in these parts.

They're quite wonderful and couldn't have been kinder to me. They haven't any money either – though they soon will have, I'm sure – and they helped me keep body and soul together by sharing their last crust (not quite that, really). They're going to be huge stars and, since we all know that yours truly is going to be one too, we've decided that, when that great day arrives, we shall act together in a play I shall write for us and the cosmos will have a new galaxy.'

His prediction would catch up with him a decade later towards the end of a trip around South America. In Santiago a cable reached him from the Lunts, who had been working exclusively for the Theatre Guild for some years . . .

'OUR CONTRACT WITH THEATRE GUILD UP IN JUNE STOP WE'RE FREE STOP WHAT ABOUT IT?'

Noël travelled back to the US on a Norwegian freighter. By the time he arrived in San Francisco he had the draft of the play under his arm.

★

Otto (Alfred Lunt) is a painter who lives with Gilda (Lynn Fontanne), an interior decorator. When asked why she doesn't marry him, she replies simply — 'Because I love him.' Marriage would spoil their relationship. The only problem is that she also loves Leo (Noël), a writer, who loves her in return. And they both love Otto, who loves both of them.

The play revolves around the complications this perilous ménage à trois creates for them and the people around them, as they realize once and for all that, while they can't live with each other, they can't live without each other either.

Act One is set in Paris. Otto returns from a business trip, overjoyed to see Gilda again but she immediately tells him he must go to the Hotel Georges V. Leo has just arrived and can't wait to see him. Otto leaves . . .

GILDA *stands quite still for a moment or two; then she sits down at a table.* LEO *comes out of the bedroom. He is thin and nervous and obviously making a tremendous effort to control himself. He walks about aimlessly for a little and finishes up looking out of the window, with his back to* GILDA.

LEO: What now?

GILDA: I don't know.

LEO: Not much time to think.

GILDA: A few minutes.

LEO: Are there any cigarettes?

GILDA: Yes, in that box.

LEO: Want one?

GILDA: No.

LEO (*lighting one*): It's nice being human beings, isn't it? I'm sure God's angels must envy us.

GILDA: Whom do you love best? Otto or me?

LEO: Silly question.

GILDA: Answer me, anyhow.

LEO: How can I? Be sensible! In any case, what does it matter?

GILDA: It's important to me.

LEO: No, it isn't — not really. That's not what's important. What we did was inevitable. It's been inevitable for years. It doesn't matter who loves who the most; you can't line up things like that mathematically. We all love each other a lot, far too much, and we've made a bloody mess of it! That was inevitable, too.

GILDA: We must get it straight, somehow.

LEO: Yes, we must get it straight and tie it up with ribbons with a bow on the top. Pity it isn't Valentine's Day!

GILDA: Can't we laugh a little? Isn't it a joke? Can't we make it a joke?

LEO: Yes, it's a joke. It's a joke, all right. We can laugh until our sides ache. Let's start, shall we?

GILDA: What's the truth of it? The absolute, deep-down truth? Until we really know that, we can't grapple with it. We can't do a thing. We can only sit here flicking words about.

LEO: It should be easy, you know. The actual facts are so simple. I love you. You love me. You love Otto. I love Otto. Otto loves you. Otto loves me. There now! Start to unravel from there.

GILDA: We've always been honest, though, all of us. Honest with each other, I mean. That's something to go on, isn't it?

LEO: In this particular instance, it makes the whole thing far more complicated. If we were ordinary moral, high-thinking citizens we could carry on a backstairs affair for weeks without saying a word about it. We could lunch and dine together, all three, and not give anything away by so much as a look.

GILDA: If we were ordinary moral, high-thinking citizens we shouldn't have had an affair at all.

LEO: Perhaps not. We should have crushed it down. And the more we crushed it down the more we should have resented Otto, until we hated him. Just think of hating Otto −

GILDA: Just think of him hating us.

LEO: Do you think he will?

GILDA (*inexorably*): Yes.

LEO (*walking about the room*): Oh, no, no − he mustn't! It's too silly. He must see how unimportant it is, really.

GILDA: There's no question of not telling him, is there?

LEO: Of course not.

GILDA: We could pretend that you just arrived here and missed him on the way.

LEO: So we could, dear − so we could.

GILDA: Do you think we're working each other up? Do you think we're imagining it to be more serious than it really is?

LEO: Perhaps.

GILDA: Do you think, after all, he may not mind quite so dreadfully?

LEO: He'll mind just as much as you or I would under similar circumstances. Probably a little bit more. Imagine that for a moment, will you? Put yourself in his place.

GILDA (*hopelessly*): Oh, don't!

LEO: Tell me one thing. How sorry were you last night, when once you realized we were in for it?

GILDA: I wasn't sorry at all. I gave way utterly.

LEO: So did I.

GILDA: Very deep inside, I had a qualm or two. Just once or twice.

LEO: So did I.

GILDA: But I stamped on them, like killing beetles.

LEO: A nice way to describe the pangs of a noble conscience!

GILDA: I enjoyed it all, see! I enjoyed it thoroughly from the very first moment. So there!

LEO: All right! All right! So did I.

GILDA (*defiantly*): It was romantic. Suddenly, violently romantic! The whole evening was 'Gala'. You looked lovely, darling − very smooth and velvety – and your manner was a dream! I'd forgotten about your French accent and the way you move your hands, and the way you dance. A sleek little gigolo!

LEO: You must try not to be bitter, dear.

GILDA: There seemed to be something new about you: something I'd never realized before. Perhaps it's having money. Perhaps your success has given you a little extra glamour.

LEO: Look at me now, sweet! It's quite chilly, this morning light. How do I appear to you now?

GILDA (*gently*): The same.

LEO: So do you, but that's because my eyes are slow at changing visions. I still see you too clearly last night to be able to realize how you look this morning. You were very got up – very got up, indeed, in your green dress and your ear-rings. It was 'Gala', all right – strong magic!

GILDA: Coloured lights, sly music, overhanging trees, paper streamers – all the trappings.

LEO: Champagne, too, just to celebrate, both of us hating it.

GILDA: We drank to Otto. Perhaps you remember that as well?

LEO: Perfectly.

GILDA: How could we? Oh, how could we?

LEO: It seemed quite natural.

GILDA: Yes, but we knew in our hearts what we were up to. It was vile of us.

LEO: I'll drink Otto's health until the day I die! Nothing could change that ever.

GILDA: Sentimentalist!

LEO: Deeper than sentiment: far, far deeper. Beyond the reach of small enchantments.

GILDA: Was that all it was to you? A small enchantment?

LEO: That's all it ever is to anybody, if only they knew.

GILDA: Easy wisdom. Is it a comfort to you?

LEO: Not particularly.

GILDA (*viciously*): Let's have some more! 'Passion's only transitory,' isn't it? 'Love is ever fleeting!' 'Time is a great healer.' Trot them all out, dear.

LEO: Don't try to quarrel with me.

GILDA: Don't be so wise and assured and knowing, then. It's infuriating.

LEO: I believe I was more to blame than you, really.

GILDA: Why?

LEO: I made the running.

GILDA: *You* made the running! (*She laughs.*)

LEO: A silly pride made me show off to you, parade my attraction for you, like a mannequin. New spring model, with a few extra flounces!

GILDA: That's my story, Leo; you can't steal it from me. I've been wallowing in self-abasement, dragging out my last night's femininity and spitting on it. I've taken the blame on to myself for the whole thing. Ernest was quite shocked; you should have been listening at the door.

LEO: I was.

GILDA: Good! Then you know how I feel.

LEO: Lot of damned hysteria.

GILDA: Possibly, but heartfelt at the moment.

LEO: Can't we put an end to this flagellation party now?

GILDA: We might just as well go on with it; it passes the time.

LEO: Until Otto comes back.

GILDA: Yes. Until Otto comes back.

LEO (*walking up and down*): I expect jealousy had something to do with it, too.

GILDA: Jealousy?

LEO: Yes. Subconscious and buried deep, but there all the same; there for ages, ever since our first meeting when you chose Otto so firmly.

GILDA: Another of those pleasant little galas! The awakening of spring! Romance in a café! Yes, sir! 'Yes, sir, three bags full!'

LEO: A strange evening. Very gay, if I remember rightly.

GILDA: Oh, it was gay, deliriously gay, thick with omens!

LEO: Perhaps we laughed at them too hard.

In Act Two, Gilda and Leo are living together in London. It's the morning after the opening night of Leo's play, Change and Decay, *and he is reading his reviews . . .*

LEO (*rolling over on his back and flinging the paper in the air*): It's a knockout! It's magnificent! It'll run a year.

GILDA: Two years.

LEO: Three years.

GILDA: Four years, five years, six years! It'll run for ever. Old ladies will be trampled to death struggling to get into the pit. Women will have babies regularly in the upper circle bar during the big scene at the end of the second act –

LEO (*complacently*): Regularly as clockwork.

GILDA: The *Daily Mail* says it's daring and dramatic and witty.

LEO: The *Daily Express* says it's disgusting.

GILDA: I should be cut to the quick if it said anything else.

LEO: The *Daily Mirror*, I regret to say, is a trifle carping.

GILDA: Getting uppish, I see. Naughty little thing!

LEO (*reading the* Daily Mirror): '*Change and Decay* is gripping throughout. The characterization falters here and there, but the dialogue is polished and sustains a high level from first to last and is frequently witty, nay, even brilliant – '

GILDA: I love 'nay'.

LEO (*still reading*): 'But' – here we go, dear! 'But the play, on the whole, is decidedly thin.'

GILDA: My God! They've noticed it.

LEO (*jumping up*): Thin – thin! What do they mean, 'thin'?

GILDA: Just thin, darling. Thin's thin all the world over and you can't get away from it.

LEO: Would you call it thin?

GILDA: Emaciated.

LEO: I shall write fat plays from now onwards. Fat plays filled with very fat people!

GILDA: You mustn't let your vibrations be upset by the *Daily Mirror*. It means to be kind. That's why one only looks at the pictures.

LEO: The *Daily Sketch* is just as bad.

GILDA (*gently*): Just as good, dear – just as good.

LEO: Let's have another look at Old Father *Times*.

GILDA: It's there, behind the *Telegraph*.

LEO (*glancing through it*): Non-committal, but amiable. A minute, if slightly inaccurate, description of the plot.

GILDA (*rising and looking over his shoulder*): Only a few of the names wrong.

LEO: They seem to have missed the main idea of the play.

GILDA: You mustn't grumble; they say the lines are provocative.

LEO: What *could* they mean by that?

GILDA: Anyhow, you can't expect a paper like *The Times* to be really interested in your petty little excursions in the theatre. After all, it is the organ of the nation.

LEO: That sounds vaguely pornographic to me.

Eventually Gilda leaves them both. Leo and Otto commiserate over a few drinks.

At one performance Alfred and Noël accidentally swapped lines. Realizing what had happened they continued to play each other's lines. Noël recalled:

'Since it was a drunk scene, nobody noticed. But then I realized that Leo (*now Alfred*) would come to a line where he had to burp. And I knew Alfred couldn't burp – so I took the line back and we finished the scene mightily pleased with ourselves. Until we exited, only to be confronted with an icy Lynn. "Nothing either of you did on that stage tonight was even *remotely* funny!"'

LEO: Where is Gilda?

OTTO: She's gone out.

LEO: Out! Why? Where's she gone to?

OTTO: I don't know.

LEO (*turning away*): How vile of you! How unspeakably vile of you both!

OTTO: It was inevitable.

LEO (*contemptuously*): Inevitable!

OTTO: I arrived unexpectedly; you were away; Gilda was alone. I love her; I've always loved her – I've never stopped for a minute, and she loves me, too.

LEO: What about me?

OTTO: I told you I was sorry about hurting you.

LEO: Gilda loves me.

OTTO: I never said she didn't.

LEO (*hopelessly*): What are we to do? What are we to do now?

OTTO: Do you know, I really haven't the faintest idea.

LEO: You're laughing inside. You're thoroughly damned well pleased with yourself, aren't you?

OTTO: I don't know. I don't know that either.

LEO (*savagely*): You are! I can see it in your eyes – so much triumph – such a sweet revenge!

OTTO: It wasn't anything to do with revenge.

LEO: It was. Of course it was – secretly thought out, planned for ages – infinitely mean!

OTTO: Shut up! And don't talk such nonsense.

LEO: Why did you do it, then? Why did you come back and break everything up for me?

OTTO: I came back to see you both. It was a surprise.

LEO: A rather cruel surprise, and brilliantly successful. You should be very happy.

OTTO (*sadly*): Should I?

LEO: Perhaps I should be happy, too; you've set me free from something.

OTTO: What?

LEO (*haltingly*): The – feeling I had for you – something very deep, I imagined it was, but it couldn't have been, could it? – now that it has died so easily.

OTTO: I said all that to you in Paris. Do you remember? I thought it was true then, just as you think it's true now.

LEO: It is true.

OTTO: Oh, no, it isn't.

LEO: Do you honestly believe I could ever look at you again, as a real friend?

OTTO: Until the day you die.

LEO: Shut up! It's too utterly beastly – the whole thing.

OTTO: It's certainly very, very uncomfortable.

LEO: Is Gilda going to leave me? To go away with you?

OTTO: Do you want her to?

LEO: Yes, I suppose so, now.

OTTO: We didn't make any arrangement or plans.

LEO: I came back too soon. You could have gone away and left a note for me – that would have heen nice and easy for you, wouldn't it?

OTTO: Perhaps it would, really. I don't know that I should have done it, though.

LEO: Why not?

OTTO: If I had, I shouldn't have seen you at all, and I wanted to see you very much.

LEO: You even wanted to see me, hating you like this? Very touching!

OTTO: You're not hating me nearly as much as you think you are. You're hating the situation: that's quite different.

LEO: You flatter yourself.

OTTO: No. I'm speaking from experience. You forget, I've been through just what you're going through now. I thought I hated you with all my heart and soul, and the force of that hatred swept me away on to the high seas, too far out of reach to be able to come back when I discovered the truth.

LEO: The truth!

OTTO: That no one of us was more to blame than the other. We've made our own circumstances, you and Gilda and me, and we've bloody well got to put up with them!

LEO: I wish I could aspire to such a sublime God's-eye view!

OTTO: You will – in time – when your acids have calmed down.

LEO: I'd like so very much not to be able to feel anything at all for a little. I'm desperately tired.

OTTO: You want a change.

LEO: It seems as if I'm going to get one, whether I want it or not.

OTTO (*laughing*): Oh, Leo, you really are very, very tender!

LEO: Don't laugh! How dare you laugh! How *can* you laugh!

OTTO: It's a good joke. A magnificent joke.

LEO (*bitterly*): A pity Gilda chose just that moment to go out, we could all have enjoyed it together.

OTTO: Like we did before?

LEO: Yes, like we did before.

OTTO: And like we shall again.

LEO (*vehemently*): No, *never* again − never!

OTTO: I wonder.

The telephone rings. LEO *goes over mechanically to answer it; he lifts up the receiver, and as he does so he catches sight of the two letters propped up against the brandy bottle. He stares at them and slowly lets the receiver drop on to the desk.*

LEO (*very quietly*): Otto.

OTTO: What is it?

LEO: Look.

OTTO *comes over to the desk, and they both stand staring at the letters.*

OTTO: Gilda!

LEO: Of course.

OTTO: She's gone! She's escaped!

LEO: Funny word to use, 'escaped'.

OTTO: That's what she's done, all the same, escaped.

LEO: The joke is becoming richer.

OTTO: Escaped from both of us.

LEO: We'd better open them, I suppose.

OTTO (*slowly*): Yes − yes, I suppose we had.

They both open the letters, in silence, and read them.

LEO (*after a pause*): What does yours say?

OTTO (*reading*): 'Goodbye, my clever little dear! Thank you for the keys of the city.'

LEO: That's what mine says.

OTTO: I wonder where she's gone?

LEO: I don't see that that matters much.

OTTO: One up to Gilda!

LEO: What does she mean, 'keys of the city'?

OTTO: A lot of things.

LEO: I feel rather sick.

OTTO: Have some sherry?

LEO: That's brandy.

OTTO: Better still.

He pours out a glass and hands it to LEO.

LEO (*quietly*): Thank you.

OTTO (*pouring one out for himself*): I feel a little sick, too.

LEO: Do you think she'll come back?

OTTO: No.

LEO: She will – she must – she must come back!

OTTO: She won't. Not for a long time.

LEO (*drinking his brandy*): It's all my fault, really.

OTTO (*drinking his*): Is it?

LEO: Yes. I've, unfortunately, turned out to be successful. Gilda doesn't care for successful people.

OTTO: I wonder how much we've lost, with the years?

LEO: A lot. I think, practically everything now.

OTTO (*thoughtfully*): Love among the artists. Very difficult, too difficult.

LEO: Do you think we could find her?

OTTO: No.

LEO: We could try.

OTTO: Do you want to?

LEO: Of course.

OTTO: Why? What would be the use?

LEO: She might explain a little – a little more clearly.

OTTO: What good would that do? We know why she's gone perfectly well.

LEO: Because she doesn't want us any more.

OTTO: Because she thinks she doesn't want us any more.

LEO: I suppose that's as good a reason as any.

OTTO: Quite.

LEO: All the same, I should like to see her just once – just to find out, really, in so many words –

OTTO (*with sudden fury*): So many words! That's what's wrong with us! So many words – too many words, masses and masses of words, spewed about until we're choked with them. We've argued and probed and dragged our entrails out in front of one another for years! We've explained away the sea and the stars and life and death and our own peace of mind! I'm sick of this endless game of three-handed, spiritual ping-pong – this battling of our little egos in one another's faces! Sick to death of it! Gilda's made a supreme gesture and got out. Good luck to her, I say! Good luck to the old girl – she knows her onions!

OTTO *refills his glass and drains it at a gulp.*

LEO: You'll get drunk, swilling down all that brandy on an empty stomach.

OTTO: Why not? What else is there to do? Here, have some more as well.

He refills LEO's *glass and hands it to him.*

LEO: All right! Here goes. (*He drains his glass.*) Now we start fair.

He refills both their glasses.

OTTO (*raising his glass*): Gilda! (*He drains it.*)

LEO (*doing the same*): Gilda! (*He drains it.*)

OTTO: That's better, isn't it? Much, much better.

LEO: Excellent. We shall be sick as dogs!

OTTO: Good for our livers.

LEO: Good for our immortal souls.

He refills the glasses, and raises his.

Our Immortal Souls!

OTTO (*raising his*): Our Immortal Souls!

They both drain them to the last drop.

LEO: I might have known it!

OTTO: What?

LEO: That there was going to be a break. Everything was running too smoothly, too well. I was enjoying all the small things too much.

OTTO: There's no harm in enjoying the small things.

LEO: Gilda didn't want me to.

OTTO: I know.

LEO: Did she tell you so?

OTTO: Yes, she said she was uneasy.

LEO: She might have had a little faith in me, I think. I haven't got this far just to be sidetracked by a few garlands.

OTTO: That's what I said to her; I said you wouldn't be touched, inside.

LEO: How about you?

OTTO: Catching up, Leo! Popular portraits at popular prices.

LEO: Good work or bad work?

OTTO: Good. An occasional compromise, but essentials all right.

LEO (*with a glint in his eye*): Let's make the most of the whole business, shall we? Let's be photographed and interviewed and pointed at in restaurants! Let's play the game for what it's worth, secretaries and fur coats and *de luxe* suites on transatlantic liners at minimum rates! Don't let's allow one shabby perquisite to slip through our fingers! It's what we dreamed many years ago and now it's within our reach. Let's cash in, Otto, and see how much we lose by it.

He refills both glasses and hands one to OTTO.

Come on, my boy!

He raises his glass.

Success in twenty lessons! Each one more bitter than the last! More and better Success! Louder and funnier Success!

They both drain their glasses.

They put down their glasses, gasping slightly.

OTTO (*agreeably*): It takes the breath away a bit, doesn't it?

LEO: How astonished our insides must be – all that brandy hurtling down suddenly!

OTTO: On Sunday, too.

LEO: We ought to know more about our insides, Otto. We ought to know why everything does everything.

OTTO: Machines! That's what we are, really – all of us! I can't help feeling a little discouraged about it every now and then.

LEO: Sheer sentimentality! You shouldn't feel discouraged at all; you should be proud.

OTTO: I don't see anything to be proud about.

LEO: That's because you don't understand; because you're still chained to stale illusions. Science dispels illusions; you ought to be proud to be living in a scientific age. You ought to be proud to know that you're a minute cog in the vast process of human life.

OTTO: I don't like to think I'm only a minute cog – it makes me sort of sad.

LEO: The time for dreaming is over, Otto.

OTTO: Never! I'll never consent to that. Never, as long as I live! How do you know that science isn't a dream, too? A monstrous, gigantic hoax?

LEO: How could it be? It proves everything.

OTTO: What does it prove? Answer me that!

LEO: Don't be silly, Otto. You must try not to be silly.

OTTO (*bitterly*): A few facts, that's all. A few tawdry facts torn from the universe and dressed up in terminological abstractions!

LEO: Science is our only hope, the only hope for humanity! We've wallowed in false mysticism for centuries; we've fought and suffered and died for foolish beliefs, which science has proved to be as ephemeral as smoke. Now is the moment to open our eyes fearlessly and look at the truth!

OTTO: What is the truth?

LEO (*irritably*): It's no use talking to you – you just won't try to grasp anything! You're content to go on being a romantic clod until the end of your days.

OTTO (*incensed*): What about you? What about the plays you write? Turgid with romance; sodden with true love; rotten with nostalgia!

LEO (*with dignity*): There's no necessity to be rude about my work – that's quite separate, and completely beside the point.

OTTO: Well, it oughtn't to be. It ought to be absolutely in accord with your cold, incisive, scientific viewpoint. If you're a writer it's your duty to write what you think. If you don't you're a cheat – a cheat and a hypocrite!

LEO (*loftily*): Impartial discussion is one thing, Otto. Personal bickering is another. I think you should learn to distinguish between the two.

OTTO: Let's have some more brandy.

LEO: That would be completely idiotic.

OTTO: Let's be completely idiotic!

LEO: Very well.

They both refill their glasses and drain them in silence.

OTTO: There's a certain furtive delight in doing something consciously that you know perfectly well is thoroughly contemptible.

LEO: There is, indeed.

OTTO: There isn't much more left. Shall we finish it?

LEO: Certainly.

OTTO *refills both glasses.*

OTTO (*handing* LEO *his*): Now what?

LEO: Now what what?

OTTO (*giggling slightly*): Don't keep on saying, 'what, what, what' – it sounds ridiculous!

LEO: I wanted to know what you meant by 'Now what?'

OTTO: Now what shall we drink to?

LEO (*also giggling*): Let's not drink to anything – let's just drink!

OTTO: All right.

He drinks.

LEO (*also drinking*): Beautiful!

OTTO: If Gilda came in now she'd be surprised all right, wouldn't she?

LEO: She'd be so surprised, she'd fall right over backwards!

OTTO: So should we.

They both laugh immoderately at this.

LEO (*wiping his eyes*): Oh, dear! Oh, dear, oh, dear, how silly! How very, very silly.

OTTO (*with sudden change of mood*): She'll never come back. Never.

LEO: Yes, she will – when we're very, very old, she'll suddenly come in – in a bath-chair!

OTTO (*sullenly*): Damn fool.

LEO (*with slight belligerence*): Who's a damn fool?

OTTO: You are. So am I. We both are. We were both damn fools in the first place, ever to have anything to do with her.

LEO (*admiringly*): You're awfully strong, Otto! Much, much stronger than you used to be.

OTTO: I've been all over the world; I've roughed it – that's what's made me strong. Every man ought to rough it.

LEO: That's the trouble with civilized life – it makes you soft. I've been thinking that for a long time. I've been watching myself getting softer and softer and softer – it's awful!

OTTO: You'd soon be all right if you got away from all this muck.

LEO: Yes, I know, but how?

OTTO (*putting his arm around his shoulders*): Get on a ship, Leo – never mind where it's going! Just get on a ship – a small ship.

LEO: How small?

OTTO: Very small indeed; a freighter.

LEO: Is that what you did?

OTTO: Yes.

LEO: Then I will. Where do very small ships sail from?

OTTO: Everywhere – Tilbury, Hamburg, Havre –

LEO: I'm free! I've suddenly realized it. I'm free!

OTTO: So am I.

LEO: We ought to drink to that, Otto. It's something worth drinking to. Freedom's been lost to us for a long, long time and now we've found it again! Freedom from people and things and softness! We really ought to drink to it.

OTTO: There isn't any more brandy.

LEO: What's that over there?

OTTO: Where?

LEO: On the thing.

OTTO (*going to it*): Sherry.

LEO: What's the matter with sherry?

OTTO: All right.

He brings over the bottle and fills their glasses.

LEO (*raising his*): Freedom!

OTTO (*doing the same*): Freedom!

> *They both drink.*

LEO: Very insipid.

OTTO: Tastes like brown paper.

LEO: I've never tasted brown paper.

OTTO: Neither have I.

> *They roar with laughter.*

LEO: Sherry's a very ludicrous word, isn't it, when you begin to analyse it?

OTTO: Any word's ludicrous if you stare at it long enough. Look at 'macaroni'.

LEO: That's Italian; that doesn't count.

OTTO: Well, 'rigmarole' then, and 'neophyte' and 'haddock'.

LEO: And 'wimple' – wimple's the word that gets me down!

OTTO: What is a wimple?

LEO: A sort of medieval megaphone, made of linen. Guinevere had one.

OTTO: What did she do with it?

LEO (*patiently*): Wore it, of course. What did you think she did with it?

OTTO: She might have blown down it.

LEO (*with slight irritation*): Anyhow, it doesn't matter, does it?

OTTO (*agreeably*): Not in the least. It couldn't matter less. I always thought Guinevere was tedious, wimple or no wimple.

LEO: I'm beginning to float a little, aren't you?

OTTO: Just leaving the ground. Give me time! I'm just leaving the ground –

LEO: Better have some more sherry.

OTTO: I'm afraid it isn't very good sherry.

LEO (*scrutinizing the bottle*): It ought to be good; it's real old Armadildo.

OTTO: Perhaps we haven't given it a fair chance.

> *He holds out his glass.* LEO *refills it and his own.*

LEO (*raising his glass*): Après moi le deluge!

OTTO: Après both of us the deluge!

> *They drain their glasses.*

LEO: I think I shall sit down now. I'm so terribly sick of standing up.

OTTO: Human beings were never meant to stand up, in the first place. It's all been a grave mistake.

They both sit on the sofa.

LEO: All what?

OTTO: All this stamping about.

LEO: I feel ever so much happier. I don't feel angry with you or with Gilda or with anybody! I feel sort of at peace, if you know what I mean.

OTTO (*putting his arm around him*): Yes, I know – I know.

LEO: Keys of the city, indeed!

OTTO: Lot of damned nonsense.

LEO: Too much sense of drama, flouncing off like that –

OTTO: We've all got too much sense of drama, but we won't have any more – from now onwards, reason and realism and clarity of vision.

LEO: What?

OTTO (*very loudly*): I said 'clarity of vision'.

LEO: I wouldn't have believed I could ever feel like this again – so still and calm, like a deep, deep pool.

OTTO: Me, too – a deep pool, surrounded with cool green rushes, with the wind rustling through them.

This flight of fancy is disturbed by a faint hiccup.

LEO (*resting his head on* OTTO's *shoulder*): Will you forgive me – for – for everything?

OTTO (*emotionally*): It's I who should ask you that!

LEO: I'm glad Gilda's gone, really – she was very wearisome sometimes. I shall miss her, though.

OTTO: We shall both miss her.

LEO: She's the only really intelligent woman I've ever known.

OTTO: Brilliant!

LEO: She's done a tremendous lot for us, Otto. I wonder how much we should have achieved without her?

OTTO: Very little, I'm afraid. Terribly little.

LEO: And now she's gone because she doesn't want us any more.

OTTO: I think she thinks we don't want her any more.

LEO: But we do, Otto – we do –

OTTO: We shall always want her, always, always, always –

LEO (*miserably*): We shall get over it in time, I expect, but it will take years.

OTTO: I'm going to hate those years. I'm going to hate every minute of them.

LEO: So am I!

OTTO: Thank God for each other, anyhow!

LEO: That's true. We'll get along, somehow – (*his voice breaks*) together –

OTTO (*struggling with his tears*): Together –

LEO (*giving way to his, and breaking down completely*): But we're going to be awfully – awfully – lonely –

They both sob hopelessly on each other's shoulders as the curtain slowly falls.

And of course Gilda returns – to them both.

★

One of the problems created by some young directors in approaching this particular piece is to emphasize what they see as a hidden 'gay agenda'. ('If darling Noël could have written it the way he wanted *to write it.')*

The clear rebuttal to that is in Noël's own words:

'Suggestion is always more interesting than statement.'

At the time of Design for Living *the Lunts had been acting almost exclusively together, usually for the Theatre Guild, for some years and perfected a style of naturalism that other actors appearing with them found difficulty getting used to – even Noël, who knew them so well but had never acted with them before.*

The preparation for the play was not without the occasional crise *and, once it was successfully over, he made the process the subject of a satirical sketch . . .*

DESIGN FOR REHEARSING

NOËL COWARD   Simon Jones
ALFRED LUNT   Barrie Ingham
LYNN FONTANNE   Rosemary Harris

First performed in a concert version at Ten Chimneys
(the Lunts' home at Genessee Depot, Wisconsin),
13 April 2003

The scene is a bare stage with a few chairs and benches dotted about and a prompt table with a script, cigarettes and chewing gum. ALFRED *and* LYNN *are discovered sitting upstage opposite each other mumbling indistinctly.* NOËL *enters in hat and coat.*

NOËL: Hello, my little dears. I thought I was early.

ALFRED: We hadn't anything else to do so we got here at 10:15.

LYNN: Darling, I had a marvellous idea.

NOËL (*taking off hat and coat*): What?

LYNN: I'm not going to say 'strawberry jam' like I did yesterday at all.

NOËL: How are you going to say it?

LYNN: Like this: 'strawberry jam'.

NOËL: Lovely. What scene shall we start with?

LYNN: You see, it's such an obvious change of mood there that it's better not to mark it too much, so if I tack 'strawberry jam' on to the rest of it and then say it quite casually like this: 'strawberry jam'.

NOËL: Ever so much better.

LYNN: I'll do it the old way if you want me to but I did feel . . .

NOËL: Try it anyhow.

LYNN: You see, I think *she* would. You be Alfred for a moment and I'll show you what I mean. (*She grips his wrists.*) 'Strawberry jam.' There!

NOËL: That's quite, quite magnificent, dear. Now what are we going to start with — you and Alfred in the second act?

ALFRED: Oh, God, I was so *awful* in that scene yesterday – just an old stodgy Scandinavian Pudding.

NOËL: I thought you were so excellent.

ALFRED: No. No. No. I was awful – dreadful. I didn't sleep a wink all night – tossing about and turning I was, and pacing the floor.

LYNN: Do you know what he did to me at 4:30 this morning?

NOËL: I tremble to think.

LYNN: His whole first act and then we cooked some eggs.

ALFRED: I loathe my face, you know – it's horrible – no bone structure. I'd like to have a face like yours.

LYNN: He's always wanted to have a face like yours.

NOËL: Let's do your scene in the second act with Alfred.

LYNN: No, darling. We can do that at home. Let's do one of your scenes.

NOËL: All right. I'd like to say one thing, Alfred, before we begin. You're raving to say you were bad in that scene yesterday – it was perfectly enchanting, all through.

ALFRED (*wailing*): Oh, no. No. No. No. It was terrible.

LYNN: I was a shell, an empty shell, that's all I was, and I had a stomach ache. – You wait until I get my words slick.

ALFRED: Do you know, Noël, this is the most *extraordinary* play! It's got a sort of – you know – an underneath – quality. It's fascinating – when I first read the script I got the most extraordinary feeling of *satisfaction* – like when I read *Karl and Anna*.

LYNN: Never mind that now, darling. We must begin.

NOËL: My entrance?

LYNN: Yes . . .

ALFRED: By the way, Noël, you did the most superb bit of business with the lid of the cigarette box yesterday. Don't change it – for God's sake don't change it!

NOËL: Well, I wasn't quite sure – I thought it might be a little overdone.

ALFRED: No. No. No. It was enchanting. Larry noticed it – He said it was perfect.

LYNN: Larry does the most marvellous imitation of you. He did it last night in Alfred's hat.

ALFRED: I suppose you know this is the best play you've ever written.

LYNN: Do you realize we've never in our lives had a complete script to work on. We're quite dazed – we really are – dazed.

ALFRED: You remember, *Caprice*?

LYNN: Oh, my God!

NOËL: Come on, my entrance.

LYNN (*kissing him*): Darling, you won't be disheartened about yesterday, will you? It was the first time I'd touched the last act without my book.

ALFRED: And don't worry about her making her entrance through the fireplace. The old girl has no bump of locality at all. She's walked through fireplaces for years – just the Santa Claus of Fifty-second Street.

NOËL: Let's not start with my entrance. We're very slick there. It's the end of the act that's so ragged.

ALFRED: That's my fault – I'm awful.

NOËL: No, it isn't – it's mine.

LYNN: I'll be all right when I get my words slick. God knows I realize I'm slow, but I've never been as slow as this. We're tired, you know – all those years learning part after part.

NOËL: Alfred's entrance.

ALFRED: All right.

They take their places. LYNN *and* NOËL *laugh hysterically –* ALFRED *enters.*

ALFRED: Hallo, Leo.

NOËL: Hallo, Otto.

ALFRED: Why did you stop laughing so suddenly?

NOËL: It's funny how lovely it is to see you.

ALFRED: Why funny?

Pause.

NOËL: Come on, Lynn.

LYNN: Oh, God! let's go back. I shall always forget that line – always – always – always.

They go back.

ALFRED: Hallo, Leo.

NOËL: Hallo, Otto.

ALFRED: Why did you stop laughing so suddenly?

NOËL: It's funny how lovely it is to see you.

ALFRED: Why funny?

Pause.

LYNN: It's no use looking at me like that. I can't do anything if you look at me like that.

ALFRED: I wasn't looking at you at all.

LYNN: Oh yes, you were – you had a sneer on your face.

ALFRED: She always picks on me when she forgets her lines.

LYNN: I was word perfect in this scene last night and now Alfred's put me off entirely.

ALFRED: Nonsense.

LYNN: No. No. It's no good. When you're in this mood I can't act with you. It's not fun.

NOËL: Will you both of you shut up and get on with it?

LYNN: We're always like this, darling. You mustn't be disheartened. What's my line?

NOËL: 'Where's Ernest?'

LYNN: Where's Ernest?

Etc., etc., etc., until:

ALFRED: Oh, did you?

NOËL: Yes I did.

ALFRED: I see.

Pause.

LYNN *and* NOËL (*together*): If only you wouldn't look like that.

LYNN: I shall never remember that line – never – never – never –

NOËL: I'll say it, then.

LYNN: No, I'll say it.

NOËL: All right – say it.

LYNN: Give it to me.

ALFRED: I see.

LYNN: If only you wouldn't look like that. You sat down there yesterday, Alfred.

ALFRED: Well, I'm standing up today.

LYNN: That's what's putting me off.

ALFRED: I don't see that it matters very much how I look.

   Etc., etc., etc., until:

LYNN: . . . It's overbalancing and disrupting everything.

NOËL: 'Distorting'.

LYNN: It's disrupting in my part.

NOËL: I bet it isn't.

LYNN: I'll show you. Where's my bag?

   They look for it.

LYNN: Here. (*She produces part.*)

NOËL (*finding place*): There you are – 'distorting'.

LYNN: Funny, I could have sworn it was 'disrupting'.

NOËL: Never mind.

ALFRED: I *knew* it was 'distorting'.

LYNN: Why didn't you say so?

ALFRED: Because you've already snapped my head off once this mormng.

LYNN: It's silly to say things like that just because you're nervous about
   going to the dentist at four-thirty.

ALFRED: It's nothing to do with the dentist.

LYNN: Oh, yes it is. (*To* NOËL.) It upsets him, you know.

ALFRED: I think you must be sickening for something. You haven't behaved
   like this since *Strange Interlude.*

LYNN: Now, Alfred.

ALFRED: So disagreeable and snappy.

NOËL (*shouting them down*): Listen, both of you – listen –

LYNN: What?

NOËL: I shall never be able to play this part –

ALFRED: Don't be so silly.

LYNN: It's our fault – we're worrying him.

NOËL: No. It's nothing to do with you – it's me – I'm wrong – I haven't
   got the feel of it – when I watch you – you're so meticulous, so superb
   it takes the ground from under my feet.

ALFRED *and* LYNN: No. No. No.

NOËL: Yes. Yes. Let's get somebody else and I'll just direct. Honestly – I'm so wretched – I shall never –

ALFRED: You're wonderful. You're going to be better than you've *ever been in your life.*

LYNN: You're so fluid and assured – you're an actor.

NOËL: No. No. No.

ALFRED: Yes. Yes. Yes. I'm the one who's going to let the play down.

NOËL: No. No. No.

LYNN: No. No. No.

ALFRED: Yes. Yes. Yes. I'm awful.

LYNN: No, darling, no. It's me not knowing my lines.

NOËL: What does it *matter* about the lines?

ALFRED: Let's go back and start all over again.

LYNN: Yes. From the very beginning.

NOËL: Don't you think we'd better start from my entrance?

LYNN: Yes, darling – your entrance.

ALFRED: It's my entrance that it gets so ragged.

NOËL: All right.

ALFRED: Hallo, Leo.

NOËL: Hallo, Otto.

ALFRED: Why did you stop laughing so suddenly?

NOËL: It's funny how lovely it is to see you.

ALFRED: Why funnny?

Pause.

ALFRED: Come on, Lynn.

LYNN (*absently*): Where's Ernest? – I was wrong about that reading in the second act – it ought to be like this. Listen – 'strawberry jam'!

Curtain.

FUMED OAK

(from *Tonight at 8:30*, 1936)

HENRY GOW	Noël Coward
DORIS, *his wife*	Gertrude Lawrence
ELSIE, *his daughter*	Moya Nugent
MRS ROCKETT, *his mother-in-law*	Alison Leggatt

Directed by Willard Stoker
Phoenix Theatre, London, 13 January 1936

It never ceased to irritate Noël that the general perception was that he could only write about duchesses, gilded youth and the general froth of society. And to be fair, the chattering classes did tend to dominate in his early plays – as they did in those of other dramatists of the time. In later years, though, he was able to show that, having been born into a lower middle-class family himself, he could understand 'ordinary' people and speak for them, as he did in parts of Cavalcade (*1931*), This Happy Breed (*1939*) *and* In Which We Serve (*1942*).

But perhaps the most inspiring of his proletarian principals was Henry Gow in the one-act play Fumed Oak *– one of the nine short plays that made up* Tonight at 8:30 (*1936*).

Henry lives a life of quiet desperation in a South London house – 'indistinguishable from several thousand others' – with his shrewish wife Doris, his cantankerous mother-in-law, Mrs Rockett, and his adenoidal daughter Elsie. As we meet them all in the first scene it is obvious that he is henpecked by all of them. Despite their incessant nagging, he says not a word.

But in the second scene, the worm turns. (I have eliminated the interjections from the three women to give Henry his monologue.)

HENRY (*to* DORRIE): Fifteen, no sixteen years ago tonight, Dorrie, you and me had a little rough and tumble in your Aunt Daisy's house in Stansfield Road, do you remember?

We had the house to ourselves, it being a Sunday, your Aunt had popped over to the Golden Calf with Mr Simmonds, the lodger, which, as the writers say, was her wont. You'd been after me for a long while, Dorrie.

I didn't know it then, but I realized it soon after, you had to have a husband, what with one sister married and the other engaged, both of them younger than you, you had to have a husband, and quick, so you fixed on me. You were pretty enough and I fell for it hook, line and sinker. Then a couple of months later you'd told me you'd clicked. You cried a hell of a lot, I remember, said the disgrace would kill your mother if she ever found out. I didn't know then that it'd take a sight more than that to kill that leathery old mare.

(*To* GRANDMA:) I expect you were in on the whole business, in a refined way of course. You knew what was going on all right, you knew that Dorrie was no more in the family way than I was, but we got married; you both saw to that, and I chucked up all the plans I had for getting on. Perhaps being a steward on a ship and seeing a bit of the world. Oh yes, all that had to go, and we settled down in rooms and I went into Ferguson's Hosiery.

I was the innocent one, not you. I found out you'd cheated me a long, long time ago, and when I found out, realized it for certain, I started cheating on you. Prepare yourself, Dorrie, my girl, you're going to be really upset this time. I've been saving! Every week for over ten years I've been earning a little bit more than you thought I was. I've managed, by hook and by crook, to put by five hundred and seventy-two pounds – d'you hear me? *Five hundred and seventy-two pounds!*

I haven't got it on me, it's in the bank. And it's not for you, it's for me – all but fifty pounds of it, that much is for you, just fifty pounds, the last you'll ever get from me – I've done what I think's fair and what I think's fair is a damn sight more than you deserve. I've transferred the freehold of this house into your name, so you'll always have a roof over your head – you can take in lodgers at a pinch, though God help the poor bastards if you do!

I'm going away. I've got my ticket here in my pocket, and my passport. My passport photo's a fair scream. I wish I could show it to you, but I don't want you to see the nice new name I've got.

Where am I going? Wouldn't you like to know? Maybe Africa, maybe China, maybe Australia. There are lots of places in the world you know nothing about, Dorrie. You've often laughed at me for reading books, but I found out a hell of a lot from books. There are islands in the South Seas for instance with cocoa palms and turtles and sunshine all the year round, you can live there for practically nothing, then there's Australia or New Zealand. With a little bit of capital I might start in a small way sheep-farming. Think of it, miles and miles of open country stretching as far as the eye can see, good fresh air, that might be very nice, might suit me beautifully. Then there's South America. There are coffee plantations there and sugar plantations and banana plantations. If I go to South America I'll send you a whole crate. 'Ave a banana, Dorrie! 'Ave a banana!

Then there's the sea. Not the sea we know at Worthing with the tide going in and out regular and the band playing on the pier. The *real* sea's what I mean. The sea that Joseph Conrad wrote about, and Rudyard Kipling and lots of other people, too, a sea with whacking great waves and water spouts and typhoons and flying-fish and phosphorus making the foam look as if it was lit up. Those people knew a thing or two I can tell you. They knew what life could be like if you give it a chance. They knew there was a bit more to it than refinement and fumed oak and lace curtains and getting old and miserable with nothing to show for it. I'm getting on a bit now, but my health's not too bad, taken all round. There's still time for me to see a little bit of real life before I conk out. I'm still fit enough to do a job of work, real work, mind you, not bowing and scraping and wearing meself out showing fussy old cows the way to the lace and chinaware and the bargain basement.

And don't start weeping and wailing either, that won't cut any ice with me. I know what you're like, I know you through and through. You're frightened now, scared out of your wits, but give you half a chance and you'd be worse than ever you were. You're a bad lot, Dorrie, not what the world would call a bad lot, but what *I* call a bad lot. Mean and cold and respectable.

And don't talk to me about 'poor little Elsie'. Poor little Elsie, my eye! I think Elsie's awful. I always have ever since she was little. She's never done anything but whine and snivel and try to get something for nothing.

Elsie can go to work in a year or so, in the meantime, you can go to work yourself, you're quite a young woman still and strong as an ox.

I'm taking my last look at you, Dorrie. I shall never see you again as long as I live.

And look what I'm looking at!

Three generations, Grandmother, Mother and Kid. Made of the same bones and sinews and muscles and glands, millions of you, millions just like you. You're past it now, Mother, you're past the thick of the fray, you're nothing but a music-hall joke, a mother-in-law with a bit of money put by. Dorrie, the next few years will show whether you've got guts or not. Maybe what I'm doing to you will save your immortal soul in the long run, that'd be a bit of all right, wouldn't it? I doubt it, though, your immortal soul's too measly.

You're a natural bully and a cheat, and I'm sick of the sight of you; I should also like to take this opportunity of saying that I hate that bloody awful slave bangle and I always have. As for you, Elsie, you've got a chance, it's a slim one, I grant you, but still it's a chance. If you learn to work and be independent and, when the time comes, give what you have to give freely and without demanding life-long payment for it, there's just a bit of hope that you'll turn into a decent human being. At all events, if you'll take one parting piece of advice from your cruel, ungrateful father, you'll spend the first money you ever earn on having your adenoids out.

Goodbye, one and all. Nice to have known you!

There have been innumerable productions of Tonight at 8:30 *over the years — the quality invariably variable, once the originals, Noël&Gertie, no longer played all the leading parts. But perhaps the most unusual was staged in Hollywood in 1940 in aid of British War Relief. Noël reported to Lornie, his personal assistant:*

'I didn't see the first bill which was young Doug [Fairbanks] and Constance Bennett in "We Were Dancing", Basil Rathbone and Gladys Cooper in "The Astonished Heart" and Binnie Barnes and Reginald Gardiner in "Red Peppers". All the reports say that Binnie was marvellous. I saw, however, the second and third bills. Roland Young in "Fumed Oak", who played it like a dim Foreign Office *attaché* and was awful, "Family Album" with Joan Fontanne [Fontaine], Claire Trevor, Philip Merivale, etc., and Aubrey Smith as "Burrows" – this was charmingly done and the success of the series, "Hands Across the Sea" with Judith Anderson, Isobel Jeans, Nigel Bruce, Ian Hunter, etc., was a lash-up on account of Zazu Pitts never having been on the stage before and playing "Mrs Wadhurst". Every laugh she got went to her head and she did more and more clowning until not one word of the play was heard. The third bill was pretty horrible except for Bart (Herbert) Marshall, Rosalind Russell, Una O'Connor and Edmund Gwynn [Gwenn] in "Still Life". "Ways and Means" was played by Brian Aherne and Greer Garson with all the lightness and speed of a performance of *King Lear* given by a church social. But the pearl of the whole evening was "Shadow Play" with Georges Metaxa and a rather ageing Jewish actress called Dorothy Stone; this was terribly macabre. Georges, who is now quite square, was completely incomprehensible and sang very loudly indeed. Dorothy Stone danced so much that I was afraid she would have heart failure; unfortunately she didn't.'

PRESENT LAUGHTER

(1939)

GARRY ESSENDINE	Noël Coward
ROLAND MAULE	James Donald
LIZ ESSENDINE	Joyce Carey
JOANNA LYPPIATT	Judy Campbell
HENRY LYPPIATT	Gerald Case
MORRIS DIXON	Dennis Price

Directed by Noël Coward
Haymarket Theatre, London, 29 April 1943

THEATRE ROYAL HAYMARKET

NOEL COWARD

in

HIS OWN PLAY

PRESENT LAUGHTER

6D.

In the Coward universe the ladies didn't always have the monopoly on excessive self-imagery.

In Present Laughter *Garry Essendine is an actor just admitting to being forty — and resisting every inch of the way.*

'I'm always acting — watching myself go by. I see myself all the time, eating, drinking, loving, suffering. My life is not my own. I belong to the public and my work.'

It was fitting that Noël created the part, since there are distinct elements of autobiography here. In a BBC radio interview in 1972 he admitted:

'Of course, Garry Essendine is me.'

As he wrote to his US manager, Jack Wilson, who was to produce the 1946 Broadway version:

'*Present Laughter* is not so much a play as a series of semi-autobiographical pyrotechnics, and it needs, over and above everything else, abundant physical vitality. I myself found it arduous to play and God knows I have the vitality of the devil. Clifton's method is more measured than mine and I suspect that because of this, in spite of his technical skill and wit and charm, he gives the audience time to see the wheels going round. I played it more violently than I have ever played anything, and swept everything and everybody along with me at a breakneck speed.'

To Clifton Webb, who was to play Garry/Noël, he wrote:

'Darling Mr Webb,

You poor foolish boy! Fancy attempting to play a part which being in itself small and rather thankless requires, above everything else, beauty and grace and sweetness. After all, you must remember, it was written with those qualities in mind and played with such exquisite finesse that you could have heard a bomb drop.

However, if you like, in your clumsy heavy footed way, to go stamping through the fabric of my dreams, that's entirely your affair.

I detected in your letter a certain whining note about the number of words you had to learn.

This complaint has been verified by those funny little Lunts who I hear are strutting about in some trumpery little piece (*O Mistress Mine*) and who also have trouble with their words.

Now, my Darling Little Webb, it is a question of concentration and Mary Baker Eddy ...You must persevere, Dear Boy, and think beautiful thoughts and if you don't make an enormous success in it, I shall come and knock the B'Jesus out of you! I consign you happily to your fate! I love you very much.'

It must be admitted that there was some cause for Webb's complaint. The part has just about as many lines as Hamlet's – but rather more laughs.

★

In Act One, Garry has an unexpected visit from a somewhat eccentric young playwright, Roland Maule ...

GARRY *motions* ROLAND *into a chair.*

GARRY: Do sit down, won't you?

ROLAND (*sitting*): Thank you.

GARRY: Cigarette?

ROLAND: No, thank you.

GARRY: Don't you smoke?

ROLAND: No.

GARRY: Drink?

ROLAND: No, thank you.

GARRY: How old are you?

ROLAND: Twenty-five, why?

GARRY: It doesn't really matter – I just wondered.

ROLAND: How old are you?

GARRY: Forty in December – Jupiter, you know – very energetic.

ROLAND: Yes, of course. (*He gives a nervous, braying laugh.*)

GARRY: You've come all the way from Uckfield?

ROLAND: It isn't very far.

GARRY: Well, it sort of *sounds* far, doesn't it?

ROLAND (*defensively*): It's quite near Lewes.

GARRY: Then there's nothing to worry about, is there? I want to talk to you about your play.

ROLAND (*gloomily*): I expect you hated it.

GARRY: Well, to be candid, I thought it was a little uneven.

ROLAND: I thought you'd say that.

GARRY: I'm glad I'm running so true to form.

ROLAND: I mean it really isn't the sort of thing you would like, is it?

GARRY: In that case why on earth did you send it to me?

ROLAND: I just took a chance. I mean I know you only play rather trashy stuff as a rule, and I thought you just might like to have a shot at something deeper.

GARRY: What is there in your play that you consider so deep, Mr Maule? Apart from the plot which is completely submerged after the first four pages.

ROLAND: Plots aren't important, it's ideas that matter. Look at Chekhov.

GARRY: In addition to ideas I think we might concede Chekhov a certain flimsy sense of psychology, don't you?

ROLAND: You mean my play isn't psychologically accurate?

GARRY (*gently*): It isn't very good, you know, really, it isn't.

ROLAND: I think it's very good indeed.

GARRY: I understand that perfectly, but you must admit that my opinion, based on a lifelong experience of the theatre, might be the right one.

ROLAND (*contemptuously*): The *commercial* theatre.

GARRY: Oh, dear. Oh, dear. Oh, dear!

ROLAND: I suppose you'll say that Shakespeare wrote for the commercial theatre and that the only point of doing anything with the drama at all is to make money! All those old arguments. What you don't realize is that the theatre of the future is the theatre of ideas.

GARRY: That may be, but at the moment I am occupied with the theatre of the present.

ROLAND (*heatedly*): And what do you do with it? Every play you appear in is exactly the same, superficial, frivolous and without the slightest intellectual significance. You have a great following and a strong personality, and all you do is prostitute yourself every night of your life. All you do with your talent is to wear dressing gowns and make witty remarks when you might be really helping people, making them think! Making them feel!

GARRY: There can be no two opinions about it. I am having a most discouraging morning.

ROLAND (*rising and standing over* GARRY): If you want to live in people's memories, to go down to posterity as an important man, you'd better do something about it quickly. There isn't a moment to be lost.

GARRY: I don't give a hoot about posterity. Why should I worry about what people think of me when I'm dead as a doornail, anyway? My worst defect is that I am apt to worry too much about what people think of me when I'm alive. But I'm not going to do that any more. I'm changing my methods and you're my first experiment. As a rule, when insufferable young beginners have the impertinence to criticize me, I dismiss the whole thing lightly, because I'm embarrassed for them and consider it not quite fair game to puncture their inflated egos too sharply. But this time, my highbrow young friend, you're going to get it in the neck. To begin with, your play is not a play at all. It's a meaningless jumble of adolescent, pseudo-intellectual poppycock. It bears no relation to the theatre or to life or to anything. And you yourself wouldn't be here at all if I hadn't been bloody fool enough to pick up the telephone when my secretary wasn't looking. Now that you are here, however, I would like to tell you this. If you wish to be a playwright you just leave the theatre of tomorrow to take care of itself. Go and get yourself a job as a butler in a repertory company, if they'll have you. Learn from the ground up how plays are constructed and what is actable and what isn't. Then sit down and write at least twenty plays one after the other, and if you can manage to get the twenty-first produced for a Sunday-night performance you'll be damned lucky!

ROLAND (*hypnotized*): I'd no idea you were like this. You're wonderful!

GARRY (*flinging up his hands*): My God!

ROLAND: I'm awfully sorry if you think I was impertinent, but I'm awfully glad too, because if I hadn't been you wouldn't have got angry and if you hadn't got angry I shouldn't have known what you were really like.

GARRY: You don't in the least know what I'm really like.

ROLAND: Oh, yes, I do – now.

GARRY: I can't see that it matters, anyway.

ROLAND: It matters to me.

GARRY: Why?

ROLAND: Do you really want to know?

GARRY: What on earth are you talking about?

ROLAND: It's rather difficult to explain really.

GARRY: What is difficult to explain?

ROLAND: What I feel about you.

GARRY: But —

ROLAND: No, please let me speak — you see, in a way I've been rather unhappy about you — for quite a long time — you've been a sort of obsession with me. I saw you in your last play forty-seven times, one week I came every night, in the pit, because I was up in town trying to pass an exam.

GARRY: Did you pass it?

ROLAND: No, I didn't.

GARRY: I'm not entirely surprised.

ROLAND: My father wants me to be a lawyer, that's what the exam was for, but actually I've been studying psychology a great deal because I felt somehow that I wasn't at peace with myself and gradually, bit by bit, I began to realize that you signified something to me.

GARRY: What sort of something?

ROLAND: I don't quite know — not yet.

GARRY: That 'not yet' is one of the most sinister remarks I've ever heard.

ROLAND: Don't laugh at me, please. I'm always sick if anyone laughs at me.

GARRY: You really are the most peculiar young man.

ROLAND: I'm all right now, though, I feel fine!

GARRY: I'm delighted.

ROLAND: Can I come and see you again?

GARRY: I'm afraid I'm going to Africa.

ROLAND: Would you see me if I came to Africa too?

GARRY: I really think you'd be happier in Uckfield.

ROLAND: I expect you think I'm mad but I'm not really, I just mind deeply about certain things. But I feel much better now because I think I shall be able to sublimate you all right.

GARRY: Good. Now I'm afraid I shall have to turn you out because I'm expecting my manager and we have some business to discuss.

ROLAND: It's all right, I'm going immediately.

GARRY: Shall I get you your script?

ROLAND: No, no – tear it up – you were quite right about it – it was only written with part of myself, I see that now. Goodbye.

GARRY: Goodbye.

★

'It's no use to go and take courses in playwriting any more than it's much use taking courses in acting. Better play to a bad matinée in Hull, it will teach you much more than a year of careful instruction.'

Television interview, 1969

Richard Briers, who played Roland in the 1965 revival, remembers:

'Ah! Roland! A very favourite part! Acting opposite Nigel Patrick was pretty tough, as he demanded a terrific pace. I was fast, too, and on the first night we played the opening scene so fast that nobody understood a word!

'I played Maule with great emotion, trying to save Garry from his awful commercial plays. After his long tirade against *my* type of plays, there was a pause and I exclaimed – "You're wonderful" and became instantly in love with him, which, of course, drove him up the wall!

'After the first night Noël looked at me – paused, and said: "You frightened me to death!"'

★

Later in the play Garry, exasperated by what he sees as the continual and unreasonable demands of his 'extended family' of wife, staff and associates, expresses himself forcefully, if a little histrionically.

GARRY: Position indeed! I have no more position than a little frightened beetle, cringing into the shadows, trying frantically to hide away from the blinding, merciless light of criticism that is for ever beating down upon me . . . I'm sick to death of being stuffed with everybody's confidences. I'm bulging with them. You all of you come to me over and over again and pour your damned tears and emotions and sentiment over me until I'm wet through. You're all just as badly behaved as I am really, in many ways a great deal worse. You believe in your lachrymose amorous hangovers whereas I at least have the grace to take mine lightly. You wallow and I laugh because I believe now and I always have believed that there's far too much nonsense talked about sex. You, Morris, happen to like taking your paltry attachments seriously. You like suffering and plunging into orgies of jealousy and torturing yourself and everyone else. That's your way of enjoying yourself. Henry's technique is a little different, he plumps for the domestic blend. That's why he got tired of Joanna so quickly. Anyhow, he's beautifully suited with poor Elvira. She's been knee-deep in pasture ever since she left Roedean! Joanna's different again. She devotes a great deal of time to sex but not for any of the intrinsic pleasures of it, merely as a means to an end. She's a collector. A go-getter and attractive, unscrupulous pirate. I personally am none of these things. To me the whole business is vastly overrated. I enjoy it for what it's worth and fully intend to go on doing so for as long as anybody's interested and when the time comes that they're not, I shall be perfectly content to settle down with an apple and a good book!

MORRIS: Well, I'll be damned!

HENRY: Of all the brazen, arrogant sophistry I've ever listened to that takes the prize for all time!

MORRIS: You have the nerve to work yourself up into a state of moral indignation about us when we all know –

GARRY: I have not worked myself into anything at all. I'm merely defending my right to speak the truth for once.

HENRY: Truth! You wouldn't recognize the truth if you saw it. You spend your whole life attitudinizing and posturing and showing off –

GARRY: And I should like to know where we should all be if I didn't! I'm an artist, aren't I? Surely I may be allowed a little licence!

MORRIS: As far as I'm concerned, it's expired.

LIZ: For heaven's sake stop shouting all of you, you'll have the roof off.

JOANNA (*rising*): I'm sick of this idiotic performance. I'm going.

HENRY (*furiously to* GARRY): And kindly don't start that old threadbare argument about none of us being able to live and breathe if it wasn't for your glorious talent.

GARRY: How dare you allude to my talent in that nasty sarcastic tone, you ungrateful little serpent!

MORRIS: Anyhow, if it hadn't been for our restraining influence you'd be in the provinces by now.

GARRY: And what's the matter with the provinces, may I ask? They've often proved to be a great deal more intelligent than London.

HENRY: Be careful! Someone might hear.

GARRY: I suppose you'll be saying next that it's your restraining influence that has allowed me to hold my position as the idol of the public for twenty years –

MORRIS: You're not the idol of the public. They'll come and see you in the right play and the right part, and you've got to be good at that. Look what happened to you in *Pity the Blind*!

GARRY: I was magnificent in *Pity the Blind*.

MORRIS: Yes, for ten days.

HENRY: If it hadn't been for us you'd have done *Peer Gynt*.

GARRY: If I so much as hear *Peer Gynt* mentioned in this house again I swear before heaven that I shall produce it at Drury Lane.

HENRY: Not on my money you won't!

GARRY: Your money indeed! Do you think I'm dependent on your miserable money to put on plays? Why, there are thousands of shrewd old gentlemen in the city who would be only too delighted to back me in anything I choose to do.

HENRY: I think it rather depends whether they are married or not.

GARRY: Oh, so we're back to that again, are we.

HENRY: No, we're not back to anything. This has been a most disgusting, degrading scene, and if it wasn't for the fact that Morris and I signed the contract for the Forum Theatre this morning we should both of us wash our hands of you for ever!

GARRY: You've what!! . . .

(*To* HENRY): Do you mean to tell me that you signed a contract for that theatre when I particularly told you that no power on God's earth would induce me to play in it?

MORRIS: Now look here, Garry –

GARRY: I will not look there. It's nothing more nor less than the most outrageous betrayal of faith and I'm deeply, deeply angry . . .

HENRY: As I told you the other day, they are doing up the whole theatre, reseating the orchestra floor which will put over a hundred on to the capacity. In addition to that they're mad to have you there and have even consented to put a shower bath into your dressing room –

GARRY: I don't care whether they've put a swimming bath in my dressing room and a squash court and a Steinway Grand. I will not play a light French comedy to an auditorium that looks like a Gothic edition of Wembley Stadium.

★

It's easy to see why – when in professional doubt – Noël would reach for and frequently appear in 'dear old Present Laughter*'.*

★

COWARD ON COMEDY

'I am light-minded. I would inevitably write a comedy if – God help me – I wanted to write a play with a message.'

Diaries, 1959

'Who can truly say there is more truth in tears than in laughter?'

'Comedy is nearly always despised in its generation and honoured more latterly, except by the public.'

'The whole of comedy depends on timing – and if you are really on your toes, you play the audience and you control the laughter. You mustn't ever let the audience get out of hand.'

'The first rule of comedy is to play quickly. I don't mean gabble. There's a difference between speed and pace. You throw your laughs away deliberately in the first act, then pull them in the last. In the first act you have to get the audience's attention – once you have it, they will repay you in the second. Play through the laughs, if you have to. It will only make the audience believe there are so many of them that they missed a few.'

THIS HAPPY BREED

(1939)

FRANK GIBBONS   Noël Coward
ETHEL GIBBONS   Judy Campbell

Directed by Noël Coward
Haymarket Theatre, London, 30 April 1943

Noël was a heart-on-the-sleeve patriot and his feelings for his country crop up again and again in his work. 'I am England — and England is me,' he told a Sunday Express *interviewer in 1965.*

Cavalcade *(1931) was the most overt and sustained expression of his emotion. In it Jane Marryot, the heroine, gives her Toast to the Future — as she has done through the decades we have shared with her during the play:*

JANE: Let's drink to the hope that one day this country of ours, which we love so much, will find dignity and greatness and peace again.

In his first night curtain speech Noël heard himself saying, 'In spite of the troublous times we are living in, it is still pretty exciting to be English' — though in later years he would reflect:

'Quite true, quite sincere; I felt it strongly, but I rather wished I hadn't said it, hadn't popped it on to the top of *Cavalcade* like a paper cap.'

As history turned out, he was to revisit the thought again not too many years later in times even more troublous. In This Happy Breed *— a sort of sequel to* Cavalcade *— the action leads up to the second 'war to end wars', and at the end of the play Noël has the working-class hero, Frank Gibbons, soliloquize to his infant grandson, who symbolizes his country's future.*

FRANK: Frankie boy, I wonder what you're going to turn out like! You're not going to get any wrong ideas, see? That is, not if I have anything to do with it . . . There's nobody here to interrupt us, so we can talk as man to man, can't we? There's not much to worry about really, so long as you remember one or two things always. The first is that life isn't all jam for anybody, and you've got to have trouble of some kind or another whoever you are. But if you don't let it get you down, however bad it is, you won't go far wrong . . . Another thing you'd better get into that little bullet head of yours is that you belong to something that nobody can't ever break, however much they try. And they'll try all right – they're trying now. Not only people in other countries who want to do us in because they're sick of us ruling the roost – and you can't blame them at that! But people here, in England. People who have let 'emselves get soft and afraid. People who go on a lot about peace and good will and the ideals they believe in, but somehow don't believe in 'em enough to think they're worth fighting for . . . The trouble with the world is, Frankie, that there are too many ideals and too little horse sense. We're human beings, we are – all of us – and that's what people are liable to forget. Human beings don't like peace and good will and everybody loving everybody else. However much they may think they do, they don't really because they're not made like that. Human beings like eating and drinking and loving and hating. They also like showing off, grabbing all they can, fighting for their rights and bossing anybody who'll give 'em half a chance. You belong to a race that's been bossy for years and the reason it's held on as long as it has is that nine times out of ten it's behaved decently and treated people right. Just lately, I'll admit, we've been giving at the knees a bit and letting people down who trusted us and allowing noisy little men to bully us with a lot of guns and bombs and aeroplanes. But don't worry – that won't last – the people themselves, the ordinary people like you and me, know something better than all the fussy old politicians put together – we know what we belong to, where we come from, and where we're going. We may not know it with our brains, but we know it with our roots. And we know another thing too, and it's this. We 'aven't lived and died and struggled all these hundreds of years to get decency and justice and freedom for ourselves without being prepared to fight fifty wars if need be – to keep 'em.

ETHEL *comes in*

ETHEL: What in the world are you doing? Talking to yourself?

FRANK: I wasn't talking to myself – I was talking to Frankie.

ETHEL: Well, I'm sure I hope he enjoyed it.

FRANK: He's stopped dribbling anyhow!

ETHEL: Come on in – supper's ready – you'd better close the windows, he might get a chill.

ETHEL *goes out.*

FRANK *closes the windows and goes back to the pram.*

FRANK: So long, son . . .

He goes out as the curtain falls.

With war duly declared, Noël determined that as part of his contribution he would write the play, the film and the song that would help his fellow countrymen and women – in however small a way – to get through it.

The play was to be Blithe Spirit *(1941), the film* In Which We Serve *(1942) and the song 'London Pride'. He recalled:*

'"London Pride" was written in the spring of 1941. I was standing on the platform of a London railway station on the morning after a bad blitz. Most of the glass in the station roof had been blown out and there was dust in the air and the smell of burning. The train I was waiting to meet was running late and so I sat on a platform seat and watched the Londoners scurrying about in the thin spring sunshine. They all seemed to me to be gay and determined and wholly admirable and for a moment or two I was overwhelmed by a wave of sentimental pride.'

Then he noticed a small wild flower growing in a crack in the concrete. It seemed to symbolize the resilience of his fellow Londoners. He remembered its name – London Pride.

'The song started in my head then and there and was finished in a couple of days . . .

'I am proud of the words of this song. They express what I felt at the time and what I still feel, i.e. London Pride.'

LONDON PRIDE

London Pride has been handed down to us.
London Pride is a flower that's free.
London Pride means our own dear town to us.
And our pride it for ever will be.
Woa, Liza,
See the coster barrows,
Vegetable marrows
And the fruit piled high.
Woa, Liza,
Little London sparrows,
Covent Garden Market where the costers cry.
Cockney feet
Mark the beat of history.
Every street
Pins a memory down.
Nothing ever can quite replace
The grace of London Town.

There's a little city flower every spring unfailing
Growing in the crevices by some London railing,
Though it has a Latin name, in town and countryside
We in England call it London Pride.

London Pride has been handed down to us.
London Pride is a flower that's free.
London Pride means our own dear town to us,
And our pride it for ever will be.
Hey, lady,
When the day is dawning
See the policeman yawning
On his lonely beat.
Gay lady,
Mayfair in the morning,
Hear your footsteps echo in the empty street.
Early rain
And the pavement's glistening.
All Park Lane

In a shimmering gown.
Nothing ever could break or harm
The charm of London Town.

In our city darkened now, street and square and crescent,
We can feel our living past in our shadowed present,
Ghosts beside our starlit Thames
Who lived and loved and died
Keep throughout the ages London Pride.

London Pride has been handed down to us.
London Pride is a flower that's free.
London Pride means our own dear town to us,
And our pride it for ever will be.
Grey city
Stubbornly implanted.
Taken so for granted
For a thousand years.
Stay, city,
Smokily enchanted,
Cradle of our memories and hopes and fears.
Every Blitz
Your resistance
Toughening,
From the Ritz
To the Anchor and Crown,
Nothing ever could override
The pride of London Town.

LIE IN THE DARK AND LISTEN

Lie in the dark and listen,
It's clear tonight so they're flying high
Hundreds of them, thousands perhaps,
Riding the icy, moonlight sky.
Men, material, bombs and maps
Altimeters and guns and charts
Coffee, sandwiches, fleece-lined boots
Bones and muscles and minds and hearts

English saplings with English roots
Deep in the earth they've left below
Lie in the dark and let them go
Lie in the dark and listen.

Lie in the dark and listen,
They're going over in waves and waves
High above villages, hills and streams
Country churches and little graves
And little citizens' worried dreams.
Very soon they'll have reached the sea
And far below them will lie the bays
And coves and sands where they used to be
Taken for summer holidays.
Lie in the dark and let them go
Lie in the dark and listen.

Lie in the dark and listen
City magnates and steel contractors,
Factory workers and politicians
Soft, hysterical little actors
Ballet dancers, 'reserved' musicians,
Safe in your warm, civilian beds.
Count your profits and count your sheep
Life is flying above your heads
Just turn over and try to sleep.
Lie in the dark and let them go
Theirs is a world you'll never know
Lie in the dark and listen.

★

With America still neutral, Noël wrote to Aleck Woollcott, a friend since the days of the Algonquin Round Table:

'I hear that Ruth Gordon and Helen Hayes among many others have been making strong representations to persuade me to give all this up and return to the theatre! If you should see them at any time, you might explain sweetly and tenderly for me that the reason I cannot at the moment return to the theatre (madly important though I know it to be) is that I am an Englishman and my country is at war!

This is a sinister and deadly war, in many ways more so than the last one. There has not been so much bloodshed as yet but, with the kind assistance of press and radio, some very dreadful things are happening to the human spirit. There is no knowing what will survive and what we shall all feel and think. I expect a lot of things will change.

P.S. I occasionally hurtle up to the front and sing firmly to the troops who are so sunk in the mud that they can't escape.'

And to Jack Wilson, his former lover and now his US manager, safely tucked away in New York:

'I honestly can't bear the thought of leaving England again – except for very brief periods – till the end of the war. The muddle and confusion and irritation is almost as bad as ever but the ordinary people are so magnificent that with all the discomforts and food rationing and cigarette shortage and blackouts, I want to be with them.

The other day I went to a certain very badly blitzed coastal town, Plymouth. The behaviour of the people in the midst of such appalling devastation was beyond praise and beyond gallantry. They were genuinely cheerful and philosophic and I never heard anyone even grumble. In the evenings between 7:30 and 9:30 there is a band on the front and the whole of the town – or what is left of it – come out and dance in the sunlight. The girls put on their bright coloured frocks and dance with the sailors and marines and soldiers. The fact that they were dancing on the exact site of a certain historic game of bowls added a little extra English nostalgia to what was one of the most touching and moving scenes I have ever seen.'

Noël looked back on those years in his second volume of autobiography, Future Indefinite (1959):

'I was a flagrant, unabashed sentimentalist and likely to remain so until the end of my days. I did love England and all it stood for. I loved its follies and apathies and curious streaks of genius;

I loved standing to attention for "God Save the King"; I loved British courage, British humour, and British understatement . . . I loved the people – the ordinary, the extraordinary, the good, the bad, the indifferent, and what is more I belonged to that exasperating, weather-sodden little island with its uninspired cooking, its muddled thinking and its unregenerate pride, and it belonged to me, whether it liked it or not.'

But a decade later, after an annual Battle of Britain dinner, he wrote in his Diary*:*

'What was it that I so minded about twenty-three years ago? An ideal? An abstract patriotism? What? . . . I wanted suddenly to stand up and shout . . . "Let's face the truth. The England we knew and loved was betrayed at Munich, revived for one short year in 1940 and was supreme in adversity, and now no longer exists." That last great war was our valediction. It will never happen again.'

THE BATTLE OF BRITAIN DINNER

New York, 1963

I have been to the 'Battle of Britain' dinner.
Held at the Hotel Shelbourne on 37th street and Lexington
And there they were, a few survivors
Of that long dead victory
And there they were too, the non-survivors
Somewhere in the air above us,
Or at any rate in our hearts
The young men who died, humorously, gaily, making jokes
Until the moment when swift blazing death annihilated them.
And there we were, raising our glasses to them
Drinking to their intolerable gallantry
And trying to make believe that their sacrifice
Was worth while
Perhaps it was worth while for them, but not for us.
They flew out of life triumphant, leaving us to see
The ideal that they died for humiliated and betrayed

Even more than it had been betrayed at Munich
To those conceited, foolish, frightened old men.
Today in our country it is the young men who are frightened
They write shrill plays about defeat and are hailed as progressive
They disdain our great heritage. They have been labelled by
    their dull
Facile contemporaries as 'Angry Young Men'
But they are not angry, merely scared and ignorant,
Many of them are not even English
But humourless refugees from alien lands
Seeking protection in our English sanity
And spitting on the valiant centuries
That made the sanity possible.
These clever ones, these terrified young men
Who so fear extinction and the atom bomb
Have little in common with the men we were remembering
    tonight.
Whatever fears they had remained unspoken. They flew daily
    and nightly into the sky
Heavily outnumbered by the enemy and saved us for one
    valedictory year
Gave us one last great chance
To prove to a bemused and muddled world
Our basic quality. All that was done.
The year was lived alone and then
Conveniently forgotten and dismissed
Except for just one night in each long year.
We raised our glasses sentimentally
An Air Vice-Marshal made a brief, appropriate speech
And then we chatted a little, oppressed by anti-climax
And finally said goodnight and went our ways.

And to that same Sunday Express *journalist:*

'I continue to tell foreigners how great we are. Before I die,
I would like once again to be able to believe this myself.'

BLITHE SPIRIT

(1941)

CHARLES CONDOMINE	Cecil Parker
RUTH CONDOMINE	Fay Compton
ELVIRA	Kay Hammond
MADAME ARCATI	Margaret Rutherford

Directed by Noël Coward
Piccadilly Theatre, London, 2 July 1941

Illustration for the programme of the Broadway production at the Booth Theatre, 1942.

Graham Greene considered it 'a weary exhibition of bad taste'. And, indeed, on the surface death and the afterlife might seem an unlikely subject of humour for a country submerged in a war. Nonetheless, despite Greene's verdict, Blithe Spirit *ran longer than the war – for 1,997 performances, a record it held for many years. Perhaps its determined avoidance of contemporary reality explained the audiences' willing suspension of disbelief.*

After his first wife, Elvira, dies, author Charles Condomine marries Ruth and they appear to be living a pleasant if uneventful and conventional life. Charles is writing The Unseen, *a book about spiritualism, and invites Madame Arcati, a medium who lives nearby, to join them and their friends, the Bradmans, for a séance, so that he can acquire the suitable 'local colour' an author needs.*

During the séance Madame Arcati accidentally conjures up the ghost of Elvira, who is visible only to Charles. This, not surprisingly, causes a certain amount of confusion.

Finally, Madame Arcati and the Bradmans depart, leaving Charles alone with his two wives . . .

CHARLES: I think I'll have a drink. (*Moves upstage to drinks table and pours whisky and soda.*) Do you want one?

RUTH: No, thank you, dear.

CHARLES (*pouring himself out a drink*): It's rather chilly in this room.

RUTH: Come over by the fire.

CHARLES: I don't think I'll make any notes tonight – I'll start fresh in the morning.

CHARLES *turns with glass in hand, sees* ELVIRA *and drops his glass on the floor.*

CHARLES: My God!

RUTH: Charles!

ELVIRA: That was very clumsy, Charles dear.

CHARLES: Elvira! – then it's true – it was you!

ELVIRA: Of course it was.

RUTH (*starts to go to* CHARLES): Charles – darling Charles – what are you talking about?

CHARLES (*to* ELVIRA): Are you a ghost?

ELVIRA (*crosses below sofa to fire*): I suppose I must be – it's all very confusing.

RUTH (*comes to right of* CHARLES, *becoming agitated*): Charles – what do you keep looking over there for? Look at me – what's happened?

CHARLES: Don't you see?

RUTH: See what?

CHARLES: Elvira.

RUTH (*staring at him incredulously*): Elvira!!

CHARLES (*with an effort at social grace*): Yes – Elvira, dear, this is Ruth – Ruth, this is Elvira.

RUTH *tries to take his arm.* CHARLES *retreats downstage left.*

RUTH (*with forced calmness*): Come and sit down, darling.

CHARLES: Do you mean to say you can't see her?

RUTH: Listen, Charles – you just sit down quietly by the fire and I'll mix you another drink. Don't worry about the mess on the carpet – Edith can clean it up in the morning. (*She takes him by the arm.*)

CHARLES (*breaking away*): But you must be able to see her – she's there – look – right in front of you – there –

RUTH: Are you mad? What's happened to you?

CHARLES: You can't see her?

RUTH: If this is a joke, dear, it's gone quite far enough. Sit down for God's sake and don't be idiotic.

CHARLES (*clutching his head*): What am I to do – what the hell am I to do!

ELVIRA: I think you might at least be a little more pleased to see me – after all, you conjured me up.

CHARLES (*above table left centre*): I didn't do any such thing.

ELVIRA: Nonsense, of course you did. That awful child with the cold came and told me you wanted to see me urgently.

CHARLES: It was all a mistake – a horrible mistake.

RUTH: Stop talking like that, Charles – as I told you before, the joke's gone far enough.

CHARLES: I've gone mad, that's what it is – I've just gone raving mad.

RUTH (*pours out brandy and brings it to* CHARLES *below piano*): Here – drink this.

CHARLES (*mechanically – taking it*): This is appalling!

RUTH: Relax.

CHARLES: How can I relax? I shall never be able to relax again as long as I live.

RUTH: Drink some brandy.

CHARLES (*drinking it at a gulp*): There, now – are you satisfied?

RUTH: Now sit down.

CHARLES: Why are you so anxious for me to sit down – what good will that do?

RUTH: I want you to relax – you can't relax standing up.

ELVIRA: African natives can – they can stand on one leg for hours.

CHARLES: I don't happen to be an African native.

RUTH: You don't happen to be a *what*?

CHARLES (*savagely*): An African native!

RUTH: What's that got to do with it?

CHARLES: It doesn't matter, Ruth – really it doesn't matter – we'll say no more about it.

CHARLES *crosses to armchair and sits.* RUTH *comes upstage of him.*

CHARLES: See, I've sat down.

RUTH: Would you like some more brandy?

CHARLES: Yes, please.

RUTH *goes up to drinks table with glass.*

ELVIRA: Very unwise – you always had a weak head.

CHARLES: I could drink you under the table.

RUTH: There's no need to be aggressive, Charles – I'm doing my best to help you.

CHARLES: I'm sorry.

RUTH (*crosses to upstage of* CHARLES *with brandy*): Here – drink this – and then we'll go to bed.

ELVIRA: Get rid of her, Charles – then we can talk in peace.

CHARLES: That's a thoroughly immoral suggestion, you ought to be ashamed of yourself.

RUTH: What is there immoral in that?

CHARLES: I wasn't talking to you.

RUTH: Who were you talking to, then?

CHARLES: Elvira, of course.

RUTH: To hell with Elvira!

ELVIRA: There now – she's getting cross.

CHARLES: I don't blame her.

RUTH: What don't you blame her for?

CHARLES (*rises and backs downstage left a pace*): Oh, God!

RUTH: Now look here, Charles – I gather you've got some sort of plan behind all this. I'm not quite a fool. I suspected you when we were doing that idiotic séance . . .

CHARLES: Don't be so silly – what plan could I have?

RUTH: I don't know – it's probably something to do with the characters in your book – how they, or one of them would react to a certain situation – I refuse to be used as a guinea-pig unless I'm warned beforehand what it's all about.

CHARLES (*moves a couple of paces towards* RUTH): Elvira is here, Ruth – she's standing a few yards away from you.

RUTH (*sarcastically*): Yes, dear, I can see her distinctly – under the piano with a zebra!

CHARLES: But, Ruth . . .

RUTH: I am not going to stay here arguing any longer . . .

ELVIRA: Hurray!

CHARLES: Shut up!

RUTH (*incensed*): How dare you speak to me like that!

CHARLES: Listen, Ruth – please listen –

RUTH: I will not listen to any more of this nonsense – I am going up to bed now, I'll leave you to turn out the lights. I shan't be asleep – I'm too upset. So you can come in and say goodnight to me if you feel like it.

ELVIRA: That's big of her, I must say.

CHARLES: Be quiet – you're behaving like a guttersnipe.

RUTH (*icily*): That is all I have to say. Goodnight, Charles.

RUTH *walks swiftly out of the room without looking at him again.*

CHARLES (*follows* RUTH *to door*): Ruth . . .

ELVIRA: That was one of the most enjoyable half-hours I have ever spent.

CHARLES (*puts down glass on drinks table*): Oh, Elvira – how could you!

ELVIRA: Poor Ruth!

CHARLES (*staring at her*): This is obviously a hallucination, isn't it?

ELVIRA: I'm afraid I don't know the technical term for it.

CHARLES (*comes downstage to centre*): What am I to do?

ELVIRA: What Ruth suggested – relax.

CHARLES: What happens if I touch you?

ELVIRA: I doubt if you can. Do you want to?

CHARLES (*sits left end of sofa*): Oh, Elvira . . . (*He buries his face in his hands.*)

ELVIRA (*to left arm of sofa*): What is it, darling?

CHARLES: I really do feel strange, seeing you again . . .

ELVIRA (*moves to right below sofa and round above it again to left arm*): That's better.

CHARLES (*looking up*): What's better?

ELVIRA: Your voice was kinder.

CHARLES: Was I ever unkind to you when you were alive?

ELVIRA: Often . . .

CHARLES: Oh, how can you! I'm sure that's an exaggeration.

ELVIRA: Not at all – you were an absolute pig that time we went to Cornwall and stayed in that awful hotel – you hit me with a billiard cue –

CHARLES: Only very, very gently . . .

ELVIRA: I loved you very much.

CHARLES: I loved you too . . . (*He puts out his hand to her and then draws it away.*) No, I can't touch you – isn't that horrible?

ELVIRA: Perhaps it's as well if I'm going to stay for any length of time . . . (*Sits left arm of sofa.*)

CHARLES: I suppose I shall wake up eventually . . . but I feel strangely peaceful now.

ELVIRA: That's right. Put your head back.

CHARLES (*doing so*): Like that?

ELVIRA (*stroking his hair*): Can you feel anything . . . ?

CHARLES: Only a very little breeze through my hair . . .

ELVIRA: Well, that's better than nothing.

CHARLES (*drowsily*): I suppose if I'm really out of my mind they'll put me in an asylum.

ELVIRA: Don't worry about that – just relax –

CHARLES (*very drowsily indeed*): Poor Ruth . . .

ELVIRA (*gently and sweetly*): To hell with Ruth.

Curtain.

Elvira decides that, if she can't return to Charles's world, he should join her in hers. Knowing his regular habits, she tampers with his car – but today it is Ruth who makes the journey. Now Charles has two ghost wives and any minute Ruth will appear. Elvira begs Charles to have Madame Arcati send her back . . .

ELVIRA: Please get rid of her. Ruth will be in in a minute.

CHARLES: Madame Arcati, would you think it most frightfully rude if I asked you to go into the dining room for a moment? My first wife wishes to speak to me alone.

MADAME ARCATI: Oh, must I? It's so lovely being actually in the room with her.

CHARLES: Only for a few minutes – I promise she'll be here when you come back.

MADAME ARCATI: Very well. Hand me my bag, will you – it's on the settee.

ELVIRA (*picking it up and handing it to her*): Here you are.

MADAME ARCATI (*taking it and blowing her a kiss*): Oh, you darling – you little darling.

MADAME ARCATI *humming ecstatically, goes into the dining room and shuts the door.*

ELVIRA: How good is she really?

CHARLES: I don't know.

ELVIRA: Do you think she really could get me back again?

CHARLES: But, my dear child . . .

ELVIRA: And don't call me your dear child – it's smug and supercilious.

CHARLES: There's no need to be rude.

ELVIRA: The whole thing's been a failure – a miserable dreary failure – and oh! what high hopes I started out with.

CHARLES: You can't expect much sympathy from me, you know. I am perfectly aware that your highest hope was to murder me.

ELVIRA: Don't put it like that, it sounds so beastly.

CHARLES: It is beastly. It's one of the beastliest ideas I've ever heard.

ELVIRA: There was a time when you'd have welcomed the chance of being with me for ever.

CHARLES: Your behaviour has shocked me immeasurably, Elvira – I had no idea you were so unscrupulous.

ELVIRA (*bursting into tears*): Oh, Charles . . .

CHARLES: Stop crying.

ELVIRA: They're only ghost tears – they don't mean anything really – but they're very painful.

CHARLES: You've brought all this on yourself, you know.

ELVIRA: That's right – rub it in. Anyhow it was only because I loved you – the silliest thing I ever did in my whole life was to love you – you were always unworthy of me.

CHARLES That remark comes perilously near impertinence, Elvira.

ELVIRA: I sat there, on the other side, just longing for you day after day. I did really – all through your affair with that brassy-looking woman in the South of France I went on loving you and thinking truly of you – then you married Ruth and even then I forgave you and tried to understand because all the time I believed deep inside that you really loved me best . . . that's why I put myself down for a return visit and had to fill in all those forms and wait about in draughty passages for hours – if only you'd died before you met Ruth everything might have been all right – she's absolutely ruined you – I hadn't been in the house a day before I realized that. Your books aren't a quarter as good as they used to be either.

CHARLES (*incensed*): That is entirely untrue . . . Ruth helped me and encouraged me with my work which is a damned sight more than you ever did.

ELVIRA: That's probably what's wrong with it.

CHARLES: All you ever thought of was going to parties and enjoying yourself.

ELVIRA: Why shouldn't I have fun? I died young, didn't I?

CHARLES: You needn't have died at all if you hadn't been idiotic enough to go out on the river with Guy Henderson and get soaked to the skin.

ELVIRA: So we're back at Guy Henderson again, are we?

CHARLES: You behaved abominably over Guy Henderson and it's no use pretending that you didn't.

ELVIRA: Guy adored me – and anyhow he was very attractive.

CHARLES: You told me distinctly that he didn't attract you in the least.

ELVIRA: You'd have gone through the roof if I'd told you that he did.

CHARLES: Did you have an affair with Guy Henderson?

ELVIRA: I would rather not discuss it if you don't mind.

CHARLES: Answer me – did you or didn't you?

ELVIRA: Of course I didn't.

CHARLES: You let him kiss you though, didn't you?

ELVIRA: How could I stop him – he was bigger than I was.

CHARLES (*furiously*): And you swore to me –

ELVIRA: Of course I did. You were always making scenes over nothing at all.

CHARLES: Nothing at all –

ELVIRA: You never loved me a bit really – it was only your beastly vanity.

CHARLES: You seriously believe that it was only vanity that upset me when you went out in the punt with Guy Henderson?

ELVIRA: It was not a punt – it was a little launch.

CHARLES: I didn't care if it was a three-masted schooner. You had no right to go!

ELVIRA: You seem to forget *why* I went! You seem to forget that you had spent the entire evening making sheep's eyes at that overblown harridan with the false pearls.

CHARLES: A woman in Cynthia Cheviot's position would hardly wear false pearls.

ELVIRA: They were practically all she was wearing.

CHARLES: I am pained to observe that seven years in the echoing vaults of eternity have in no way impaired your native vulgarity.

ELVIRA: That was the remark of a pompous ass.

CHARLES: There is nothing to be gained by continuing this discussion.

ELVIRA: You always used to say that when you were thoroughly worsted.

CHARLES: On looking back on our married years, Elvira, I see now, with horrid clarity, that they were nothing but a mockery.

ELVIRA: You invite mockery, Charles – it's something to do with your personality, I think, a certain seedy grandeur.

CHARLES: Once and for all, Elvira –

ELVIRA: You never suspected it but I laughed at you steadily from the altar to the grave – all your ridiculous petty jealousies and your fussings and fumings –

CHARLES: You were feckless and irresponsible and morally unstable – I realized that before we left Budleigh Salterton.

ELVIRA: Nobody but a monumental bore would have thought of having a honeymoon at Budleigh Salterton.

CHARLES: What's the matter with Budleigh Salterton?

ELVIRA: I was an eager young bride, Charles – I wanted glamour and music and romance – all I got was potted palms, seven hours every day on a damp golf course and a three-piece orchestra playing 'Merrie England'.

CHARLES: It's a pity you didn't tell me so at the time.

ELVIRA: I did – but you wouldn't listen – that's why I went out on the moors that day with Captain Bracegirdle. I was desperate.

CHARLES: You swore to me that you'd gone over to see your aunt in Exmouth!

ELVIRA: It was the moors.

CHARLES: With Captain Bracegirdle?

ELVIRA: With Captain Bracegirdle.

CHARLES (*furiously*): I might have known it – what a fool I was – what a blind fool! Did he make love to you?

ELVIRA (*sucking her finger and regarding it thoughtfully*): Of course.

CHARLES: Oh, Elvira!

ELVIRA: Only very discreetly – he was in the cavalry, you know . . .

CHARLES: Well, all I can say is that I'm well rid of you.

ELVIRA: Unfortunately you're not.

CHARLES: Oh yes I am – you're dead and Ruth's dead – I shall sell this house lock, stock and barrel and go away.

ELVIRA: I shall follow you.

CHARLES: I shall go a long way away – I shall go to South America – you'll hate that, you were always a bad traveller.

ELVIRA: That can't be helped – I shall have to follow you – you called me back.

CHARLES: I did *not* call you back!

ELVIRA: Well, somebody did – and it's hardly likely to have been Ruth.

CHARLES: Nothing in the world was further from my thoughts.

ELVIRA: You were talking about me before dinner that evening.

CHARLES: I might just as easily have been talking about Joan of Arc but that wouldn't necessarily mean that I wanted her to come and live with me.

ELVIRA: As a matter of fact she's rather fun.

CHARLES: Stick to the point.

ELVIRA: When I think of what might have happened if I'd succeeded in getting you to the other world after all – it makes me shudder, it does honestly . . . it would be nothing but bickering and squabbling for ever and ever and ever. I swear I'll be better off with Ruth – at least she'll find her own set and not get in my way.

CHARLES: So I get in the way, do I?

ELVIRA: Only because I was idiotic enough to imagine that you loved me, and I sort of felt sorry for you.

CHARLES: I'm sick of these insults – please go away.

ELVIRA: There's nothing I should like better – I've always believed in cutting my losses. That's why I died.

CHARLES: Of all the brazen sophistry –

ELVIRA: Call that old girl in again – set her to work – I won't tolerate this any longer – I want to go home.

ELVIRA *starts to cry.*

CHARLES: For heaven's sake don't snivel.

The spectral Ruth finally appears and the two women gang up to nag Charles. Appalled by the prospect the future holds, he leaves them both.

★

The original Madame Arcati was Margaret Rutherford who, because of the subsequent film version, became everyone's conception of the part – but not Noël's. He wrote to Jack Wilson about the production:

'The great disappointment is Margaret Rutherford, whom the audience love, because the part is so good, but who is actually very, very bad indeed. She is indistinct, fussy and, beyond her personality, has no technical knowledge or resources at all. She merely fumbles and gasps and drops things and throws many of my best lines down the drain. She is . . . mortification to me, because I thought she would be marvellous. I need hardly say that she got a magnificent notice. So much for that.'

Ironically, he had experienced great difficulty in persuading the lady to take the part in the first place. She respected spiritualism and felt the play was an attack on it. It took impresario Binkie Beaumont's most silken manner – and an expensive lunch – to persuade her that it was an attack on fraudulent mediums. 'Very well,' Miss Rutherford finally said, 'but I must warn you that I regard this as a very serious play, almost a tragedy. I don't see it as a comedy at all.' Which is why her earnest performance makes it so funny.

Other actors have seen the role differently. Penelope Keith, for instance, saw her as 'a woman of enormous energy and enthusiasm, with a consuming belief in her supernatural powers'. One suspects this view of medium-as-professional will prevail.

Elvira is also open to interpretation. Judy Campbell – the only actress to play opposite Noël himself – told Maria Aitken, who played Elvira in the National Theatre revival of 1976, that Noël had sent her a note reading: 'Don't forget – Elvira is a ghost in gumboots!' 'Which I took to mean,' said Maria, 'that one shouldn't waft around too much.'

★

Noël was perpetually fascinated by the subject of stars and the nature of stardom. 'I don't know what it (star quality) is, but I've got it,' he once said. But he often tried to define it, as in the essay that follows.

HOW I WONDER WHAT YOU ARE

What is it that stars have that others haven't? Is it an earthy quality or a spiritual quality? Is it concrete, abstract, animal, vegetable or mineral? There will obviously never be a satisfactory answer. A young girl decides to go on the stage. She is strikingly beautiful and by no means untalented. She is adequately taught at an acting school or by the better method of playing small parts in a repertory company. After a year or so she procures a job in London for which she receives honourable mention in the *Sunday Times* and an 'Among others' in the *Daily Telegraph*. She at once acquires an agent, or has one thrust upon her, and her future is shining with promise. Twenty years later, having played two leading parts, one on tour and one in the West End in a play that ran only a fortnight, bits in movies, snippets on the radio and an endless succession of heroine's friends, she one day looks at herself in the mirror and, if she is wise, notes that she is not quite so strikingly beautiful as she was, marries a well-disposed dentist in Kettering and is heard of no more. If she is not wise she sticks doggedly to the Theatre and finally has to be assisted to the grave by the Actors' Benevolent Fund.

This, I admit is a gloomy picture but it is not an unusual one . . .

This extra 'something' is an amalgam of various elements; vitality, sex appeal, an intriguing voice (nearly all big stars have distinctive voices), an individual style of movement and some sort of chemical emanation, of which she may or may not be conscious, which places her on a different plane from her possibly more talented colleagues. The balanced mixture of all these ingredients is recognized as 'personality' or, in other words, 'Star Quality'. Very very occasionally this 'Star Quality' may be acquired by years of experience, determination and the assurance of polished technique, but as a general rule it is something that people either have or have not and when they have, it is unmistakable.

In any event this fortunately endowed creature, whoever she may be, is hailed, within a relatively short space of time, as a Star, and it is in this glorious moment that the rot usually starts to set in. Her hitherto unblemished character begins, subtly at first, to suffer that 'sea change – into something rich and strange'. The name in lights, tumultuous applause, hosts of admirers, acres of first-night flowers and extravagant publicity all contribute their insidious magic until, a few years later, we see, bowing graciously to us on an opening night, a triumphant, assured, fascinating, adored, rip-snorting megalomaniac.

The grim fact must be faced: that the majority of the theatre-going public would rather pay their money to see an extraordinary creature than an ordinary one. An extraordinary actress playing a relatively ordinary part may indeed lay waste the author's original intentions, but she will bring to that part a certain quality, a composite of her own personal magnetism, her reputation and her acquired technique which will hypnotize the audience into loving her. An ordinary, possibly better actress, playing the same part honestly and with loyal adherence to the author's text, will usually succeed in being little more than accurate. She will, of course, be effusively thanked by the author, director and the management and, if she happens to be an understudy, cheered to the echo by the gallery, but the business will drop steadily until the star returns to the cast. From the point of view of the dedicated drama enthusiasts this is indeed a desperate injustice as is the world outside it.

He confided to his Diary *in 1955:*

'Poor darling glamorous stars everywhere, their lives are so lonely and wretched and frustrated. Nothing but applause, flowers, Rolls-Royces, expensive hotel suites, constant adulation. It's too pathetic and wrings the heart.'

STAR QUALITY

(1967)

In Noël's last completed play, Star Quality *– adapted from his short story of the same name – he tackled the subject again. The text which follows is taken from Noël's original version, which has never been produced; but an adaptation by Chris Luscombe, with Penelope Keith as Lorraine Barrie, was staged at the Apollo Theatre, London on 8 August 2001.*

The star Lorraine Barrie has agreed to appear in Dark Heritage, *a play by a new playwright, Bryan Snow. Miss Barrie is notoriously temperamental, but Bryan sees no sign of it as readings begin. Tony Orford, the director's assistant, who has witnessed the phenomenon more times than he cares to recall, enlightens him . . .*

BRYAN: You're not being very encouraging.

TONY: Cheer up – it's all part of life's rich pattern.

BRYAN: Oh, shut up.

TONY: The whole thing is primarily biological and it began way back in the beginning of the world when the Almighty, for personal reasons best known to Himself, arranged that ladies should be constructed differently from gentlemen.

BRYAN: I don't know what you're talking about.

TONY: All temperamental scenes made by all temperamental female stars since the theatre was first invented have been based on that inescapable fact. It is drummed into their fluffy little heads from infancy onwards that they possess something unique and infinitely precious that every man they meet desires more than anything else. They receive cart-loads of flowers on opening nights whereas the poor leading man considers himself lucky if his cousin gives him one carnation wrapped in damp cellophane.

BRYAN: Aren't male actors ever temperamental?

TONY: Only very rarely. They cannot afford to be. They can be morose, nervous, wretched and miscast and sometimes tearful but that is as far as it goes. They must press on gallantly and stand aside for the leading lady, present her graciously to the audience and dress in a less comfortable dressing room. They must give up cheerfully many privileges their talent has earned them, all to feed the already overweening vanity of some gifted, self-indulgent, domineering harridan whose every thought and feeling is motivated by sex-consciousness, treachery and illusion.

BRYAN: You make it a little too obvious that you don't care for women.

TONY: Don't be silly. I adore women, but not in what is known as 'that way'. Some of my best friends are women and they're a damn sight more loyal and sweet to me than they are to each other. Above all, I love great big diamond-studded glamour stars. They fascinate me. I love all their little tricks and carry-ons; their unscrupulousness, their inflexible determination, their courage, their magnificent dishonesty with themselves and with everyone else. I love and pity their eternal gullibility and their tragic, silly loneliness. In our darling Lorraine, for instance, you have a glittering example of *bona-fide*, sizzling megalomania. She could only exist in the theatre or the film studios. No other career, not even that of a brilliantly successful courtesan, could ever provide enough food for her ravening ego.

BRYAN: You seem to have left out one very important thing – her talent.

TONY: Oh no, I was leaving that to the last. That's the pay-off, the definitive answer to all the silly riddles. That's her basic power, her superb natural gift for acting. I don't suppose she has ever acted really badly in her life. I don't believe she could if she tried. That is her one reality, the foundation upon which the whole structure of her charm and person-ality rests, and, believe you me, it's rock solid.

BRYAN: I'm glad you admit that at any rate.

TONY: Calm down, there's a good boy. You've missed the entire point.

BRYAN: I certainly have, and a bloody good job too.

TONY: You helped me up on to my favourite tub and I started thumping it too soon. It's silly to issue storm-warnings when the sky is clear and we haven't even left the harbour. Am I forgiven?

BRYAN: There's nothing to forgive. But I still don't quite believe you when you say you're devoted to Lorraine.

TONY: Perhaps 'devoted' is overstating it a little. But I like her more than you think I do and I admire her for something that is beyond definition and beyond praise, her star quality. Whether she was born with it, or how and where she managed to acquire it, I neither know nor care, but it's there all right. It's there as strongly in comedy as in tragedy. I once caught her at a matinée in Manchester. The play was lousy, the fortnight's notice was up on the board and the audience so dull that I thought half of them must be dead. That was during the first act.

Suddenly you are aware that you are in the presence of something very great indeed – something abstract that is beyond definition and beyond praise. Quality – star quality plus. It is there as strongly in comedy as in tragedy, magical and unmistakable, and the hair will rise on your addled little head, chills will swirl up and down your spine and you will solemnly bless the day that you were born. All this, of course, only applies if you happen to love the theatre, and I suspect that you might learn to if you stick around a bit.

BRYAN: You're just as stage-struck as I am.

TONY: And you need never again accuse me, in that prim disapproving voice of yours, of not liking women, because it just doesn't make sense. Nobody can love the theatre without liking women because they are the most fascinating, unpredictable and exciting part of it.

Here endeth the first lesson.

AGE CANNOT WITHER

(Unfinished, 1967)

NAOMI KEMBLE	Sally Ann Howes
STELLA MILVERTON	Hayley Mills
JUDY CRAVEN	Rosemary Harris

First performed in concert in an abridged version
at The Players Club, New York, 10 December 2002

*Every playwright worth the name has plays in his bottom drawer that
were either unfinished or unproduced and Noël was no exception. He
started* Age Cannot Wither *in 1967.*

'I have done an act and a half . . . and I am now letting it simmer
for a little. I shall probably finish it within the next few weeks.'

Diary, 14 May 1967

'As far as dialogue is concerned it is very good, but I had a
terrible time trying to get the curtain down. Finally, with a
scream of relief, I managed it and shall now wait until I return
home from London next week before starting the second act.
I have it fairly clearly constructed in my mind, so it shouldn't
be too difficult.'

Diary, 8 June 1967

*But then events in the outside world intervened – the lingering illness
of his secretary, Lorn Loraine, the death of old friends Spencer Tracy and
Dorothy Parker. He was 'too agitated' and never to be 'good and ready'
to tackle it again.*

*Nonetheless, what remains is vintage – if little known – Coward. It's as
if the two heroines of* Fallen Angels *(1925), Julia Sterroll and Jane
Banbury, were now in their sixties . . .*

The scene is the drawing room of the Kembles' flat in Bryanston Square. JONATHAN *is reading* The Times. NAOMI *is on the telephone.*

NAOMI: Very well then, four-thirty. I shall want Paul for my rinse and Miss Massingham for my nails. – She's away? But she only got back from her holiday two weeks ago – Seaford? – Her mother can't possibly be ill in Seaford, it's supposed to be so bracing. – No, not Miss Churt. She's a sadist, she uses her orange stick like a spear. – What about the dusty looking one with horn-rimmed glasses? – Miss Dadlett. Yes, all right, we'll settle for Miss Dadlett. She's rather inclined to hum little tunes while she's wielding the buffer but perhaps you could warn her in advance that I have no ear for music? Yes – Four-thirty. Thank you so much. (*She hangs up.*)

JONATHAN: There's been an earthquake in Malta. It lasted for three minutes.

NAOMI: Poor Jane Etheridge.

JONATHAN: What's Jane Etheridge got to do with it?

NAOMI: She lives there, doesn't she?

JONATHAN: The Etheridges are in Gibraltar.

NAOMI: Well, it's the same sort of thing, isn't it? I mean, they're both naval bases. Isn't it time you went to the club? Stella and Judy will be here in a minute.

JONATHAN: I shan't bite them.

NAOMI: You don't like Stella and it's no use pretending you do. You always say she rubs you up the wrong way.

JONATHAN: Judy, on the other hand, always smoothes me down so it levels things out. I'm devoted to Judy, provided she hasn't got that ghastly husband with her.

NAOMI: Robert's all right, so long as you keep him off the Common Market.

JONATHAN: He's a pompous windbag. I can't think why she ever married him in the first place.

NAOMI: The first place was thirty-five years ago. He's probably changed, we're all liable to. I expect he was beautiful as the day and tremendously romantic looking when he was young. I can still see traces of sex-appeal.

JONATHAN: I can't.

NAOMI: It would be most unsuitable if you could.

JONATHAN: When did it actually *start*?

NAOMI: When did *what* actually start?

JONATHAN: This gruesome annual hen-party idea?

NAOMI: Centuries ago, about a month after we'd left St Ursula's. We all happened to meet by chance at Peter Jones and had lunch together. And it isn't in the least gruesome. It enables us to keep in touch: we reminisce like mad and have a lovely time.

JONATHAN: It seems so set and unspontaneous, like Christmas. I wonder you don't give each other presents.

NAOMI: We do sometimes. A couple of years ago Judy gave me that poodle's head clip with a ruby eye, but the eye fell out and I've never had another one put in.

JONATHAN: It would at least be gracious to wear it. It might encourage her to give you another.

NAOMI: I can't go about wearing a blind poodle.

JONATHAN: I could understand it if you were really close friends, but you barely clap eyes on each other for the rest of the year.

NAOMI: I expect we would if we could, but we all live in different places. Judy's in Paris most of the time, Stella has to stay with Alec in that awful family mausoleum in Perthshire. She only manages to get to London once in every six months.

JONATHAN: We must count our blessings.

NAOMI: I can't think why you're so beastly about poor Stella. She's never done you any harm.

JONATHAN: She's too large and over-friendly, like a sheepdog. I always feel that she expects me to throw a stick for her.

NAOMI: She can't help being large. She never stops doing exercises and dieting. Judy thinks it's glandular. She was always fairly stocky even as a girl.

JONATHAN: I bet the hell she was. She was probably captain of the hockey team as well.

NAOMI: As a matter of fact, she was. She won two silver cups and a complete set of Chaucer in tooled leather.

JONATHAN: Serves her right.

NAOMI: There's time for you to get your hair cut before lunch if you hurry.

JONATHAN: I don't *want* to get my hair cut.

NAOMI: It's getting awfully long at the sides. You don't want to wander about the West End looking scruffy, do you?

JONATHAN: I don't want to wander about the West End anyway, scruffy or not. I'm going straight to the club.

NAOMI: Well, what's stopping you?

JONATHAN: Curiosity.

NAOMI: How do you mean, *curiosity*? What are you so curious about?

JONATHAN: I want to see how your old girls are holding up. In comparison with you, I mean.

NAOMI: And how do you think *I'm* holding up?

JONATHAN: Surprisingly well, all things considered.

NAOMI: I can't say I find that 'all things considered' very reassuring. All *what* things considered?

JONATHAN: The March of Time for one. We're none of us getting any younger.

NAOMI: I accept that cliché with the contempt it deserves.

JONATHAN (*ignoring her interruption*): Except, of course, Stella. She'll be back in 'rompers' in a couple of years, if she doesn't watch out.

NAOMI: I wish you'd lay off Stella. She seems to be becoming an obsession with you. It's some form of repressed sex-antagonism, I expect. You've probably been secretly in love with her for years without being aware of it. A psychiatrist would put you right in a minute.

JONATHAN: Nonsense.

NAOMI: The subconscious can be more devious than you realize. Ronnie Willford would be a gibbering lunatic at this very minute if he hadn't gone to that man in Mount Street.

JONATHAN: Ronnie Willford will *still* be a neurotic old auntie however many men he went to in Mount Street. I was at Cambridge with him and I know. He had a horrible Siamese cat which bit everybody and he was always fainting in chapel.

NAOMI: The man in Mount Street at least told him what was wrong with him and set him on an even keel.

JONATHAN: Rubbish. All he told him was that he had homosexual tendencies and ought to have a cold bath every morning and go for long walks.

NAOMI: Anyway, he's completely relaxed now and jolly as a sandboy from morning till night.

JONATHAN: Jolly *with* a sandboy from morning till night is probably nearer the mark.

STELLA MILVERTON *comes in. She is a heavily-built, cheerful-looking woman in her sixties.*

STELLA: I stopped Mrs Rothwell announcing me, because she looked flustered. I expect she's got something just coming to the boil. (*She kisses* NAOMI *and turns to* JONATHAN.) I can't think what *you're* doing here, Jonathan. Husbands are strictly forbidden.

JONATHAN (*as they shake hands*): I'm leaving immediately.

STELLA: I thought I was going to be late, because Jane rang up in a tremendous state of excitement just as I was leaving the house. They're going to let her play Paula Tanqueray at the next RADA matinée!

NAOMI: Surely she's a little young for Paula Tanqueray?

STELLA: They're always too young for everything at the RADA. Last year a girl of fourteen played King Lear. She was quite splendid.

NAOMI: Darling Jonathan, as you seem determined to linger on where you're not wanted, you might at least make yourself useful and mix us a Dry Martini.

JONATHAN: All right. (*He goes to the drink table.*)

STELLA (*settling herself on the sofa*): I'm bursting with news.

NAOMI: Well, don't say anything important until Judy comes.

STELLA: Oh, nothing world-shattering. Just tit-bits like poor Mona's caesarian and that sex maniac who murdered all those girls in Glasgow turning out to be Maisie's cousin.

JONATHAN: Who's Maisie?

STELLA: My new cook. She's gaunt and grey and aggressively respectable. You can imagine what a state she's in, poor thing.

JONATHAN: Even if she were a fluffy blonde, I should think she'd find the situation fairly embarrassing. One doesn't discover a murderer in the family every day of the week.

STELLA: She's terrified that she might have to go into the witness box and give evidence.

NAOMI: I see her point. I should hate going into a witness box myself.

STELLA: It wouldn't be the faintest use if she did anyway. She's a terrible mumbler. I can't understand half of what she's talking about when she's standing bang in front of me.

JONATHAN (*handing her a cocktail*): Here's your Martini. I've put in a zest of lemon, is that all right?

STELLA: I'd never say no to a zest of anything. (*She sips it.*) It's perfect.

JONATHAN (*handing Naomi hers*): Here you are, darling.

NAOMI: Thanks.

JONATHAN: I really am leaving now, so you can begin letting your hair down. Give my love to Judy. (*He blows them a kiss and goes out.*)

STELLA: Dear Jonathan. He always looks so elegant. How on earth does he manage to keep his figure?

NAOMI: He doesn't. He just happens to be made like that. He's terribly lazy and never takes a scrap of exercise.

STELLA: Perhaps he has very small bones.

NAOMI: Possibly, I've never looked.

STELLA: Alec never stops doing exercises. He huffs and puffs for hours every morning. He's even bought one of those idiotic rowing-machines and I have to clamber over it to get into the bath. I wouldn't mind if it did any good but it doesn't. I tried it myself every day for six weeks.

NAOMI (*laughing*): Oh, Stella. You must have looked awfully funny!

STELLA: There was no one to see what I looked like. I didn't do it in public.

NAOMI: And there were no results at all?

STELLA: Oh, there were results all right. I felt sick, gave myself a splitting headache and wrenched my shoulder.

NAOMI: Perhaps you could have shots of some sort, why don't you ask your doctor? – you know, hormones and things.

STELLA: No, thank you. Linda Fergurson had hormone injections and grew a black cavalry moustache in under a week.

MRS ROTHWELL *flings open the door.*

MRS ROTHWELL (*announcing*): Mrs Craven.

JUDY CRAVEN *enters. Of the three ladies she is the most chic. She is expertly dressed, dyed and made-up. Not a hair is out of place.* MRS ROTHWELL *withdraws, closing the door behind her.*

JUDY (*kissing* NAOMI): Dearest Naomi – Here we go again. (*She kisses* STELLA.) I can hardly believe a year has gone by since last time. It might have been last Tuesday.

NAOMI (*admiringly*): Well! I must say you certainly do look –

JUDY (*holding up her hand*): Don't say it. I know perfectly well I look wonderful. If I didn't after all I've been through, I'd shoot myself.

NAOMI: How do you mean – 'all you've been through'? *What* have you been through?

JUDY (*dramatically*): The full treatment! Face lift, breast lift, the lot. I had to suck Ovaltine through a straw for four whole days. It was hell.

STELLA: You don't mean to say you really – ?

JUDY: I certainly do, and what's more I wouldn't go through it again if my chin fell down to my knees. It was perfectly beastly and I loathed every minute of it.

STELLA (*starry-eyed*): You always were the brave one at school. Do you remember striking Miss Lockhart with a hockey stick?

NAOMI: Never mind about Miss Lockhart and hockey sticks for the moment. This is serious. (*To* JUDY.) When did all this happen? How long ago?

JUDY: Seven months ago. On the fifth of November, as a matter of fact. Gunpowder, treason and plot.

NAOMI: Where?

JUDY: Vienna. It was just one long dreamy waltz.

NAOMI: Why didn't you write and tell us?

JUDY: I wanted it to be a surprise.

STELLA: Well, you got your wish. It most emphatically is.

NAOMI: What did Robert say?

JUDY: He said – 'What's the matter, old girl, you look a bit seedy?'

STELLA: Oh, Judy! How discouraging. After all that trouble!

JUDY: I suppose it was in a way. Not that I expected him to rush at me in a frenzy of sudden, uncontrolled lust, but I would have liked a casual comment like – 'That hat suits you' or 'Your trip to Vienna certainly seems to have done you good.' But not a bit of it. He just went back to his *Times* crossword and asked me for a dismissive verb starting with B in six letters.

STELLA: I can think of several in four letters.

NAOMI: Well, all I can say is that I think you've been downright underhand, underhand and crafty.

JUDY: Believe me, 'underhand' is the last word to describe the operation. He snipped and stitched away at me for three and a half hours.

NAOMI: *Who* did the operation?

JUDY: Professor Krindling, of course.

NAOMI (*horrified*): Professor Krindling! You must have been mad. He's well known to be the biggest charlatan in the business.

JUDY: Charlatan or no charlatan, you've got to admit he did a wonderful job on me.

NAOMI: You took a terrible risk.

JUDY: Nonsense.

NAOMI: He was the one who was responsible for Mary Kinnerton's strawberry chin.

JUDY: Mary Kinnerton's chin was always a worry anyway. Whatever he did to it couldn't have made all that much difference.

STELLA: Fancy knowing somebody who's actually been to Krindling! What's he like?

JUDY: Absolutely hideous with tufts of black hair bursting from his ears but gentle as a dove.

NAOMI: He sounds a horror.

JUDY: Well, he isn't a horror – he's an angel. And he's an absolute fanatic over his job, a hundred per cent dedicated. He used to sit on my bed and tell me the most fascinating things. You've no idea what you can have done to you nowadays, if you really put your mind to it. You can even have your sex changed at the drop of a hat.

NAOMI: King's Road, Chelsea must be knee deep in discarded bowlers.

JUDY: It's all very fine to laugh and make silly jokes.

NAOMI: I'm not laughing, not really. Actually, I'm thoroughly shocked and horrified. I hate the whole idea of this undignified scampering after Youth. I intend to grow old as gracefully as I can and let nature take its course.

JUDY: Then you'd better give up those blue rinses to start with and eat a lot of chocolate eclairs.

STELLA (*laughing*): Touché!

NAOMI (*crossly*): I don't know what you mean by 'touché'. I see nothing wrong in trying to make the best of oneself. A little self-discipline never hurt anybody. But I draw the line at plastic surgery, unless it's a medical necessity.

JUDY: Well, I find it a medical necessity to look at least ten years younger than I really am, so you can come off your high horse and stop being so pompous.

NAOMI: I don't mean to be pompous, really I don't. It's just that I can't bear the idea of mutton dressed as lamb.

JUDY: Do you think *I* look like mutton dressed as lamb?

NAOMI: No, I can't honestly say that I do. But is it really worth the effort? I mean does it really make you *feel* younger and happier and more able to cope with everything?

JUDY: Yes, it does. It most certainly does.

STELLA: The sad thing about the whole business is that nobody's really fooled.

JUDY: That's not the point. I don't give a hoot whether other people are fooled or not. I shan't care when everybody knows perfectly well that I'm eight-five, so long as I don't *look* it. It's a question of personal satisfaction. I should hate to get out of my bath and look in the glass and see everything hanging about.

NAOMI: Even now there must be a certain amount hanging about.

JUDY: That's just where you're wrong, there isn't, thanks to the dear professor. A snip here and a tuck there have worked wonders. I'll show you if you like.

NAOMI: Not before lunch, dear.

JUDY: Really, Naomi. You should try not to be so prim and hidebound.

NAOMI: It's nothing to do with being prim and hidebound. I just don't want Mrs Rothwell to come in and see you prancing about stripped to the waist.

JUDY: I hadn't planned on doing the dance of the seven veils.

NAOMI: I also feel that to examine scar tissue just before Steak Béarnaise might be a bit off-putting.

JUDY: All right – all right – have it your own way. I merely thought you might be interested.

NAOMI (*soothingly*): But I *am* interested. I also think it was frightfully brave of you to have it done at all. A little sly perhaps to have been so secretive about it.

JUDY: You could hardly expect me to put an announcement in *The Times*.

STELLA: What I want to know is – did it *hurt*?

JUDY: No, not really. It itched a bit and I felt as if I'd been scalped but it soon wore off. My face swelled up, of course, and looked like a vast Victoria plum for several days. Every time I looked in the glass I got the giggles and that *did* hurt like hell, I must say.

STELLA: Do you think *we* ought to have it done?

NAOMI: What do you mean 'we'? Speak for yourself. Personally, I have no intention of being tampered with.

JUDY: What a ghastly expression. It's only little girls on Wimbledon Common who get tampered with.

STELLA: Oh no, it isn't. Muriel Bailey gets tampered with every time she goes in the tube.

NAOMI: Poor Muriel. She's always been terribly unpunctual. Perhaps that explains it.

STELLA (*to* JUDY): Did you tell Robert you were going to have it done?

JUDY: Of course I told him. I always tell Robert everything.

STELLA: What did he say?

JUDY: 'Anything for a change'!

NAOMI: Has it made any difference to his feeling for you?

JUDY: If by that you mean what I think you mean, you ought to be ashamed of yourself.

NAOMI: I only wondered.

JUDY: Robert and I haven't indulged in any of that sort of thing since nineteen forty-five.

STELLA: Victory year.

JUDY: And we wouldn't have then, if Mrs Anstruther hadn't been in the Isle of Wight.

NAOMI: That horrible woman! I can never remember her first name.

JUDY: Neither can Robert, I asked him only the other day. He thinks it was Hermione but he wouldn't take a bet on it.

STELLA: Did you mind at the time? About Mrs Anstruther, I mean?

JUDY: Of course, I did. I was heartbroken. I even hired a private detective to follow them everywhere.

NAOMI: And did he?

JUDY: Yes, but without very satisfactory results. According to his report they went into the New Gallery Cinema and never came out.

STELLA: Perhaps it was *Ben Hur.*

NAOMI (*with a luxurious sigh*): Isn't it lovely getting old? I wouldn't care now if Jonathan slept with a different woman every night.

JUDY: It's possible that *they* would.

NAOMI: That was a very bitchy thing to say. Jonathan is still a very attractive man.

JUDY: Yes, but not really in that way.

NAOMI: Certainly in 'that way'. He's particularly alluring to the Young. Debutantes fall for him in droves. Only the other day the eldest Hatherton girl asked him point blank to take her to Paris for the weekend.

JUDY: If he had, I expect 'point blank' would have been the operative phrase.

NAOMI: If you're trying to insinuate –

JUDY: I'm not trying to insinuate anything. I'm merely rejecting your fanciful image of dear old Jonathan as a rampaging Casanova. He'll be sixty-eight next birthday. I know that because Robert's is the day before and they always send each other cards.

NAOMI: There's no accounting for the sex-urge. Ninon de Lenclos went on having lovers until she was pushing ninety.

JUDY: Then she must have been a conceited old ass.

NAOMI (*going to the drink table*): Would anyone like another nip?

STELLA: Yes, please. I'm looking forward to the day when I don't have to worry whether I look nice or not.

JUDY: When that day dawns, it will be your last.

STELLA: Do you really think that when I'm a gnarled old crone of ninety-five I shall still fuss about my hair?

JUDY: Certainly. If you've got any left, and if you haven't, you'll fuss about your wig. Old habits die hard.

STELLA: Oh, God!

JUDY: It's nothing to be depressed about. On the contrary, it shows a certain spiritual nobility. My Aunt Esther died on her eighty-ninth birthday painted up to the eyes.

NAOMI: Had she led a very giddy life?

JUDY: Lord, yes. Three husbands and strings of lovers. One of them was rumoured to be the station-master at Kettering.

STELLA: You mean she was a natural sex-pot?

JUDY: She certainly was. We were none of us allowed to see her until after we'd been confirmed.

STELLA (*seriously*): But she really liked sex for sex's sake? I mean it was necessary to her?

JUDY: I suppose it must have been.

STELLA: Well, it isn't to me. It never was.

JUDY: But you must have liked going to bed with people when you were young?

STELLA: I never went to bed with people when I was young. I was occasionally mauled a bit at dances and I once had a set-to with my cousin Stephen in the maze at Hampton Court.

NAOMI: How dreadful. There isn't even anywhere to sit down!

STELLA: He didn't seem to want to *sit* down.

JUDY: All right. We'll settle for the fact that you were a virgin until you married Robert. But what happened then?

STELLA: How do you mean 'what happened then'? The usual thing, I suppose.

JUDY: You were in love with him, weren't you?

STELLA: Of course, I was. I was dotty about him.

JUDY: Then didn't you *enjoy* it?

STELLA: Not at first, I was too agitated. Later on I got sort of used to it. I suppose it *is* rather habit-forming.

JUDY: Oh, Stella – Really!

STELLA: There's no need to look so shocked. I just don't happen to be a voluptuary.

JUDY: It certainly takes more than thirty years of marriage and one set-to in the Hampton Court maze to make a voluptuary.

STELLA: I really do rather resent your tone of patronage, Judy. We can't all go about swooning over men years younger than we are and working ourselves into states and plunging our heads into gas ovens.

JUDY: It's mean of you to bring that up. It happened years ago and I only put my head in a little way to see what it felt like but it made me sneeze, so I took it out again.

NAOMI: That was Derek What's-his-name, wasn't it?

JUDY: Yes. That was Derek What's-his-name, all right. He certainly was a killer.

NAOMI: He had no back to his head.

JUDY: I never noticed the back of his head. I was always too busy looking at the front. As a matter of fact, I saw him in the Ritz Bar only a few months ago.

STELLA: How did he look?

JUDY: Bright red and bald as an egg.

NAOMI: Oh dear — it does seem sad, doesn't it?

JUDY: Not to me it doesn't. I was absolutely delighted.

NAOMI: Did you see who was with him?

JUDY: Not very clearly. They were right at the other end of the bar near the door.

NAOMI: Perhaps it was Mildred.

JUDY: Not unless she's recently joined the Navy.

NAOMI (*fascinated*): Oooh, just fancy! Derek of all people. Upper deck or lower?

JUDY: Upper, but only just.

STELLA: It's no surprise to me, I always had my suspicions about Derek. There was something in the way he played the piano.

JUDY: Come now, Stella. He did at least play the piano beautifully.

STELLA: Too much Debussy.

NAOMI: None of the men in my life have been able to play a note on anything. Jonathan did buy a ukelele soon after we were married but it gave him a blister on his thumb and he threw it into the fire.

STELLA: Like that beastly Roman emperor and those little boys.

JUDY: What on earth are you talking about?

STELLA: I can't remember his name off hand but I know he used to throw little boys into the fire after he'd had his way with them.

JUDY: Italians are naturally cruel, I'm afraid. Look how they whack away at those wretched donkeys in Capri.

STELLA: This drink's terribly strong. If lunch doesn't happen soon, I shall fall down.

NAOMI: It should be ready any minute.

JUDY: Couldn't you ring a bell or something?

NAOMI: Good Heavens, no. Mrs Rothwell would have a fit. She's terribly highly strung.

JUDY: One should never allow oneself to be dominated by servants.

NAOMI: That feudal attitude won't wash nowadays, Judy. If anything upset Mrs Rothwell, I should be done for. Also, when the bell rings in the kitchen, it really is deafening. Enough to give anyone a nervous breakdown.

JUDY: That could be fixed by wedging in a bit of rag.

NAOMI: Then it wouldn't ring at all, so we should be back where we started.

STELLA: Wouldn't it be awful if we really were?

JUDY: Really were *what*?

STELLA: Back where we started. On the threshold of life – young and eager and oversexed.

NAOMI: Speak for yourself. I wasn't oversexed.

JUDY: What about Miss Mowforth? You were barmy about her.

NAOMI: That had nothing to do with sex, it was a spiritual relationship.

JUDY: You kept a snapshot of her in fencing-bloomers in your handkerchief drawer.

NAOMI: What about you and Doctor Pringle? I remember you fainting dead away when he sounded your chest.

JUDY: That wasn't passion. I was sickening for mumps.

STELLA: You were too old for mumps.

JUDY: Nevertheless, I had them all right. Is mumps them or it?

NAOMI: It must be them. You can't have a mump all by itself.

STELLA: Isn't it lucky that we're all reasonably healthy? Considering our ages I mean.

JUDY: I'm not reasonably healthy. I'm a martyr to practically everything. I cough and sniffle from November to May and in June I get hay fever, which torments me until the end of September.

NAOMI: At least you have October to look forward to.

STELLA (*earnestly*): I still maintain that we're fantastically lucky. We might be bedridden or crippled with arthritis or bent double like croquet-hoops. Instead we're all three sound in wind and limb and ready for anything.

JUDY: You always exaggerate so. We're far from being ready for anything, except lunch. And it doesn't look as if we're ever going to get that.

NAOMI: You must be patient, it's a cheese soufflé. She couldn't possibly start it until you'd both got here. You might have been stuck in a traffic jam and it would have sunk like a stone. Would you like another little nip?

JUDY: If I had another little nip I shouldn't be able to tell the difference between a cheese soufflé and a steak and kidney pudding.

STELLA: At least nothing agitating is likely to happen to any of us now, we're too old. Except getting ill and dying, of course.

JUDY: Do stop harping on how old we are. It's undermining. I'm beginning to feel as though I couldn't get out of this chair without help.

NAOMI: I doubt if you can. It's a perfect beast, like a hip-bath. Even quite young people get stuck in it.

STELLA: I'd hate to get ill but I don't believe I shall mind dying all that much.

JUDY: It's easy enough to say that now but just you wait until the time comes. You'll probably be in the most awful frizz.

STELLA: I don't know why you should assume that. Lots of people are calm as cucumbers on their death beds and think up lovely memorable things to say to comfort everybody.

JUDY: I doubt if I shall. I'm more likely to be in a tearing rage and insult people right and left.

NAOMI (*thoughtfully*): I shall cry, I expect. Not the boo-hooing, snuffly kind of crying, but just gentle, helpless tears, because everyone is being so kind to me.

JUDY: Perhaps they won't be.

NAOMI: Of course they will. People are always kind at death beds. They smooth your pillows and keep putting their fingers to their lips and tiptoeing about the darkened room.

JUDY: That would drive me mad to start with.

STELLA: Why don't we change the subject to something more cheerful? Lunch, for instance!

NAOMI: I wish you'd shut up about lunch. It'll be ready in a minute.

STELLA: I'm famished and it's nearly a quarter to two.

JUDY: Perhaps Mrs Rothwell has had some sort of accident.

NAOMI: Mrs Rothwell could never have an accident. You only have to look at her.

STELLA: I wish I could look at her. I've never wanted to look at anybody so much in my life.

JUDY: Three grandmothers! It really does seem grotesque, doesn't it? Almost indecent.

NAOMI: What's indecent about it? I don't know what you mean.

JUDY: The way we behave and dress and carry on. It's all so unsuitable somehow.

STELLA: What on earth are you talking about?

JUDY: I think nineteenth-century grandmothers were far more attractive and impressive than twentieth-century ones. They were yellowish and frail and infinitely more understanding and smelt vaguely of lavender water.

STELLA: Mine didn't. She had a voice like a foghorn and smelt dreadful.

NAOMI: What of?

STELLA: Mothballs, principally, but there was something else as well, I can't quite describe it –

JUDY: Well, be a dear and don't try.

NAOMI: Actually, I do rather see what Judy means. Nobody seems to get comfortably old any more. I'm sure we should all three of us find life far less agitating if we'd given up at fifty and were content to sit about clanking with cameo brooches.

JUDY: Old and grey and full of sleep and nodding by the fire.

STELLA: I'd rather sit in Antoine's, where at least there's someone to nod to.

JUDY: I still maintain that we present the wrong image.

STELLA: Who to?

JUDY: The world in general and our grandchildren in particular. How can we expect them to rush to us with their tiny troubles when we're always having our hair set and our nails done?

STELLA: You're getting your generations mixed, dear. My grand-daughter's last tiny trouble had to be dealt with by that very dubious doctor in St John's Wood.

NAOMI: Jennifer *is* an exception, Stella. You must admit that.

STELLA: I don't admit anything of the sort. The majority of the young today are morally irresponsible. Jennifer was just a bit careless. She was always vague as a child.

NAOMI: I think to become pregnant at the age of eighteen and a half is carrying vagueness a little too far.

JUDY: She inherits a lot of it from her mother.

STELLA: I resent that, Judy. Harriet was a bit forgetful, I agree, but she had a brilliant mind.

JUDY: She left two bull terrier puppies in the ladies lavatory at Paddington. If that isn't vague I should like to know what is.

NAOMI: Oh, poor things! What happened to them?

JUDY: The usual routine. Lost Property Office, Battersea Dogs' Home, advertisements in the *Daily Telegraph*. She got them back eventually.

NAOMI: Thank God for that. I can't bear to think of dogs being left about and forsaken. They must suffer so dreadfully not being able to explain anything to anybody.

STELLA: I don't suppose abandoned babies on doorsteps have too good a time, either.

NAOMI: At least they don't run the risk of being put into strange kennels and getting bitten by other abandoned babies.

STELLA: I don't care what you say about us presenting the wrong image, Judy. I still think we have every reason to congratulate ourselves.

JUDY: What on earth for?

STELLA (*vehemently*): Because we've survived! We've cleared all the hazards and hurdles and ditches. All we have to do now is to canter serenely down the home stretch.

NAOMI: Your phraseology is over-ebullient, Stella, it always was. We're none of us capable of cantering anywhere. It's as much as I can do to stagger from the top of Sloane Street to Harrods.

STELLA: You know perfectly well what I mean. We've all three of us been through the mill in our different ways and at last, at long last, we can afford to put our feet up and relax. There really isn't much that can happen to us now.

JUDY: For God's sake, touch wood!

STELLA: I wouldn't dream of touching wood. In my opinion all those foolish old superstitions encourage disaster rather than prevent it.

NAOMI: That's a superstition in itself.

STELLA: I don't in the least mind being thirteen at table and I can't wait to walk under ladders.

NAOMI: I'm afraid you'll have to until after lunch. Unless I can persuade Mrs Rothwell to set up the kitchen steps outside the dining-room door.

MRS ROTHWELL *enters.*

MRS ROTHWELL (*announcing*): Luncheon is served, Madame.

MRS ROTHWELL *withdraws leaving the door open.* NAOMI *ushers the others out.*

And on what better line could one wish to exit?

★

'There's room for everything in the theatre. I think there's still room for a drama or a comedy or a play about kitchen sinks or tramps or whatever – that's fine, providing they're good enough. But there's still room for a charming upper middle-class family, who have hearts and limbs and feel and think, jut the same as anybody else does. And even dukes and duchesses. There are still a few extant!'

★

'The theatre still spells magic for many millions of people and that magic should be a source of deep pride to all those who are privileged to serve in it.'

THE SONGS

Where are the songs we sung
When love in our hearts was young? . . .

Where, in the shadows that we have to pass among,
Lie those songs that once we sung?

Operette, 1938

Noël at the piano at Goldenhurst.

PLAY, ORCHESTRA, PLAY

Listen to the strain
It plays once more for us,
There it is again,
The past in store for us.
Wake
In the memory some forgotten song,
To break
The rhythm – driving us along
And make
Harmony again a last encore for us.

Play, orchestra, play,
Play something light and sweet and gay
For we must have music
We must have music
To drive our fears away.
While our illusions
Swiftly fade for us,
Let's have an orchestra score.
In the confusions
The years have made for us,
Serenade for us,
Just once more.
Life needn't be grey,
Although it's changing day by day,
Though a few old dreams may decay,
Play, orchestra, play.

Shadow Play, Tonight at 8:30 (1936)

Probably Noël's most famous song is 'Mad Dogs and Englishmen'. It was composed in his head on a motor trip in the Far East in early 1930 between Hanoi and Tonkin, and he sang it to his travelling companion, Jeffrey Amherst

'on the verandah of a small jungle guest house. Not only Jeffrey, but the gecko lizards and the tree frogs gave every vocal indication of enthusiasm.'

Noël's own enthusiasm for the song was somewhat tempered on the eve of the Second World War when he asked Winston Churchill's advice on how he could best contribute to the war effort.

'It was, on the whole, an unsuccessful little interview. I was aware throughout that he was misunderstanding my motives and had got it firmly into his mind that I wished to be a glamorous secret agent. I tried vainly to disabuse him of this by assuring him that nothing was further from my thoughts, and that even if my heart were set on such a course, the very fact of my celebrity value would prove an insuperable obstacle. I emphasized repeatedly my firm conviction that my brain and creative intelligence could be of more service to the Government than my theatrical ability. I think the word "intelligence" must have been the monkey wrench, because at the mere mention of it he said irascibly, "You'd be no good in the intelligence service." I endeavoured, with growing inward irritation, to explain that I didn't mean "The Intelligence" in inverted commas, but my own personal intelligence, which was not in inverted commas. He would have none of it, however, and went off at a great tangent about the Navy (which in any event was preaching to the already converted). Finally, warming to his subject, he waved his hand with a bravura gesture and said dramatically: "Get into a warship and see some action! Go and sing to them when the guns are firing – that's your job!" With, I think, commendable restraint, I bit back the retort that if the morale of the Royal Navy was at such low ebb that the troops were unable to go into action without my singing "Mad Dogs and Englishmen" to them, we were in trouble at the outset and that, although theoretically "Singing when the guns are firing" sounds extremely gallant, it is, in reality, impracticable, because during a naval battle all ship's

companies are at action stations, and the only place for me to
sing would be in the ward-room by myself.'

Future Indefinite, 1950

*The song later became the cause of an Anglo-American dispute. When
Churchill and Roosevelt met on the British battleship HMS Prince of
Wales to draw up the Atlantic Charter, their respective aides were troubled
to hear what seemed to be a 'heated altercation' during a private session.*

*The argument turned out to be about the sequence of the words in
'Mad Dogs'. Did 'In Bangkok at twelve o'clock/They foam at the
mouth and run' come at the end of the first refrain or the second?*

*Noël was later asked by Churchill to adjudicate. 'I'm afraid, Prime
Minister,' he said, 'the President was right and you were wrong.'
Churchill gave him that bulldog glare and finally said – 'Bwitain
can take it!'*

MAD DOGS AND ENGLISHMEN

In tropical climes there are certain times of day
When all the citizens retire
To tear their clothes off and perspire.
It's one of those rules that the greatest fools obey,
Because the sun is much too sultry
And one must avoid its ultra-violet ray.

Papalaka papalaka papalaka boo,
Papalaka papalaka papalaka boo,
Digariga digariga digariga doo,
Digariga digariga digariga doo.

The natives grieve when the white men leave
     their huts,
Because they're obviously definitely nuts!

Mad dogs and Englishmen
Go out in the midday sun,

The Japanese don't care to,
The Chinese wouldn't dare to,
Hindoos and Argentines sleep firmly
    from twelve to one,
But Englishmen detest a siesta.
In the Philippines
There are lovely screens
To protect you from the glare.

In the Malay States
There are hats like plates
Which the Britishers won't wear.
At twelve noon
The natives swoon
And no further work is done.
But mad dogs and Englishmen
Go out in the midday sun.

It's such a surprise for the Eastern
    eyes to see
That though the English are effete,
They're quite impervious to heat.
When the white man rides every
    native hides his glee,
Because the simple creatures hope he
Will impale his solar topee on a tree.

Bolyboly bolyboly bolyboly baa,
Bolyboly bolyboly bolyboly baa,
Habaninny habaninny habaninny haa
Habaninny habaninny habaninny haa.

It seems such a shame
When the English claim
The earth
That they give rise to such hilarity and mirth.

Mad dogs and Englishmen
Go out in the midday sun.

The toughest Burmese bandit
Can never understand it.
In Rangoon the heat of noon
Is just what the natives shun.
They put their Scotch or Rye down
And lie down.

In a jungle town
Where the sun beats down
To the rage of man and beast,
The English garb
Of the English sahib
Merely gets a bit more creased.
In Bangkok
At twelve o'clock
They foam at the mouth and run,
But mad dogs and Englishmen
Go out in the midday sun.

Mad dogs and Englishmen
Go out in the midday sun.
The smallest Malay rabbit
Deplores this stupid habit.
In Hongkong
They strike a gong
And fire off a noonday gun
To reprimand each inmate
Who's in late.
In the mangrove swamps
Where the python romps
There is peace from twelve to two,
Even caribous
Lie around and snooze,
For there's nothing else to do.
In Bengal
To move at all
Is seldom, if ever done,
But mad dogs and Englishmen
Go out in the midday sun.

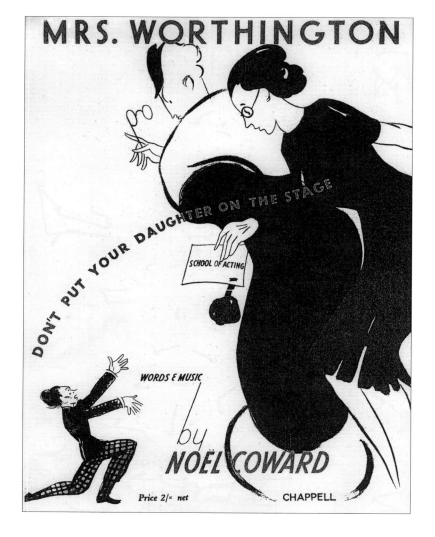

A close second would have to be 'Mrs Worthington' (1936), a song that was never part of any show and mostly sung by Noël himself — or any misguided wannabe Noël. It expressed a nightmare that haunted him throughout his professional life . . .

'Its universal appeal lies, I believe, in its passionate sincerity. It is a genuine *cri de coeur* and as such cannot fail to ring true. Unhappily, its effectiveness, from the point of view of propaganda, has been negligible. I had hoped, by writing it, to discourage misguided maternal ambition, to deter those dreadful eager mothers from making beasts of themselves, by boring the hell out of me and wasting their own and my time, but I have not succeeded. On the contrary, the song seems to

have given them extra impetus and ninety-nine out of a
hundred of the letters they write to me refer to it with roguish
indulgence, obviously secure in the conviction that it could not
in any circumstances apply to them. This is saddening, of course,
but, realizing that the road of the social reformer is paved with
disillusion, I have determined to rise above it.'

MRS WORTHINGTON

Regarding yours, dear Mrs Worthington,
Of Wednesday the 23rd,
Although your baby
May be
Keen on a stage career,
How can I make it clear,
That this is not a good idea.
For her to hope,
Dear Mrs Worthington,
Is on the face of it absurd,
Her personality
Is not in reality
Inviting enough,
Exciting enough
For this particular sphere.

Don't put your daughter on the stage,
    Mrs Worthington,
Don't put your daughter on the stage,
The profession is overcrowded
And the struggle's pretty tough
And admitting the fact
She's burning to act,
That isn't quite enough.
She has nice hands, to give the wretched girl
    her due,
But don't you think her bust is too
Developed for her age?
I repeat
Mrs Worthington,

Sweet
Mrs Worthington,
Don't put your daughter on the stage.

Don't put your daughter on the stage,
    Mrs Worthington,
Don't put your daughter on the stage,
She's a bit of an ugly duckling,
You must honestly confess,
And the width of her seat
Would surely defeat
Her chances of success,
It's a loud voice, and though it's not exactly flat,
She'll need a little more than that
To earn a living wage,
On my knees,
Mrs Worthington,
Please,
Mrs Worthington,
Don't put your daughter on the stage.

Don't put your daughter on the stage,
    Mrs Worthington,
Don't put your daughter on the stage,
Though they said at the school of acting
She was lovely as Peer Gynt,
I'm afraid on the whole
An ingénue role
Would emphasize her squint,
She's a big girl, and though her teeth are
    fairly good
She's not the type I ever would
Be eager to engage,
No more buts,
Mrs Worthington,
NUTS,
Mrs Worthington,
Don't put your daughter on the stage.
Don't put your daughter on the stage,
    Mrs Worthington,

Don't put your daughter on the stage,
One look at her bandy legs should prove
She hasn't got a chance,
In addition to which
The son of a bitch
Can neither sing nor dance,
She's a *vile* girl and uglier than mortal sin,
One look at her has put me in
A tearing bloody rage.
That sufficed,
Mrs Worthington,
Christ!
Mrs Worthington,
Don't put your daughter on the stage.

★

'Marvellous Party' lets down Nounou, Nada and Nell and everyone else who drifted into that celebrated soirée . . .

'During the summer of 1937 or 1938, I forget which, Elsa Maxwell gave a party in the South of France. It was a "Beach" party and when she invited Grace Moore, Beatrice Lillie and me, she explained that we were to "come as we were" and that it would be "just ourselves". When we arrived (as we were) we discovered that "just ourselves" meant about a hundred of us, all in the last stages of evening dress. We also discovered that one of the objects of the party was for us to entertain. As we were on holiday and had no accompanist and were not in any way prepared to perform, we refused. Elsa was perfectly understanding, but the other guests were a trifle disgruntled. I believe Beattie was persuaded to sing, but Grace and I held firm. This whole glittering episode was my original inspiration for "I've Been to a Marvellous Party". Beattie eventually sang the song in *Set to Music* wearing slacks, a fisherman's shirt, several ropes of pearls, a large sun-hat and dark glasses. She has sung it a great deal since.'

As you can see, Noël never quite made up his mind as to whether he'd 'been' or 'went' to that marvellous party.

...een to a marvellous party
Elise made an entrance with hay!
I'd never have guessed
From her fisherman's vest
That her bust had been whittled away
Poor Lulu got fried on Chianti
And talked about esprit de corps
The French fleet was doing a stroke with me
when suddenly Cyril screamed Fiddledidee
And ripped off his trousers and jumped in the sea
I couldn't have liked it more!

Quite for no reason
I'm here for the season
And high as a kite
Living in sin
With Maud at Cap Ferrat
Which couldn't be right
Everyone's here and frightfully gay
Nobody cares what people say
Tho' the Riviera
Seems really much queerer
Than Rome at its height
Yesterday night

I've been to a marvellous party
With Tiger and Boo Boo and Nell
It was in the fresh air
And we went as we were
And we stayed as we were which was Hell
Poor Clare skulked singing at midnight
And didn't stop singing till four
Daphne Pop-Dever got very light
Piggie and Jane had a hand to hand fight
And Lulu struck Maud and went out like
I couldn't have liked it more

I've been to a marvellous party
We didn't start dinner till ten
And young Bobbie Carr
Did a stunt at the bar
With a lot of extraordinary men
Poor Lola was there looking frightful
And Michael arrived with a whore
We knew the excitement was bound to begin
When Laura demolished a bottle of gin
And scratched her veneer with a cuttie
I couldn't have liked it more!

I'VE BEEN TO A MARVELLOUS PARTY

Quite for no reason
I'm here for the Season
And high as a kite,
Living in error
With Maud at Cap Ferrat
Which couldn't be right.
Everyone's here and frightfully gay,
Nobody cares what people say.
Though the Riviera
Seems really much queerer
Than Rome at its height,
Yesterday night –

I've been to a marvellous party
With Nounou and Nada and Nell,
It was in the fresh air
And we went as we were
And we stayed as we were
Which was Hell.
Poor Grace started singing at midnight
And didn't stop singing till four;
We knew the excitement was bound to begin
When Laura got blind on Dubonnet and gin
And scratched her veneer with a Cartier pin,
I couldn't have liked it more.

I've been to a marvellous party,
I must say the fun was intense,
We all had to do
What the people we knew
Would be doing a hundred years hence.
Dear Cecil arrived wearing armour,
Some shells and a black feather boa,
Poor Millicent wore a surrealist comb
Made of bits of mosaic from St Peter's in Rome,
But the weight was so great that she had to
   go home,
I couldn't have liked it more.

People's behaviour
Away from Belgravia
Would make you aghast,
So much variety
Watching Society
Scampering past,
If you have any mind at all
Gibbon's divine *Decline and Fall*
Seems pretty flimsy,
No more than a whimsy,
By way of contrast
On Saturday last —

I've been to a marvellous party,
We didn't start dinner till ten
And young Bobbie Carr
Did a stunt at the bar
With a lot of extraordinary men;
Dear Baba arrived with a turtle
Which shattered us all to the core,
The Grand Duke was dancing a foxtrot
    with me
When suddenly Cyril screamed Fiddledidee
And ripped off his trousers and jumped
    in the sea,
I couldn't have liked it more.

I've been to a marvellous party,
Elise made an entrance with May,
You'd never have guessed
From her fisherman's vest
That her bust had been whittled away.
Poor Lulu got fried on Chianti
And talked about *esprit de corps*.
Maurice made a couple of passes at Gus
And Freddie, who hates any kind of a fuss,
Did half the Big Apple and twisted his truss,
I couldn't have liked it more.

I've been to a marvellous party,
We played the most wonderful game,

Maureen disappeared
And came back in a beard
And we all had to guess at her name!
We talked about growing old gracefully
And Elsie who's seventy-four
Said, 'A, it's a question of being sincere,
And B, if you're supple you've nothing to fear.'
Then she swung upside down from a glass
    chandelier,
I couldn't have liked it more.

Set to Music (1939)

★

' "The Stately Homes of England" is English not only in subject matter but in its Anglo-Saxon attitude. Only the English can be self-deprecatory *and* literate at the same time. But woe betide anyone who is *not* English and tries to deprecate us!

'Note the key lines –

To prove the upper classes
Have still the upper hand

'And one knows, does one not, that they still do – even though the hand might be a mite more impoverished? One simply does not bruit it abroad, does one?'

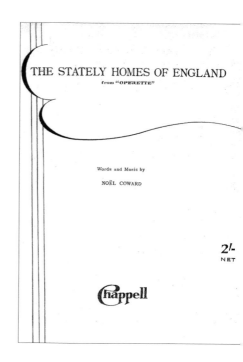

Noël recorded it and sang it all over the world 'and it has been popular with everyone with the exception of a Mayoress in New Zealand, who said it let down the British Empire'.

THE STATELY HOMES OF ENGLAND

(Quartette)

Lord Elderley, Lord Borrowmere,
Lord Sickert and Lord Camp
With every virtue, every grace,
Ah what avails the sceptred race,
Here you see – the four of us,
And there are so many more of us
Eldest sons that must succeed.
We know how Caesar conquered Gaul
And how to whack a cricket ball;
Apart from this, our education
Lacks co-ordination.
Though we're young and tentative
And rather rip-representative,
Scions of a noble breed,
We are the products of those homes
    serene and stately
Which only lately
Seem to have run to seed!

The Stately Homes of England,
How beautiful they stand,
To prove the upper classes
Have still the upper hand;
Though the fact that they have to be
    rebuilt
And frequently mortgaged to the hilt
Is inclined to take the gilt
Off the gingerbread,
And certainly damps the fun
Of the eldest son –
But still we won't be beaten,
We'll scrimp and scrape and save,
The playing fields of Eton
Have made us frightfully brave –
And though if the Van Dycks have to go
And we pawn the Bechstein Grand,

We'll stand
By the Stately Homes of England.

Here you see
The pick of us,
You may be heartily sick of us,
Still with sense
We're all imbued.
Our homes command extensive views
And with assistance from the Jews
We have been able to dispose of
Rows and rows and rows of
Gainsboroughs and Lawrences,
Some sporting prints of Aunt Florence's,
Some of which were rather rude.
Although we sometimes flaunt our family
    conventions,
Our good intentions
Mustn't be misconstrued.

The Stately Homes of England
We proudly represent,
We only keep them up for
Americans to rent.
Though the pipes that supply the bathroom
    burst
And the lavatory makes you fear the worst,
It was used by Charles the First
Quite informally,
And later by George the Fourth
On a journey north.
The State Apartments keep their
Historical renown,
It's wiser not to sleep there
In case they tumble down;
But still if they ever catch on fire
Which, with any luck, they might
We'll fight
For the Stately Homes of England.

The Stately Homes of England,

Though rather in the lurch,
Provide a lot of chances
For Psychical Research –
There's the ghost of a crazy younger son
Who murdered, in thirteen fifty-one,
An extremely rowdy Nun
Who resented it,
And people who come to call
Meet her in the hall.
The baby in the guest wing,
Who crouches by the grate,
Was walled up in the west wing
In fourteen twenty-eight.
If anyone spots
The Queen of Scots
In a hand-embroidered shroud,
We're proud
Of the Stately Homes of England.

Reprise – Act Two

Lord Elderley, Lord Borrowmere,
Lord Sickert and Lord Camp,
Behold us in our hours of ease,
Uncertain, coy and hard to please.
Reading in *Debrett* of us,
This fine Patrician quartette of us,
We can feel extremely proud,
Our ancient lineage we trace
Back to the cradle of the Race
Before those beastly Roman bowmen
Bitched our local Yeomen.
Though the new democracy
May pain the old Aristocracy
We've not winced nor cried aloud,
Under the bludgeonings of chance what
    will be – will be.
Our heads will still be
Bloody but quite unbowed!

The Stately Homes of England
In valley, dale and glen
Produce a race of charming,
Innocuous young men.
Though our mental equipment may be slight
And we barely distinguish left from right,
We are quite prepared to fight
For our principles,
Though none of us knows so far
What they really are.
Our duty to the nation,
It's only fair to state,
Lies not in procreation
But what we procreate;
And so we can cry
With kindling eye
As to married life we go,
What ho!
For the Stately Homes of England!

The Stately Homes of England,
Although a trifle bleak,
Historically speaking,
Are more or less unique,
We've a cousin who won the Golden Fleece
And a very peculiar fowling-piece
Which was sent to Cromwell's niece,
Who detested it,
And rapidly sent it back
With a dirty crack.
A note we have from Chaucer
Contains a bawdy joke.
We also have a saucer
That Bloody Mary broke.
We've two pairs of tights
King Arthur's Knights
Had completely worn away.
Sing Hey!
For the Stately Homes of England!

Operette (1938)

Patriotism, jingoism — or simply chauvinism — was a subject that Noël came back to again and again in his work.

The French may have coined the word, but the English have certainly put a fine polish on it. After all, as used to be said in less politically correct times, 'Foreigners begin at Calais.'

And apart from the 'old enemy', there was another lot who needed to study the Marquess of Queensberry rules . . .

Noël wrote this next song in 1943 at the height of the war. The BBC promptly banned it as being almost treasonable — a sense of irony not being high on the Calvinist priorities inherited from Lord Reith.

'I shall never cease to be surprised at the sublime silliness . . . After all, "Let's help the dirty swine again / To occupy the Rhine again" and "Let's give them full air parity / And treat the rats with charity" are not, as phrases, exactly oozing with brotherly love.'

Ironically it was Winston Churchill who rescued it. He insisted Noël sing it at dinner parties until he was hoarse. And on this particular point Churchill and FDR were in total accord.

DON'T LET'S BE BEASTLY
TO THE GERMANS

We must be kind –
And with an open mind
We must endeavour to find
A way –
To let the Germans know that when the war
    is over
They are not the ones who'll have to pay.
We must be sweet –
And tactful and discreet
And when they've suffered defeat
We mustn't let
Them feel upset
Or ever get
The feeling that we're cross with them or
    hate them,
Our future policy must be to reinstate them.

Don't let's be beastly to the Germans
When our victory is ultimately won,
It was just those nasty Nazis who persuaded
    them to fight
And their Beethoven and Bach are really far
    worse than their bite,
Let's be meek to them –
And turn the other cheek to them
And try to bring out their latent sense of fun.
Let's give them full air parity
And treat the rats with charity,
But don't let's be beastly to the Hun.

We must be just –
And win their love and trust
And in addition we must
Be wise
And ask the conquered lands to join our
    hands to aid them.

That would be a wonderful surprise.
For many years —
They've been in floods of tears
Because the poor little dears
Have been so wronged and only longed
To cheat the world,
Deplete the world
And beat
The world to blazes.
This is the moment when we ought to sing
   their praises.

Don't let's be beastly to the Germans
When we've definitely got them on the run —
Let us treat them very kindly as we would
   a valued friend —
We might send them out some Bishops as
   a form of lease and lend,
Let's be sweet to them -
And day by day repeat to them
That 'sterilization' simply isn't done.
Let's help the dirty swine again —
To occupy the Rhine again,
But don't let's be beastly to the Hun.

Don't let's be beastly to the Germans
When the age of peace and plenty has begun.
We must send them steel and oil and coal and
   everything they need
For their peaceable intentions can be always
   guaranteed.
Let's employ with them a sort of 'strength
   through joy' with them,
They're better than us at honest manly fun.
Let's let them feel they're swell again and bomb
   us all to hell again,
But don't let's be beastly to the Hun.

Don't let's be beastly to the Germans
For you can't deprive a gangster of his gun

Though they've been a little naughty to the
    Czechs and Poles and Dutch
But I don't suppose those countries really
    minded very much.
Let's be free with them and share the BBC
    with them.
We mustn't prevent them basking in the sun.
Let's soften their defeat again – and build their
    bloody fleet again,
But don't let's be beastly to the Hun.

★

There was, however, one country that Noël did like. And during those post-war years when he seemed unable to do anything to please in his own land, it was America that always appreciated his talent and allowed him to re-emerge as a star of cabaret and live television.

So, not surprisingly . . .

I LIKE AMERICA

I don't care for China,
Japan's far too small,
I've rumbled the Rio Grande,
I hate Asia Minor,
I can't bear Bengal
And I shudder to think
Of the awful stink
On the road to Samarkand.

The heat and smell
Must be sheer hell
On the road to Samarkand.

I like America,
I have played around
Every slappy-happy hunting ground
But I find America – okay.
I've been about a bit
But I must admit

That I didn't know the half of it
Till I hit the USA.

No likely lass
In Boston, Mass.
From passion will recoil.
In Dallas, Tex,
They talk of sex
But only think of oil.
New Jersey dames
Go up in flames
If someone mentions – bed.
In Chicago, Illinois
Any girl who meets a boy
Giggles and shoots him dead!
But I like America
Its Society
Offers infinite variety
And come what may
I shall return some day
To the good old USA.

I've loathed every acre
From Cannes to Canton,
I also deplore Bombay,
I've jeered at Jamaica
And seen through Ceylon,
And exploded the myth
Of those Flying Fith
On the Road to Mandalay.

We'll never mith
Those blasted fith
On the roads to Mandalay.

But I like America,
I have travelled far
From Northumberland to
     Zanzibar
And I find America – okay.
I've roamed the Spanish Main

Eaten sugar-cane
But I never tasted cellophane
Till I struck the USA.
All delegates
From Southern States
Are nervy and distraught.
In New Orleans
The wrought-iron screens
Are dreadfully overwrought.
Beneath each tree in Tennessee
Erotic books are read.
And when alligators thud
Through the Mississippi mud
Sex rears its ugly head.
But – I like America,
Every scrap of it,
All the sentimental crap of it
And come what may
Give me a holiday
In the good old USA.

Ace of Clubs (1950)

Patriotic to a fault though he was, Noël was perfectly capable of seeing his own countrymen's idiosyncrasies and idiocies. After all, 'Mad Dogs' had its tongue fairly far into its cheek in 1930. By the end of the Second World War he could sense a nation ready to face its uncertain future by looking over its shoulder to the safety of its imperial and colonizing past . . .

'The next song was written and firmly sung in Calcutta in 1944. Only a very few outraged "Indian Colonels" protested and it was a great success.'

I WONDER WHAT HAPPENED TO HIM?

The India that one read about
And may have been misled about
In one respect has kept itself intact.
Though 'Pukka Sahib' traditions may have cracked
And thinned
The good old Indian army's still a fact.
That famous monumental man
The Officer and Gentleman
Still lives and breathes and functions from Bombay
   to Katmandu.
At any moment one can glimpse

Matured or embryonic 'Blimps'
Vivaciously speculating as to what became of who.
Though Eastern sounds may fascinate your ear
When West meets West you're always sure to hear –

Whatever became of old Bagot?
I haven't seen him for a year.
Is it true that young Forbes had to marry that Faggot
He met in the Vale of Kashmir?
Have you had any news
Of that chap in the 'Blues'.
Was it Prosser or Pyecroft or Pym?
He was stationed in Simla, or was it Bengal?
I know he got tight at a ball in Nepal
And wrote several four-letter words on the wall.
I wonder what happened to him!

Whatever became of old Shelley?
Is it true that young Briggs was cashiered
For riding quite nude on a push-bike through Delhi
The day the new Viceroy appeared?
Have you had any word
Of that bloke in the 'Third',
Was it Southerby, Sedgwick or Sim?
They had him thrown out of the club in Bombay
For, apart from his mess bills exceeding his pay,
He took to pig-sticking in *quite* the wrong way.
I wonder what happened to him!

One must admit that by and large
Upholders of the British Raj
Don't shine in conversation as a breed.
Though Indian army officers can read
A bit
Their verbal wit – has rather run to seed.
Their splendid insularity
And roguish jocularity
Was echoing through when Victoria was Queen.
In restaurants and dining-cars,
In messes, clubs and hotel bars
They try to maintain tradition in the way it's always been

Though worlds may change and nations disappear
Above the shrieking chaos you will hear –

Whatever became of old Tucker?
Have you heard any word of young Mills
Who ruptured himself at the end of a chukka
And had to be sent to the hills?
They say that young Lees
Had a go of DTs
And his hopes of promotion are slim.
According to Stubbs, who's a bit of a louse,
The silly young blighter went out on a 'souse',
And took two old tarts into Government House.
I wonder what happened to him!

Whatever became of old Keeling?
I hear that he got back from France
And frightened three nuns in a train in Darjeeling
By stripping and waving his lance!
D'you remember Munroe,
In the PAVO?
He was tallish and mentally dim.
That talk of heredity can't be quite true,
He was dropped on his head by his ayah at two,
I presume that by now he'll have reached GHQ.
I'm *sure* that's what happened to him!

Whatever became of old Archie?
I hear he departed this life
After rounding up ten sacred cows in Karachi
To welcome the Governor's wife.
D'you remember young Phipps
Who had *very* large hips
And whose waist was excessively slim?
Well, it seems that some doctor in Grosvenor Square
Gave him hormone injections for growing his hair
And he grew something here, and he grew
    something there.
I wonder what happened to her – him?

★

Elaine Stritch and Noël Coward,
from the programme for
the Broadway production of
Sail Away.

*Wherever you stuck a pin in the map, the chances were that Noël had
already been there on his own travels . . .*

I TRAVEL ALONE

The world is wide, and when my day is done
I shall at least have travelled free,
Led by this wanderlust that turns my eyes to far
    horizons.
Though time and tide won't wait for anyone,
There's one illusion left for me
And that's the happiness I've known alone.

I travel alone,
Sometimes I'm East,
Sometimes I'm West,
No chains can ever bind me;
No remembered love can ever find me;
I travel alone.
Fair though the faces and places I've known,
When the dream is ended and passion has flown
I travel alone.
Free from love's illusion, my heart is my own:
I travel alone.

*Just as so many of the characters in his plays are inclined to make a
hasty exit before the final curtain to resolve a tricky situation – Elyot
and Amanda in* Private Lives *. . . Garry and Liz in* Present
Laughter *. . . the benighted house guests in* Hay Fever *– so would
Noël be inclined to leave a scene that didn't please. A relationship gone
wrong, a play that hadn't worked out. His personal philosophy was
simply to –*

SAIL AWAY

A different sky,
New worlds to gaze upon,
The strange excitement of an unfamiliar shore,
One more goodbye,
One more illusion gone,
Just cut your losses
And begin once more.

When the storm clouds are riding through a winter sky
Sail away – sail away.
When the love-light is fading in your sweetheart's eye
Sail away – sail away.
When you feel your song is orchestrated wrong
Why should you prolong
Your stay?
When the wind and the weather blow your dreams
   sky high
Sail away – sail away – sail away!

When the friends that you've counted on have let
   you down
Sail away – sail away!
But when soon or late
You recognize your fate
That will be your great,
Great day.
On the wings of the morning with your own true love
Sail away –
Sail away –
Sail away!

Sail Away (1961)

The only trouble is that when you do sail away – even if you are
travelling alone – there are all those other people . . .

WHY DO THE WRONG PEOPLE TRAVEL?

Travel they say improves the mind,
An irritating platitude
Which frankly, *entre nous*,
Is very far from true.
Personally I've yet to find
That longitude and latitude
Can educate those scores
Of monumental bores
Who travel in groups and herds and troupes
Of various breeds and sexes,
Till the whole world reels
To shouts and squeals
And the clicking of Rolliflexes.

Why do the wrong people travel, travel, travel,
When the right people stay back home?
What compulsion compels them
And who the hell tells them
To drag their cans to Zanzibar
Instead of staying quietly in Omaha?
The Taj Mahal
And the Grand Canal
And the sunny French Riviera
Would be less oppressed
If the Middle West
Would settle for somewhere rather nearer.
Please do not think that I criticize or cavil
At a genuine urge to roam,
But why, oh why, do the wrong people travel
When the right people stay back home
And mind their business,
When the right people stay back home
With *Cinerama,*
When the right people stay back home,

I'm merely asking
Why the right people stay back home?

Just when you think romance is ripe
It rather sharply dawns on you
That each sweet serenade
Is for the Tourist Trade.
Any attractive native type
Who resolutely fawns on you
Will give as his address
American Express.
There isn't a rock
Between Bangkok
And the beaches of Hispaniola,
That does not recoil
From suntan oil
And the gurgle of Coca-Cola.

Why do the wrong people travel, travel, travel,
When the right people stay back home?
What explains this mass mania
To leave Pennsylvania
And clack around like flocks of geese,
Demanding dry martinis on the Isles of Greece?
In the smallest street
Where the gourmets meet
They invariably fetch up
And it's hard to make
Them accept a steak
That isn't served rare and smeared with ketchup.
Millions of tourists are churning up the gravel
While they gaze at St Peter's dome,
But why, oh why, do the wrong people travel
When the right people stay back home
And eat hot doughnuts,
When the right people stay back home
With all those benefits,
When the right people stay back home?
I sometimes wonder
Why the right people stay back home!

Why do the wrong people travel, travel, travel,
When the right people stay back home?
What peculiar obsessions
Inspire those processions
Of families from Houston, Tex,
With all those cameras around their necks?
They will take a train
Or an aeroplane
For an hour on the Costa Brava,
And they'll see Pompeii
On the only day
That it's up to its ass in molten lava.
It would take years to unravel – ravel – ravel
Every impulse that makes them roam
But why oh why do the wrong people travel
When the right people stay back home
With all that Kleenex,
When the right people stay back home
With all that lettuce,
When the right people stay back home
With all those Kennedys?
Won't someone tell me
Why the right
I say the right people stay back home?

Sail Away (1961)

Sail Away *made Elaine Stritch a star, if a sometimes wandering one –
and Noël occasionally felt the need to correct her course . . .*

'Darling Stritchie,

I hope that you are well; that your cold is better; that you are
singing divinely; that you are putting on weight; that you are
not belting too much; that your skin is clear and free from spots
and other blemishes; that you are delivering my brilliant material
to the public in the manner in which it should be delivered;
that you are not making too many God-damned suggestions;
that your breath is relatively free from the sinful taint of alcohol;

that you are going regularly to confession and everywhere else that is necessary to go regularly. I also hope that you are not encouraging those dear little doggies to behave in such a fashion on the stage that they bring disrepute to the fair name of Equity and add fuel to the already prevalent suspicion that our gallant little company is not, by and large, entirely normal. I also hope that you are not constantly taking those silly Walter Kerrs and Agnes BS De Mille to the Pavillon for lunch every day. They only exhaust you and drain your energy and, however much you want to keep in with them, you must remember that your first duty is to me and the Catholic church – in that order.

I remain yours sincerely with mad hot kisses.'

WORLD WEARY

When I'm feeling dreary and blue,
I'm only too
Glad to be left alone,
Dreaming of a place in the sun.
When day is done;
Far from a telephone;
Bustle and the weary crowd
Make me want to cry out loud,
Give me something peaceful and grand
Where all the land
Slumbers in monotone.

I'm world weary, world weary,
Living in a great big town,
I find it so dreary, so dreary,
Everything looks grey or brown,
I want an ocean blue,
Great big trees,
A bird's eye view
Of the Pyrenees,
I want to watch the moon rise up
And see the great red sun go down,
Watching clouds go by
Through a Winter sky
Fascinates me
But if I do it in the street,
Every cop I meet
Simply hates me,
Because I'm world weary, world weary,
I could kiss the railroad tracks,
I want to get right back to nature and relax.

Get up in the morning at eight,
Relentless Fate
Drives me to work at nine;
Toiling like a bee in a hive
From four to five

Whether it's wet or fine,
Hardly ever see the sky,
Buildings seem to grow so high.
Maybe in the future I will
Perhaps fulfil
This little dream of mine.

I'm world weary, world weary,
Living in a great big town,
I find it so dreary, so dreary,
Everything looks grey or brown,
I want a horse and plough,
Chickens too,
Just one cow
With a wistful moo,
A country where the verb to work
Becomes a most improper noun;
I can hardly wait
Till I see the great
Open spaces,
My loving friends will not be there,
I'm so sick of their
God-damned faces,
Because I'm world weary, world weary,
Tired of all these jumping jacks,
I want to get right back to nature and relax.

This Year of Grace! (US, 1928)

★

Among his other talents Noël had a particularly strong and instinctive
sense of the times he was living in and the way they were changing . . .

This is a changing world, my dear,
New songs are sung – new stars appear,
Though we grow older year by year,
Our hearts can still be gay.

Pacific 1860 (1946)

While he himself was in many ways a creation of the twenties, he was also able to stand back and sense the angst all too close to the surface of the frenzied gaiety.

As the years went by and the evidence of social malaise became more obvious, Noël's comment on it became more explicit. Yes, women were now free to bob their hair, raise their hemlines and even − smoke cigarettes. But were they really any happier? Were any of us?

By 1925 in On with the Dance *he had summed it up. In a sophisticated little sketch,*

'Hermione Baddeley who stood about in evening dress looking drained and far from healthy, while (Alice) Delysia, as her French governess, lectured her in a worldly manner about the debauched life she was all too obviously leading.

'I thought of the tune while I was having tea. The usual dash for the piano and the thing was done. But for some reason I wrote the song in four flats, whereas I had always kept to three flats previously.'

POOR LITTLE RICH GIRL

You're only
A baby,
You're lonely,
And maybe
Some day soon you'll know
The tears
You are tasting
Are years
You are wasting,
Life's a bitter foe,
With fate it's no use competing,
Youth is so terribly fleeting;
By dancing
Much faster,
You're chancing
Disaster,
Time alone will show.

Poor little rich girl,
You're a bewitched girl,
Better beware!
Laughing at danger,
Virtue a stranger,
Better take care!
The life you lead sets all your nerves a jangle,
Your love affairs are in a hopeless tangle,
Though you're a child, dear,
Your life's a wild typhoon.
In lives of leisure
The craze for pleasure
Steadily grows.
Cocktails and laughter,
But what comes after?
Nobody knows.
You're weaving love into a mad jazz pattern,
Ruled by Pantaloon.
Poor little rich girl, don't drop a stitch too soon.

The role you are acting,
The toll is exacting.
Soon you'll have to pay.
The music of living,
You lose in the giving,
False things soon decay.
These words from me may surprise you,
I've got no right to advise you,
I've known life too well, dear,
Your own life must tell, dear,
Please don't turn away.

★

And in This Year of Grace! *in 1928 his warning was even more specific.*

'The high tone of moral indignation implicit in the lyric impressed a number of people, notably the late Aimée Semple McPherson.'

DANCE LITTLE LADY

Though you're only seventeen
Far too much of life you've seen,
Syncopated child.
Maybe if you only knew
Where your path was leading to
You'd become less wild.

But I know it's vain
Trying to explain
While there's this insane
Music in your brain.

Dance, dance, dance little lady,
Youth is fleeting – to the rhythm
    beating
In your mind.
Dance, dance, dance little lady,
So obsessed with second best.
No rest you'll ever find,
Time and tide and trouble
Never, never wait.
Let the cauldron bubble
Justify your fate.
Dance, dance, dance little lady,
Leave tomorrow behind.

When the saxophone
Gives a wicked moan,
Charleston hey hey,
Rhythms fall and rise,
Start dancing to the tune,
The band's crooning –
For soon
The night will be gone,
Start swaying like a reed
Without heeding
The speed
That hurries you on.
Nigger melodies
Syncopate your nerves
Till your body curves
Drooping – stooping,
Laughter some day dies
And when the lights are starting to
    gutter
Dawn through the shutter
Shows you're living in a world of lies.

By the time the flamboyant twenties fizzled out into the apprehensive thirties, it was quite clear to Noël what was happening to his century – even though, when he included the song in Cavalcade (1931), *it was not even a third over . . .*

TWENTIETH-CENTURY BLUES

Why is it that civilized humanity
Must make the world so wrong?
In this hurly-burly of insanity
Our dreams cannot last long.
We've reached a deadline –
The Press headline – every sorrow,
Blues value
Is News value
Tomorrow.

Blues,
Twentieth-Century Blues,
Are getting me down.
Who's
Escaped those weary
Twentieth-Century Blues.
Why,
If there's a God in the sky,
Why shouldn't he grin?
High
Above this dreary
Twentieth-Century din,
In this strange illusion,
Chaos and confusion,
People seem to lose their way.
What is there to strive for.
Love or keep alive for? Say –
Hey, hey, call it a day.
Blues,
Nothing to win or to lose.
It's getting me down.
Blues,
I've got those weary Twentieth-Century Blues.

It was, he felt,

'ironic in theme and musically rather untidy. It is also exceedingly difficult to sing, but in the play it achieved its purpose. It struck the right note of harsh discordance and typified . . . the curious hectic desperation I wished to convey.'

Ten years and another world war later, he saw little point in preaching. Humour was the only possible answer. What idiot could say 'Happy Days Are Here Again', when it was perfectly obvious that . . .

THERE ARE BAD TIMES
JUST AROUND THE CORNER

(*Las Vegas version, 1955*)

They're nervous in Nigeria
And terribly cross in Crete,
In Bucharest
They are so depressed
They're frightened to cross the street,
They're sullen in Siberia
And timid in Turkestan,
They're sick with fright
In the Isle of Wight
And jittery in Japan,
The Irish groan and shout, lads,
Maybe because they're Celts,
They know they're up the spout, lads,
And so is everyone else.
Hurray! Hurray! Hurray!
Trouble is on the way.

There are bad times just around the corner,
There are dark clouds hurtling through the sky
And it's no use whining
About a silver lining
For we *know* from experience that they won't roll by,
With a scowl and a frown
We'll keep our spirits down
And prepare for depression and doom and dread,
We're going to *un*pack our troubles from our old kit bag
And wait until we drop down dead.

There are bad times just around the corner,
The horizon's gloomy as can be,
There are black birds over
The greyish cliffs of Dover
And the vultures are hovering round the Christmas tree.
We're an *un*happy breed

And ready to stampede
When we're asked to remember what Lincoln said,
We're going to *un*tense our muscles till they sag sag sag
And wait until we drop down dead.

They're morbid in Mongolia
And querulous in Quebec,
There's not a man
In Baluchistan
Who isn't a nervous wreck,
In Maine the melancholia
Is deeper than tongue can tell,
In Monaco
All the croupiers know
They haven't a hope in Hell.
In far away Australia
Each wallaby's well aware
The world's a total failure
Without any time to spare.
Hurray! Hurray! Hurray!
Suffering and dismay.

There are bad times just around the corner,
We can all look forward to despair,
It's as clear as crystal
From Brooklyn Bridge to Bristol
That we *can't* save Democracy
And we don't much care.
At the sound of a shot
We'd just as soon as not
Take a hot-water bag and retire to bed
And while the press and the politicians nag nag nag
We'll wait until we drop down dead.

There are bad times just around the corner
And the outlook's absolutely vile,
You can take this from us
That when they Atom bomb us
We are *not* going to tighten our belts and smile smile smile,
We are in such a mess
It couldn't matter less

If a world revolution is just ahead,
We'd better all learn the lyrics of the old 'Red Flag'
And wait until we drop down dead.
A likely story
Land of Hope and Glory,
Wait until we drop down dead.

★

First, last and always there was − the Theatre. *The Gospel according to Coward:*

'The Theatre . . . is a house of strange enchantments, a temple of dreams.'

It never mattered to him if he was watching a Broadway or West End hit or an inept music-hall act on a bad night in a provincial theatre, as long as the players were giving all they had in them to give.

In 'Red Peppers' − *part of the* Tonight at 8:30 *sequence − George and Lily Pepper are touring the halls in an act loosely assembled in prehistory by George's parents. But by the mid-thirties the Red Peppers are slipping slowly down the bill.*

When Lynn Fontanne read the play she wrote to Noël . . . 'Their utter third-ratedness is so awfully pathetic. You know exactly why (aside from the pitiful business of their act) they have never been and never could be successful.'

In the two songs he wrote for Gertie and himself you can feel for all those thousands of performers who, twice nightly, would paste on a little spurious self-confidence with their Leichner No. 6 make-up and go out there to 'knock 'em dead'.

The Red Peppers first appear as a couple of disreputable sailors on shore leave . . .

HAS ANYBODY SEEN OUR SHIP?

What shall we do with the drunken sailor?
So the saying goes.
We're not tight but we're none too bright,
Great Scott! I don't suppose!
We've lost our way
And we've lost our pay,
And to make the thing complete,
We've been and gone and lost the bloomin'
    fleet!

Has anybody seen our ship?
The HMS *Peculiar*.
We've been on shore
For a month or more,
And when we see the Captain we shall get
    'what for'.
Heave ho, me hearties,
Sing Glory Hallelujah,
A lady bold as she could be

Pinched our whistles at 'The Golden Key'.
Now we're in between the devil and the deep
   blue sea.
Has anybody seen our ship?

What's to be done with the girls on shore
Who lead our Tars astray?
What's to be done with the drinks galore
That make them pass away?
We got wet ears
From our first five beers –
After that we lost control,
And now we find we're up the blinking pole!

Has anybody seen our ship?
The HMS *Disgusting*.
We've three guns aft
And another one fore
And they've promised us a funnel for the next
   world war.
Heave ho, me hearties,
The quarterdeck needs dusting.
We had a binge last Christmas year,
Nice plum puddings and a round of beer,
But the Captain pulled his cracker and we cried,
   'Oh dear!'
Has anybody seen our ship?

Has anybody seen our ship?
The HMS *Suggestive*.
She sailed away
Across the bay,
And we haven't had a smell of her since New
   Year's Day.
Heave ho, me hearties,
We're getting rather restive.
We pooled our money, spent the lot,
The world forgetting by the world forgot,
Now we haven't got a penny for the you know
   what!
Has anybody seen our ship?

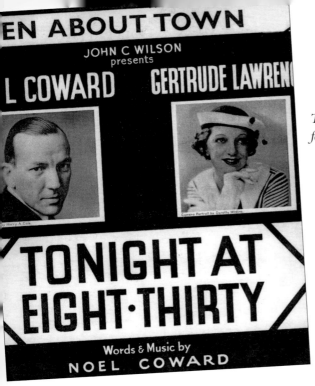

Then a frenzied quick change into formal white tie as a couple of toffs . . .

MEN ABOUT TOWN

We're two chaps who
Find it thrilling
To do the killing,
We're always willing
To give the girls a treat.
Just a drink at the Ritz,
Call it double or quits,
Then we feel the world is at our feet.
Top hats, white spats
Look divine on us,
There's a shine on us,
Get a line on us
When we come your way.
Gad! Eleven o'clock!
Let's pop into the Troc
Ere we start the business of the day.

As we stroll down Picc-Piccadilly
In the bright morning air,
All the girls turn and stare,
We're so nonchalant and frightfully debonair.
When we chat to Rose, Maud or Lily
You should see the way their boyfriends frown,
For they know without a doubt
That their luck's right out,
Up against a couple of men about town.

As we stroll down Picc-Piccadilly
All the girls say, 'Who's here?
Put your hat straight, my dear,
For it's Marmaduke and Percy Vere de Vere.'
As we doff hats, each pretty filly
Gives a wink at us and then looks down
For they long with all their might
For a red-hot night
When they see a couple of men about town.

★

To the end of his life Noël could play and sing the music-hall songs of his Edwardian youth with total recall. Theatre, for him, whatever form it took, should be entertainment for the people.

'My plays are written for the public and not for that small galaxy of scruffy critics and pretentious *savants* who know little and do less.'

Diaries, 1956

'I've never written for the intelligentsia. Sixteen curtain calls and closed on Saturday.'

Interview with the *Daily Mirror*

If a show – play or musical – didn't find an audience, it had by definition failed. Even if he had written it himself. Which caused him to question one of the fundamental so-called truths by which all thespians swore . . .

WHY MUST THE SHOW GO ON?

The world for some years
Has been sodden with tears
On behalf of the Acting profession,
Each star playing a part
Seems to expect the 'Purple Heart',
It's unorthodox
To be born in a box
But it needn't become an obsession,
Let's hope we have no worse to plague us
Than two shows a night at Las Vegas.
When I think of physicians
And mathematicians
Who don't earn a quarter the dough,
When I look at the faces
Of people in Macy's
There's one thing I'm burning to know:

Why must the show go on?
It can't be all that indispensable,
To me it really isn't sensible
On the whole
To play a leading role
While fighting those tears you can't control,
Why kick up your legs
When draining the dregs
Of sorrow's bitter cup?
Because you have read
Some idiot has said,
'The Curtain must go up!'
I'd like to know why a star takes bows
Having just returned from burying her spouse.
Brave boop-a-doopers,
Go home and dry your tears,
Gallant old troupers,
You've bored us all for years
And when you're so blue,
Wet through

And thoroughly woe-begone,
Why must the show go on?
Oh Mammy!
Why must the show go on?

We're asked to condole
With each tremulous soul
Who steps out to be loudly applauded,
Stars on opening nights
Sob when they see their names in lights,
Though people who act
As a matter of fact
Are financially amply rewarded,
It seems, while pursuing their calling,
Their suffering's simply appalling!
But butchers and bakers
And candlestick makers
Get little applause for their pains
And when I think of miners
And waiters in 'Diners'
One query for ever remains:

Why must the show go on?
The rule is surely not immutable,
It might be wiser and more suitable
Just to close
If you are in the throes
Of personal grief and private woes.
Why stifle a sob
While doing your job
When, if you use your head,
You'd go out and grab
A comfortable cab
And go right home to bed?
Because you're not giving us much fun,
This 'Laugh Clown, Laugh' routine's been
    overdone,
Hats off to Show Folks
For smiling when they're blue
But more *comme-il-faut* folks

Are sick of smiling through,
And if you're out cold,
Too old
And most of your teeth have gone,
Why must the show go on?
I sometimes wonder
Why must the show go on?

Why must the show go on?
Why not announce the closing night of it?
The public seem to hate the sight of it,
Dear, and so
Why you should undergo
This terrible strain we'll never know.
We know that you're sad,
We know that you've had
A lot of storm and strife
But is it quite fair
To ask us to share
Your dreary private life?
We know you're trapped in a gilded cage
But for Heaven's sake relax and be your age,
Stop being gallant
And don't be such a bore,
Pack up your talent,
There's always plenty more
And if you lose hope
Take dope
And lock yourself in the john,
Why must the show go on?
I'm merely asking –
Why must the show go on?

★

On what was to have been a long trip to the Far East in 1928, Noël experienced a breakdown, which caused him to leave ship in Hawaii. Luckily, he found himself in the care of friends, who insisted he stay at their beach cottage in Mokuleia to recuperate.

'I firmly resisted the temptation to work during those weeks ...
A tune certainly did slip through the barricade one day while
I was on the beach and, between walking and dozing in the
sun, I lazily fitted words to it. It lay forgotten at the back of my
mind for many months, until it emerged, nearly a year later, as
'A Room with a View' in the revue *This Year of Grace!*.

A ROOM WITH A VIEW

HE I've been cherishing
 Through the perishing
 Winter nights and days
 A funny little phrase
 That means
 Such a lot to me
 That you've got to be
 With me heart and soul
 For on you the whole
 Thing leans.

SHE Won't you kindly tell me what you're
   driving at,
 What conclusion you're arriving at?

HE Please don't turn away
 Or my dream will stay
 Hidden out of sight
 Among a lot of might-
 Have-beens!

HE A room with a view – and you,
 With no one to worry us,
 No one to hurry us – through
 This dream we've found,
 We'll gaze at the sky – and try
 To guess what it's all about,
 Then we
 Will figure out – why
 The world is round.

SHE We'll be as happy and contented
 As birds upon a tree,
 High above the mountains and the sea.

BOTH   We'll bill and we'll coo-oo-oo
        And sorrow will never come,
        Oh, will it ever come – true,
        Our room with a view?

SHE   I'm so practical
        I'd make tactical
        Errors as your wife,
        I'd try to set your life
        To rights.
        I'm upset a bit
        For I get a bit
        Dizzy now and then
        Following your mental flights.

HE   Come with me and leave behind the noisy
            crowds,
        Sunlight shines for us above the clouds.

SHE   My eyes glistened too
        While I listened to
        All the things you said,
        I'm glad I've got a head
        For heights.

        A room with a view – and you,
        And no one to give advice,
        That sounds a paradise – few
        Could fail to choose,
        With fingers entwined we'll find
        Relief from the preachers who
        Always beseech us to mind
        Our Ps and Qs.

HE   We'll watch the whole world pass before us
        While we are sitting still,
        Leaning on our own window-sill.

BOTH   We'll bill and we'll coo-oo-oo,
        And maybe a stork will bring
        This, that and t'other thing – to
        Our room with a view.

No songwriter, major or minor, can fail to deal with the one subject that defines humanity: love. Noël was no exception. But how do you define it?

WHAT IS LOVE?

Tell me – tell me – tell me, what is love?
Is it some consuming flame;
Part of the moon, part of the sun,
Part of a dream barely begun?
When is the moment of breaking – waking?
Skies change, nothing is the same,
Some strange magic is to blame;
Voices that seem to echo round me and above,
Tell me, what is love, love, love?

Bitter-Sweet (1929)

There was the 'in-loveness' of being in love . . .

SOMETHING VERY STRANGE

This is not a day like any other:
This is something special and apart.
Something to remember
When the coldness of December
Chills my heart.

Something very strange
Is happening to me,
Every face I see
Seems to be smiling.
All the sounds I hear,
The buses changing gear,
Suddenly appear
To be beguiling.
Nobody is melancholy,
Nobody is sad,

Not a single shadow on the sea.
Some Magician's spell
Has made this magic start
And I feel I want to hold each shining
    moment in my heart.
Something strange and gay
On this romantic day
Seems to be
Happening to me.

Something very strange
Is happening to me,
Every cat I see
Seems to be purring.
I can clearly tell
In every clanging bell
Some forgotten melody
Recurring.
Tinker, tailor, soldier, sailor,
Beggar-man or thief,
Every single leaf
On every tree
Seems to be aware
Of something in the air.
And if only I were younger I'd put
    ribbons in my hair.
Something strange and gay
On this romantic day
Seems to be
Happening to me!

Sail Away (1961)

YOU WERE THERE

SIMON   Was it in the real world
Or was it in a dream?
Was it just a note from some eternal theme?
Was it accidental
Or accurately planned?
How could I hesitate
Knowing that my fate
Led me by the hand?

You were there,
I saw you and my heart stopped beating,
You were there.
And in that first enchanted meeting
Life changed its tune,
The stars, the moon
Came near to me.
Dreams that I dreamed,
Like magic seemed
To be clear to me, dear to me.
You were there.
Your eyes looked into mine and faltered.
Everywhere
The colour of the whole world altered.
False became true,
My universe tumbled in two,
The earth became heaven, for you
Were there.

VICKY   How can we explain it,
The spark, and then the fire?
How add up the total
Of our hearts' desire?
Maybe some magician,
A thousand years ago –
Wove us a subtle spell
So that we could tell
So that we could know –

You were there,
I saw you and my heart stopped beating,
You were there
And in that first enchanted meeting
Life changed its tune,
The stars, the moon
Came near to me.
Dreams that I dreamed,
Like magic seemed
To be clear to me, dear to me.
You were there,
Your eyes looked into mine and faltered.
Everywhere
The colour of the whole world altered.
False became true,
My universe tumbled in two,
The earth became heaven, for you
Were there.

Shadow Play, from *Tonight at 8:30* (1936)

★

In Noël's mind each of his book musicals had a waltz at its heart and they were invariably a problem. In the case of Bitter–Sweet *(1929)* . . .

'The book had been completed long since, but the score had been causing me trouble, until one day, when I was in a taxi on my way back to the [New York] apartment after a matinée [of his revue, *This Year of Grace!*] the 'I'll See You Again' waltz dropped into my mind, whole and complete, during a twenty minute traffic block.

'The song, I am happy to say, has been sung incessantly by everybody. It has proved over the years to be the greatest song hit I have ever had or am ever likely to have . . . It is as popular today as when it was first heard, and I am still fond of it and very proud of it.'

I'LL SEE YOU AGAIN

CARL   All my life I shall remember knowing you,
All the pleasure I have found in showing you
The different ways
That one may phrase
The changing light, and changing shade;
Happiness that must die,
Melodies that must fly,
Memories that must fade,
Dusty and forgotten by and by.

SARAH   Learning scales will never seem so sweet again
Till our Destiny shall let us meet again.

CARL   The will of Fate
May come too late.

SARAH When I'm recalling these hours we've had
       Why will the foolish tears
       Tremble across the years,
       Why shall I feel so sad,
       Treasuring the memory of these days
       Always?

CARL   I'll see you again,
       Whenever Spring breaks through again;
       Time may lie heavy between,
       But what has been
       Is past forgetting.

SARAH This sweet memory,
       Across the years will come to me;
       Though my world may go awry,
       In my heart will ever lie
       Just the echo of a sigh,
       Goodbye.

BOTH   I'll see you again,
       I live each moment through again.
       Time has lain heavy between,
       But what has been
       Can leave me never;
       Your dear memory
       Throughout my life has guided me.
       Though my world has gone awry,
       Though the years my tears may dry,
       I shall love you till I die,
       Goodbye.

       Though my world has gone awry,
       Though the end is drawing nigh,
       I shall love you till I die,
       Goodbye!

In writing Conversation Piece *in 1934 he encountered a similar block.*

'I knew I could never complete the score without a main theme, and sat for ten days at the piano gloomily facing the fact that my talent had withered . . . I finally decided to give up, poured myself a stiff whisky, switched off the piano light and was about to go up to bed in despair when "I'll Follow My Secret Heart" suddenly emerged in the key of G flat, a key I had never played before.'

Paul, the soi-disant *Duc de Chaucigny-Varennes, has brought his 'ward', Melanie, to Regency Brighton with the intention of finding her a rich husband. Being a mere man, he is unaware of what is perfectly obvious to the audience from the outset – that she is in love with him . . .*

I'LL FOLLOW MY SECRET HEART

MELANIE   A cloud has passed across the sun,
The morning seems no longer gay.
With so much business to be done,
Even the sea looks grey.
C'est vrai. C'est vrai.
It seems that all the joy has faded from the day
As though the foolish world no longer wants to play.

PAUL   (*speaking*): Go and dress.

MELANIE   (*speaking*): What shall I wear? A black crêpe with a little bonnet?

PAUL   What on earth is the matter with you this morning?

MELANIE   White, white for a bride. But the sun ought to shine on a bride.

PAUL   You're not a bride yet.

MELANIE   But I shall be soon, shall I not? A very quiet aristocratic bride with a discreet heart!

(*Sings.*) You ask me to have a discreet heart
Until marriage is out of the way

But what if I meet
With a sweetheart so sweet
That my wayward heart cannot obey
A single word that you may say?

PAUL   (*speaking*): Then we shall have to go away.

MELANIE   (*sings*): No. For there is nowhere we could go
Where we could hide from what we know
Is true.
Don't be afraid I'll betray you
And destroy all the plans you have made,
But even your schemes
Must leave room for my dreams.
So when all I owe to you is paid
I'll still have something of my own,
A little prize that's mine alone.

I'll follow my secret heart
My whole life through,
I'll keep all my dreams apart
Till one comes true.
No matter what price is paid.
What stars may fade
Above,
I'll follow my secret heart
Till I find love.

★

And, of course, there is love satirical . . .

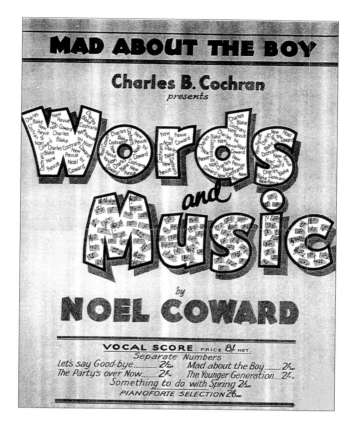

MAD ABOUT THE BOY

SOCIETY WOMAN

I met him at a party just a couple of years ago,
He was rather over-hearty and ridiculous
But as I'd seen him on the Screen
He cast a certain spell.
I basked in his attraction for a couple of hours or so,
His manners were a fraction too meticulous,
If he was real or not I couldn't tell
But like a silly fool, I fell.

Mad about the boy,
I know it's stupid to be mad about the boy,
I'm so ashamed of it
But must admit
The sleepless nights I've had about the boy.

On the Silver Screen
He melts my foolish heart in every single scene.
Although I'm quite aware
That here and there
Are traces of the cad about the boy,
Lord knows I'm not a fool girl,
I really shouldn't care,
Lord knows I'm not a schoolgirl
In the flurry of her first affair.
Will it ever cloy?
This odd diversity of misery and joy,
I'm feeling quite insane
And young again
And all because I'm mad about the boy.

SCHOOLGIRL

Home work, home work,
Every night there's home work,
While Elsie practises the gas goes pop,
I wish, I wish she'd stop,
Oh dear, oh dear,
Here it's always 'No, dear,
You can't go out again, you must stay home,
You waste your money on that common
    Picturedrome,
Don't shirk – stay here and do your work.'

Yearning, yearning,
How my heart is burning.
I'll see him Saturday in *Strong Man's Pain*
And then on Monday and on Friday week again.
To me he is the sole man
Who can kiss as well as Colman,
I could faint whenever there's a close-up of his lips,
Though John Barrymore is larger
When my hero's on his charger
Even Douglas Fairbanks Junior hasn't smaller hips.
If only he could know
That I adore him so.

Mad about the boy,
It's simply scrumptious to be mad about the boy,
I know that quite sincerely
Housman really
Wrote *The Shropshire Lad* about the boy.
In my English Prose
I've done a tracing of his forehead and his nose
And there is, honour bright,
A certain slight
Effect of Galahad about the boy.
I've talked to Rosie Hooper,
She feels the same as me,
She says that Gary Cooper
Doesn't thrill her to the same degree.
In *Can Love Destroy?*
When he meets Garbo in a suit of corduroy,
He gives a little frown
And knocks her down.
Oh dear, oh dear, I'm mad about the boy.

COCKNEY

Every Wednesday afternoon
I get a little time off from three to eleven,
Then I go to the Picture House
And taste a little of my particular heaven.
He appears
In a little while,
Through a mist of tears
I can see him smiling
Above me.
Every picture I see him in,
Every lover's caress,
Makes my wonderful dreams begin,
Makes me long to confess
That if ever he looked at me
And thought perhaps it was worth the trouble to
Love me,
I'd give in and I wouldn't care
However far from the path of virtue he'd

Shove me,
Just supposing our love was brief,
If he treated me rough
I'd be happy beyond belief,
Once would be enough.

Mad about the boy,
I know I'm potty but I'm mad about the boy.
He sets me 'eart on fire
With love's desire,
In fact I've got it bad about the boy.
When I do the rooms
I see 'is face in all the brushes and the brooms.
Last week I strained me back
And got the sack
And 'ad a row with Dad about the boy.
I'm finished with Navarro,
I'm tired of Richard Dix,
I'm pierced by Cupid's arrow
Every Wednesday from four till six.
'Ow I should enjoy
To let 'im treat me like a plaything or a toy,
I'd give my all to him
And crawl to him,
So 'elp me Gawd, I'm mad about the boy.

TART

It seems a little silly
For a girl of my age and weight
To walk down Piccadilly
In a haze of love.
It ought to take a good deal more to get a bad girl
 down,
I should have been exempt, for
My particular kind of Fate
Has taught me such contempt for
Every phase of love,
And now I've been and spent my last half-crown
To weep about a painted clown.

Mad about the boy,
It's pretty funny but I'm mad about the boy,
He has a gay appeal
That makes me feel
There's maybe something sad about the boy.
Walking down the street,
His eyes look out at me from people that I meet,
I can't believe it's true
But when I'm blue
In some strange way I'm glad about the boy.
I'm hardly sentimental,
Love isn't so sublime,
I have to pay my rental
And I can't afford to waste much time,
If I could employ
A little magic that would finally destroy
This dream that pains me
And enchains me,
But I can't because I'm mad about the boy.

There was almost an extra verse when the song was included in the
New York version of the revue, Set to Music *(1938). It was to have*
been sung by a soberly-suited businessman . . .

Mad about the boy,
It's most peculiar but I'm mad about the boy.
No one but Dr Freud
Could have enjoyed
The vexing dreams I've had about the boy.
When I told my wife
She said she'd never heard such nonsense in her life.
Her lack of sympathy
Embarrassed me
And made me, frankly, glad about the boy!
My doctor can't advise me,
He'd help me if he could.
Three times he's tried to psychoanalyse me

But it's just no good.
People I employ
Have the impertinence to call me 'Myrna Loy'.
I rise above it,
Frankly love it,
For I'm absolutely mad about the boy!

Fortunately, wiser counsels prevailed. It was only 1938. And it was
Boston . . .

★

A BAR ON THE PICCOLA MARINA

(*as sung at Las Vegas*)

I'll sing you a song,
It's not very long,
Its moral may disconcert you,
Of a mother and wife
Who most of her life
Was famed for domestic virtue.
She had two strapping daughters and a rather dull son,
And a much duller husband, who at sixty-one
Elected to retire
And later on, expire.
Sing Hallelujah, Hey nonny-no, Hey nonny-no,
    Hey nonny-no!
He joined the feathered choir.
Having laid him to rest
By special request
In the family mausoleum
As his widow repaired
To the home they had shared,
Her heart sang a gay *Te Deum*
And then in the middle of the funeral wake,
While adding some liquor to the Tipsy Cake
She briskly cried, 'That's done.

My life's at last begun.
Sing Hallelujah, Hey nonny-no, Hey nonny-no,
   Hey nonny-no!
It's time I had some fun.
Today, though hardly a jolly day,
At least has set me free,
We'll all have a lovely holiday
On the island of Capri!'

In a bar on the Piccola Marina
Life called to Mrs Wentworth-Brewster,
Fate beckoned her and introduced her
Into a rather queer
Unfamiliar atmosphere.
She'd just sit there, propping up the bar
Beside a fisherman who sang to a guitar.
When accused of having gone too far
She merely cried, 'Funiculi!
Just fancy me!
Funicula!'
When he bellowed '*Che Bella Signorina!*'
Sheer ecstasy at once produced a
Wild shriek from Mrs Wentworth-Brewster,
Changing her whole demeanour.
When both her daughters and her son said,
'Please come home, Mama,'
She murmured rather bibulously, 'Who d'you think
   you are?'
Nobody can afford to be so lahdy-bloody-da
In a bar on the Piccola Marina.

Every fisherman cried,
'*Viva Viva*' and '*Che Ragazza*',
When she sat in the Grand Piazza
Everybody would rise,
Every fisherman sighed,
'*Viva Viva che bell' Inglesi*',
Someone even said, 'Whoops-a-daisy!'
Which was quite a surprise.
Each night she'd make some gay excuse

And beaming with good will
She's just slip into something loose
And totter down the hill.

To the bar on the Piccola Marina
Where love came to Mrs Wentworth-Brewster,
Hot flushes of delight suffused her,
Right round the bend she went,
Picture her astonishment,
Day in, day out, she would gad about
Because she felt she was no longer on the shelf.
Night out, night in, knocking back the gin
She's cry 'Hurrah!
Funicula
Funiculi
Funic yourself!'
Just for fun three young sailors from Messina
Bowed low to Mrs Wentworth-Brewster
Said '*Scusi*' and politely goosed her.
Then there was quite a scena.
Her family, in floods of tears, cried,
'Leave these men, Mama.'
She said, 'They're just high-spirited, like all
    Italians are,
And most of them have a great deal more to
    offer than Papa
In a bar on the Piccola Marina.'

*Love may come to everyone — but all too often it doesn't stay. And
when 'the days dwindle down to a precious few', that may actually be
a relief.*

BRONXVILLE DARBY AND JOAN

We do not fear the verdict of posterity,
Our lives have been too humdrum and mundane,
In the twilight of our days
Having reached the final phase
In all sincerity
We must explain:

We're a dear old couple and we HATE one another
And we've hated one another for a long, long time,
Since the day that we were wed, up to the present,
Our lives, we must confess,
Have been progressively more unpleasant.
We're just sweet old darlings who despise one another
With a thoroughness approaching the sublime,
But through all our years
We've been affectionately known
As the Bronxville Darby and Joan.

Our Golden Wedding passed with all our family,
An orgy of remembrance and rue,
In acknowledgement of this
We exchanged a loving kiss
A trifle clammily
Because we knew:

We're a dear old couple who DETEST one another,
We've detested one another since our bridal night,
Which was squalid, unattractive and convulsive
And proved, beyond dispute,
That we were mutually repulsive.
We're just sweet old darlings who torment one another
With the utmost maliciousness and spite,
And through all our years
We've been inaccurately known
As the Bronxville Darby and Joan.

We're a dear old couple and we LOATHE one another
With a loathing that engulfs us like a tidal wave,
With our deep sub-conscious minds we seldom dabble
But something *must* impel

The words we spell
When we're playing 'Scrabble'.
We're just sweet old darlings who ABHOR one another
And we'll bore each other firmly to the grave,
But through all our years we've been referred to more or less
As the Bronxville Porgy and Bess.

Sail Away (1961)

NEVER AGAIN

Over now,
The dream is over now,
Maybe it really wasn't so important anyhow.
What's been can't be again
Reluctantly I see,
My heart is free again,
Belongs to me again,
The brief illusion I lived for has gone.
No more confusion and tears from now on;
To start again
And break my heart again
If you should ask me to,
I'd say, 'To hell with you!
Away with you!'

No, never again,
Never the strange unthinking joy,
Never the pain;
Let me be wise,
Let me learn to doubt romance,
Try to live without romance,
Let me be sane.
Time changes the tune.
Changes the pale unwinking stars,
Even the moon,
Let me be soon
Strong enough to flout romance –
And say, 'You're out, romance,'
Never again!

Set to Music (1938)

Two songs sum up Noël's considered attitude to love. First, Manon, the diseuse in Bitter-Sweet, expresses her wistful experience of life. If love were all . . . but it never is.

IF LOVE WERE ALL

Life is a very rough and tumble
For a humble
Diseuse.
One can betray one's troubles never,
Whatever
Occurs,
Night after night,
Have to look bright,
Whether you're well or ill
People must laugh their fill.
You mustn't sleep
Till dawn comes creeping.
Though I never really grumble
Life's a jumble.

Indeed –
And in my efforts to succeed
I've had to formulate a creed –

I believe in doing what I can,
In crying when I must,
In laughing when I choose.
Heigho, if love were all
I should be lonely,
I believe the more you love a man,
The more you give your trust,
The more you're bound to lose.
Although when shadows fall
I think if only –
Somebody splendid really needed me,
Someone affectionate and dear,
Cares would be ended if I knew that he
Wanted to have me near.
But I believe that since my life began
The most I've had is just
A talent to amuse.
Heigho, if love were all!

Though life buffets me obscenely,
It serenely
Goes on.
Although I question its conclusion,
Illusion
Is gone.
Frequently I
Put a bit by
Safe for a rainy day.
Nobody here can say
To what, indeed,
The years are leading.
Fate may often treat me meanly,
But I keenly
Pursue
A little mirage in the blue.
Determination helps me through.

But if love is too volatile to be dependable, one can always count on friendship, the quality Noël celebrates in the last song he wrote – specifically for his life companion, Graham Payn.

COME THE WILD, WILD WEATHER

Time may hold in store for us
Glory or defeat,
Maybe never more for us
Life will seem so sweet
Time will change so many things,
Tides will ebb and flow,
But wherever fate may lead us
Always we shall know –

Come the wild, wild weather,
Come the wind and the rain,
Come the little white flakes of snow.
Come the joy, come the pain,
We shall still be together
When our life's journey ends,
For wherever we chance to go
We shall always be friends.
We may find while we're travelling through
    the years
Moments of joy and love and happiness,
Reason for grief, reason for tears.
Come the wild, wild weather,
If we've lost or we've won,
We'll remember these words we say
Till our story is done.

Waiting in the Wings (1960)

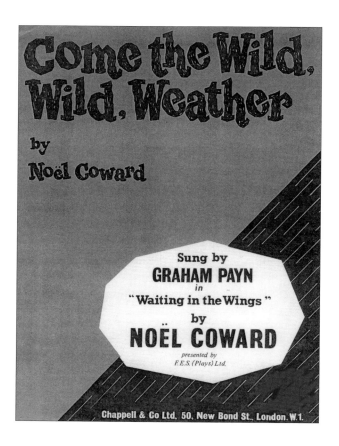

THE VERSE

Feeling the world so shadowed, and the time,
Essential to clear processes of thought,
So much accelerated, I have sought
Relief by these excursions into rhyme.

'Personal Note' from *Collected Verse*

methuen

Noël Coward Collected Verse

COWARD

Noël Coward Collected Verse

'Throughout most of the years of my life, since approximately nineteen hundred and eight, I have derived a considerable amount of private pleasure from writing verse . . . I find it quite fascinating to write at random, sometimes in rhyme, sometimes not. I am trying to discipline myself away from too much discipline, by which I mean that my experience and training in lyric writing has made me inclined to stick too closely to a rigid form. It is strange that technical accuracy should occasionally banish magic, but it does. The carefully rhymed verses, which I find very difficult not to do, are, on the whole, less effective and certainly less moving than the free ones. The writing of free verse, which I am enjoying so very much, is wonderful exercise for my mind and for my vocabulary. Most of what I have already done I really feel is good and is opening up, for me, some new windows. My sense of words, a natural gift, is becoming more trained and selective, and I suspect, when I next sit down to write a play, things may happen that have never happened before.'

During the years of World War II in particular, when Noël was travelling extensively on government business, he would amuse himself and pass the time on endless journeys by writing 'verse letters' to his family – and to Lorn Loraine, 'my beloved secretary and English representative for forty-six years', in particular. Lorn, he claimed, was

'an expert at squeezing the maximum of business information and personal news into rhymed cables which, together with my also rhymed replies, has afforded us both a lot of amusement . . . Additionally, I once churned out a few cheerful little couplets riding on a camel in the Sahara desert which, so far as I can remember, were too obscene to be preserved for posterity. As, however, they happened to be blown away in a sandstorm, they may after all be preserved for posterity and be discovered centuries hence like the Dead Sea Scrolls. As they were unsigned, I hereby seize the opportunity of publicly disowning them.'

A number of themes recur in Noël's verses. One of them – perhaps surprisingly – was religion. He was ambivalent at best about it but returned to it time and again – often flippantly . . .

' "Oh, God!" That remark no longer has any dramatic significance. One uses it when one can't find a taxi!'

'If God rings, tell him I'm not in.'

When asked in an interview about his attitude to God, he replied:

'We've never been intimate – but maybe we do have a few things in common.'

But that was in public, where a Coward bon mot was expected. To his Diary (1964) he confided . . .

'My mind is . . . not really attuned to the Church of England or any other church for that matter. I loathe all that insistence on being a miserable sinner and asking for forgiveness. The traditional part of it is all right with the squeaky hymns and the choir (mixed) and the best bibs and tuckers and all the age-old carry-on, but the fundamental faith underlying it is missing in me. I never have felt and don't feel now the call of the Holy Spirit, and I suspect I never shall.'

'I have no more faith in men of science being infallible than I have in men of God being infallible, principally on account of them being men.'

                                        Diary, 1 July 1946

At other times he was less charitably inclined . . .

LINES TO GOD

(*Unpublished*)

If I should ultimately meet my God,
He will not be the God of Love or Battles,
He'll be some under God whose job it is
To organize sharp sounds and things that rattle.
He'll be the one who, all my life on earth,
Can, most sadistically, my spirit shatter
With little hammerings and sudden shouts
And hollow ricochets of empty mirth.

★

Surprisingly, perhaps, tucked away among some miscellaneous correspondence, is an undated prayer:

Most merciful God,
grant we pray thee, that we may never forget
that as followers of Christ we are
the observed of all men, and that
our failures may cause others to
stumble; that in a measure God
places his honour in our hands.

Help us that we may be true and
Loyal to the best and highest we know
And that we may show this truth and
Loyalty in every activity of our daily life.

Grant to us the royal gift of courage.

Give unto us a keen sense of honour,
That we may never give ourselves the
Benefit of the doubt.

★

'The Grim Reaper', Noël called him. Or 'Time's wingèd chariot',
which he claimed was beginning to goose him. He was speaking about
Death.

'Death's very laughable, such a cunning little mystery. All done
with mirrors.'

Elyot in Private Lives (1930)

'I would prefer Fate to allow me to go to sleep when it's my
proper bedtime. I never have been one for staying up too late.'

Diaries, 1967

'Old age is cruel and death much kinder when it is gentle.'

Diaries, 1953

Noël was fortunate enough to be granted the last two.

I'M HERE FOR A SHORT VISIT ONLY

I'm here for a short visit only
And I'd rather be loved than hated
Eternity may be lonely
When my body's disintegrated
And that which is loosely termed my soul
Goes whizzing off through the infinite
By means of some vague, remote control
I'd like to think I was missed a bit.

Strangely, for someone of so many accomplishments, Noël frequently
worried that he would be forgotten. To the end of his days the past was
always part of his present.

'Those I have really loved are with me in moments of memory
– whole and intact and unchanged.'

'I can enjoy retrospective laughter again and again, but
retrospective tears, never.'

WHEN I HAVE FEARS

When I have fears, as Keats had fears,
Of the moment I'll cease to be
I console myself with vanished years
Remember laughter, remembered tears,
And the peace of the changing sea.

When I feel sad, as Keats felt sad,
That my life is so nearly done
It gives me comfort to dwell upon
Remembered friends who are dead and gone
And the jokes we had and the fun.

How happy they are I cannot know
But happy am I who loved them so.

Love was another hardy perennial — though Noël was the first to admit it was not a subject at which he personally shone . . .

I AM NO GOOD AT LOVE

I am no good at love
My heart should be wise and free
I kill the unfortunate golden goose
Whoever it may be
With over-articulate tenderness
And too much intensity.

I am no good at love
I batter it out of shape
Suspicion tears at my sleepless mind
And, gibbering like an ape,
I lie alone in the endless dark
Knowing there's no escape

I am no good at love
When my easy heart I yield
Wild words come tumbling from my mouth

Which should have stayed concealed;
And my jealousy turns a bed of bliss
Into a battlefield.

I am no good at love
I betray it with little sins
For I feel the misery of the end
In the moment that it begins
And the bitterness of the last goodbye
Is the bitterness that wins.

THIS IS TO LET YOU KNOW

This is to let you know
That there was no moon last night
And that the tide was high
And that on the broken horizon glimmered the lights of ships
Twenty at least, like a sedate procession passing by.

This is to let you know
That when I'd turned out the lamp
And in the dark I lay
That suddenly piercing loneliness, like a knife,
Twisted my heart, for you were such a long long way away.

This is to let you know
That there are no English words
That ever could explain
How, quite without warning, lovingly you were here
Holding me close, smoothing away the idiotic pain.

This is to let you know
That all that I feel for you
Can never wholly go.
I love you and miss you, even two hours away,
With all my heart. This is to let you know.

I KNEW YOU WITHOUT ENCHANTMENT

I knew you without enchantment
And for some years
We went our usual ways
Meeting occasionally
Finding no heights nor depths among our days
Shedding no tears
Every so often when we felt inclined
Lying like lovers in each other's arms
Feeling no qualms
In our light intimacy
So resolute we were in heart and mind
So steeled against illusion, deaf and blind
To all presentiment, to all enchantment
(I knew you without enchantment).

It is so strange
Remembering that phase
Those unexacting, uneventful days
Before the change
Before we knew this serio-comic, tragic
Most unexpected, overwhelming magic.
I knew you without enchantment.

And today I cannot think of you without
    my heart
Suddenly stopping
Or, in those long grey hours we spent apart
Dropping, dropping
Down into desolation like a stone.
To be alone
No longer means to me clear time and space
In which to stretch my mind.

I see your face
Between me and the space I used to find
Between me and the other worlds I seek
There stands your sleek
And most beloved silhouette

And yet
I can remember not so long ago
We neither of us cared
Nor dared
To know
How swiftly we were nearing the abyss
(This foolish, quite ungovernable bliss)
Let's not regret
That empty life before. It was great fun
And hurt no one
There was no harm in it
At certain moments there was even charm in it.

But oh my dearest love, there was no spell
No singing heaven and no wailing hell.
I knew you without enchantment.

Luckily, not every form of love is so volatile.

In a TV interview he was asked to sum his life up in a single word. After an uncharacteristically long pause, he replied . . .

'Well, now comes the terrible decision as to whether to be corny or not.

'The answer *is* one word. Love.

'To know that you are among people you love and who love you. That has made all the successes wonderful – much more wonderful than they'd have been anyway.

'And that's it, really . . .'

★

Ladies loomed large in Noël's life, both personal and professional. Those he worked with and those he created – Gertie, Bea Lillie, Mary Martin, Yvonne Printemps, Elaine Stritch, Mrs Worthington, Mrs Wentworth-Brewster, Alice (Who Was Always At It Again) to name but a few . . .

We know God made trees
And the birds and the bees
And the seas for the fishes to swim in,
We are also aware
That he has quite a flair
For creating quite exceptional women . . .

This was part of his introduction on the cabaret debut of his friend Marlene Dietrich at the Café de Paris in 1954. It continued:

When Eve said to Adam
'Start calling me Madam,'
The world became far more exciting.
Which turns to confusion
The modern delusion
That sex is a question of lighting.
For female allure,
Whether pure or impure,
Has seldom reported a failure,
As I know and you know,
From Venus and Juno
Right down to *La Dame aux Camélias.*
This glamour, it seems,
Is the substance of dreams
To the most imperceptive perceiver.
The Serpent of Nile
Could achieve with a smile
Far quicker results than Geneva.
Though we all might enjoy
Seeing Helen of Troy
As a gay, cabaret entertainer,
I doubt that she could
Be one quarter as good
As our legendary, lovely Marlene.

Marlene – like Noël – was her own self-invention. One of the things that endeared her to him. They would look out for each other and not be afraid to speak their mind. When Marlene was agonizing over her tortuous affair with Yul Brynner, Noël wrote to her:

'Oh, darling,

Your letter filled me with such a lot of emotions, the predominant one being rage that you should allow yourself to be so humiliated and made so unhappy by a situation once and for all. It is really beneath your dignity, not your dignity as a famous artist and a glamorous star, but your dignity as a human, only too human being.

Curly is attractive, beguiling, tender and fascinating, but he is not the only man in the world who merits those delightful adjectives . . .

To hell with Goddamned "L'Amour". It always causes far more trouble than it's worth. Don't run after it. Don't court it. Keep it waiting offstage until you are good and ready for it and even then treat it with the suspicious disdain that it deserves . . . I am sick to death of you waiting about in empty houses and apartments with your ears strained for the telephone to ring. Snap out of it, girl! A very brilliant writer once said (Could it have been me?) 'Life is for the living.' Well, that is *all* it is for, and living *does not* consist of staring in at other people's windows and waiting for crumbs to be thrown to you. You've carried on this hole in corner, overcharged, romantic, unrealistic nonsense long enough.

Stop it. Stop it. Stop it. Other people need you . . .

Unpack your sense of humour, and get on with living and ENJOY IT!'

★

Mrs Mallory was entirely Noël's own – but based on a lifetime's observation of this rather sad sub-species of the species . . .

MRS MALLORY

Mrs Mallory went to a Psychiatrist
On the advice of Mrs Silvera
Who had been twice divorced
And considered herself to be maladjusted.
Mrs Mallory, who had never been divorced at all,
Considered that she also was maladjusted
Not for any specific reason, really,
Nothing you could put your finger on
But a definite feeling of dissatisfaction

With life in general and Mr Mallory in particular,
And Deidre too who was no comfort and solace to her mother
Though at her age she should have been
But she was an unpredictable character
Who devoted too much time to 'Rock-n-Roll'
And none at all to domestic science
And helping in the house and keeping a wary eye open
For Mr Right to come along and sweep her away
To a series of social triumphs
In Washington possibly, or at least Baltimore,
Which Mrs Mallory could read about in the gossip columns
And then send the cuttings to Irma in Minneapolis
Who would have to read them whether she liked it or not.

Mrs Mallory lay on the Psychiatrist's sofa
With her arms relaxed at her sides
And her feet sticking up, one to the right and one to the left
Like a mermaid's tail.
The Psychiatrist sat behind her out of range
And waited politely for her to begin to talk,
Which she was only too eager to do.
After the first shyness had worn off
And he had asked her a few routine questions.
But she talked and talked and talked and talked.
So much, so much came tumbling out of her,
More than she would ever have believed possible,
But then of course, unlike Mrs Silvera, he didn't interrupt
And say things like, 'That reminds me of when I went to
    Atlantic City
With my first husband' or 'I feel exactly the same, dear, naturally
But I have to control my feelings on account of being so strictly
    raised.'
The Psychiatrist didn't seem to be reminded of anything at all.
He sat there so quietly that once Mrs Mallory looked round
To see if he had dropped off, but he hadn't;
There he was scribbling away on a pad and occasionally
    nodding his head.
She told him all about Deidre
And Mr Mallory coming home from the Rotarian lunch
And taking his pants off on the landing

And shouting 'Everything I have is yours, you're part of me!'
So loudly that Beulah had come out of the kitchen
And seen him with his lower parts showing
And his hat still on.
She also told the Psychiatrist about the man in the subway
Who had pressed himself against her from behind
And said something that sounded like 'Ug Ug'
Which was the one thing she had never told Mrs Silvera,
Perhaps on account of her having been so strictly raised.
She told him as well about the extraordinary dream she
    had had
On the night following the Beedmeyers' anniversary party
But when she was in the middle of it,
Before she had even got to the bit about the horse,
He suddenly rose and smiled and said that he hoped to see
    her next Friday.
At the same time.

She got up from the couch
Feeling a little dizzy and aware that her left foot had gone
    to sleep
But when she stamped at it it was all right.
She felt much better when she got home
And much less maladjusted
And when Mr Mallory came home from the office
She had put on her new hostess gown
Which she had worn only twice
Once at the Beedmeyers and the other time at the Palisades
Country Club
On Christmas Eve.
Also she had rubbed some 'Shalimar' behind her ears
And greeted him with an all embracing, welcoming smile
But it was none of it any use really
When dinner was over they looked at television as they
    always did
Until it was time to go to bed,
Mr Mallory spent longer in the bathroom than usual
And the 'Shalimar' began to wear off.
But when he did come back in his pajamas
It didn't seem to matter much anyway

Because he merely belched and said 'Excuse me' automatically,
Blew her a perfunctory kiss and got into his own bed,
Later on, after he had read *McCall's* for a little,
He switched off the light.

Mrs Mallory lay in the darkness
With her arms relaxed at her sides
And her feet up, one to the right and one to the left
Like a mermaid's tail
And a tear rolled down her face all the way to her chin.

★

*And for every insensitive Mrs Worthington or overly-sensitive Mrs
Mallory there were those innumerable – not to say unmentionable –
ladies who would corner him on social occasions. Of which there were
all too many.*

SOCIAL GRACE

I expect you've heard this a million times before
But I absolutely adored your last play
I went four times – and now to think
That here I am actually talking to you!
It's thrilling! Honestly it is, I mean,
It's always thrilling isn't it to meet someone really celebrated?
I mean someone who really does things.
I expect all this is a terrible bore for you.
After all you go everywhere and know everybody.
It must be wonderful to go absolutely everywhere
And know absolutely everybody and – Oh dear –
Then to have to listen to someone like me,
I mean someone absolutely ordinary just one of your public.
No one will believe me when I tell them
That I have actually been talking to the great man himself.
It must be wonderful to be so frightfully brainy
And know all the things that you know
I'm not brainy a bit, neither is my husband,
Just plain humdrum, that's what we are.

But we do come up to town occasionally
And go to shows and things. Actually my husband
Is quite a critic, not professionally of course,
What I mean is that he isn't all that easily pleased.
He doesn't like everything. Oh no, not by any means.
He simply hated that thing at the Haymarket
Which everybody went on about. 'Rubbish!' he said,
Straight out like that, 'Damned Rubbish!'
I nearly died because heaps of people were listening.
But that's quite typical of him. He just says what he thinks.
And he can't stand all this highbrow stuff —
Do you know what I mean? — All these plays about people being
    miserable
And never getting what they want and not even committing
    suicide
But just being absolutely wretched. He says he goes to the theatre
To have a good time. That's why he simply loves all your things,
I mean they relax him and he doesn't have to think.
And he certainly does love a good laugh.
You should have seen him the other night when we went to
    that film
With what's-her-name in it — I can't remember the title.
I thought he'd have a fit, honestly I did.
You must know the one I mean, the one about the man who
    comes home
And finds his wife has been carrying on with his best friend
And of course he's furious at first and then he decides to teach
    her a lesson.
You must have seen it. I wish I could remember the name
But that's absolutely typical of me, I've got a head like a sieve,
I keep on forgetting things and as for names — well!
I just cannot for the life of me remember them.
Faces yes, I never forget a face because I happen to be naturally
    observant
And always have been since I was a tiny kiddie
But names! — Oh dear! I'm quite hopeless.
I feel such a fool sometimes
I do, honestly.

I'VE GOT TO GO OUT AND BE SOCIAL

I've got to go out and be social,
I've got to go out and be social,
I've got to be bright
And extremely polite
And refrain from becoming too loose or too tight
And I mustn't impose conversational blight
On the dolt on my left
And the fool on my right.
I must really be very attractive tonight
As I have to go out and be social.

I have to go out and be social,
I've got to go out and be social,
I have to forget
The Bohemian set
And discuss with the flower of *Burke* and *Debrett*
The fall of the franc and the National Debt,
I have to regret
That the weather is wet
There's so much that I can't afford to forget –
As I have to go out and be social.

THE SHORT STORIES

'The abyss of years lies between me and the sort of modern short story which begins in the middle of a sentence, wanders on for a while through a jungle of confused word–images and psychological abstractions, and comes to an end in the middle of another sentence.'

Noël Coward
from the introduction to *The Collected Short Stories*

'Being primarily a dramatist, short stories have been an absorbing experiment in form, lying somewhere between a play and a novel. I found them fascinating to write, but far from easy. They demand perhaps a little less rigid self-discipline than a play, and a great deal more than a novel. In a novel there is room for divergencies and irrelevances, in a play there is none; in a short story, just a little, but it must be strictly rationed.'

★

'Worked all the morning and came to the conclusion that I love writing fiction. It is hard going but it has the lovely satisfaction about it that good, bad or indifferent, there it is and it has not got to be translated through someone else's personality.'

Diaries, 8 November 1949

★

In 1937 Noël and Gertie were playing on Broadway in Tonight at 8:30, *an exhausting production that involved their playing three different roles every evening, which often also involved dancing and singing.*

Consequently, when local society hostess, Cobina Wright – an Elsa Maxwell-ish character with the added advantage of money – invited Noël for a quiet weekend in the Hamptons, he unthinkingly accepted. It would, she promised, be 'just us'. He should perhaps have been alerted by the car ride out there, where he was accompanied by Clifton Webb, drinking brandy and wearing 'ear muffs and a camel's hair coat'.

'All in all the journey seemed longer than the one on the Trans-Siberian railway, though without the amusing frontier stations.'

When they arrived, he found himself in the next room to Webb, who proceeded to snore 'in the exact rhythm of the Hallelujah Chorus'.

The next day he awoke to see from his window 'a long caravan of Rolls-Royces and Pierce-Arrows . . . like a funeral cortège for some eminent gangster, except minus the flowers'. The 'just us' had arrived.

What predictably transpired over the next several hours he turned into a 1939 story called 'What Mad Pursuit?' and in 1947 into the play Long Island Sound.

Since the protagonists were still alive, their identity was necessarily somewhat blurred in the telling, but it is clear in retrospect that Cobina Wright was Louise Steinhauser, Grace Moore was Irene Marlow, Carol Lombard was Carola Binney, not to mention

'a contingent of film cowboys whose names were household words splashing about in the indoor pool [and] several second generation publishers *en famille* and the Governor's wife of a minor British colony, to name but a few "who shall be nameless".'

A further small distraction was the fact that, as was her custom, Grace Moore insisted on singing a large part of her repertoire, while refreshing herself 'from the mouth of a bottle of blended whiskey during the pauses'. Lily Daché, the milliner, managed to lose a valuable earring, which turned up in Monty Woolley's beard. The ordeal ended with Noël retiring to bed, only to find it occupied by Cobina's husband, his own having been taken by the overly-emotional Miss Moore.

At which point Noël packed his bag, tiptoed out of the house and hitchhiked his way back to New York.

WHAT MAD PURSUIT

I

Evan Lorrimer's celebrity value was unquestionably high. In the course of twenty years he had written no less than eleven novels; a volume of war poems, tinged with whimsical bitterness; one play which had been much praised by the London critics and run nearly two months; a critical survey of the life and times of Madame de Staël entitled *The Life and Times of Madame de Staël*; sundry essays and short stories for the more literary weeklies; and an autobiography. The autobiography had been on the whole the least successful of his works, but he in no way regretted having written it. For years he had been aware that incidents, journeys, and personal experiences had been accumulating in his mind until it had come to a point when he could no longer feel free to pursue his historical researches. He felt himself to be congested, or, to put it more crudely, constipated, and that unless he could get rid of this agglomeration of trivia, his real genius, which was writing graphically of the past in terms of the present, would atrophy. The autobiography, therefore, was a sort of cathartic and as such achieved its object. Hardly had the corrected and revised manuscript been delivered to the publishers before he was at work again, drafting out with renewed energy and clarity of thought his great novel of the Restoration, *A London Lady*. There was no doubt in his mind that if *My Steps Have Faltered,* which was the title of the autobiography, had not been written when it was, *A London Lady* would never have been written at all. The success of *A London Lady* transcended by far everything else he had ever written. It went into several editions within the first few weeks of its publication. It was elected, without one dissentient vote, as the Book Society's choice for the month of February. The most important moving picture company in Hollywood acquired the film rights of it at an even higher price than they had paid for *The Life of Saint Paul*, which had been awarded the Pulitzer Prize for the year before, and in addition to all this, its sales in America surpassed those of England a hundredfold before it had been out six weeks. It was on the suggestion of Evan's New York publishers, Neuman Bloch, that he had agreed to do a short lecture tour in the States. He had been naturally apprehensive of the idea at first, but after a certain amount of coaxing, and tempted by the prospect of visiting America for the first time in such singularly advantageous circumstances – full expenses there and back, a tour of only eight weeks visiting the principal towns, and a guaranteed fee for each lecture that appeared to be little short of fantastic – he gathered his courage together, made exhaustive notes on the subjects on which he intended to speak, and set sail on the *Queen Mary*.

Now it would be foolish to deny that Evan Lorrimer enjoyed publicity. Everyone enjoys publicity to a certain degree. It is always pleasant to feel that your name is of sufficient interest to the world to merit a prominent position in the daily newspapers. For many years past, Evan had been privately gratified to read such phrases as 'Of course Evan Lorrimer was there, suave and well-groomed as usual', or 'That inveterate first-nighter, Evan Lorrimer, arrived a few minutes before the curtain rose and was seen chatting laughingly to Lady Millicent Cawthorne in the foyer', or 'Evan Lorrimer whose new novel, *A London Lady*, has caused such a sensation, was the guest of honour at the Pen and Pencil Club on Sunday evening'. Such allusions, guileless and dignified, are immensely agreeable. Unimportant perhaps in their essence, but in their implication very important indeed. Just as millions of little coral animals in so many years construct a barrier reef against the sea, so can these small accolades, over a period of time, build, if not quite a barrier reef, at least a fortification against the waves of oblivion. Evan felt this very strongly. His reviews he read as a matter of course, regarding them rightly as part of the business. Naturally he was pleased when they were good and pained when they were bad, but the gossip columns were different. They were both unprejudiced and uncritical; they contented themselves with the simple statement that he was here or there with so-and-so, or accompanied by such-and-such, and by their repetitious banality did more to consolidate his reputation than all the carefully phrased opinions of the literati put together. But Evan, well used as he was to being photographed and interviewed and occasionally signing a few autograph books, was certainly unprepared for the violence of his reception in New York. From the moment the ship paused at Quarantine turmoil engulfed him. He was belaboured with questions by over a dozen reporters at the same time, photographed waving to mythical friends by no less than fifteen cameras simultaneously, hurried on to the dock where he was met by Neuman Bloch, Mrs Bloch, the firm's publicity agent, several more reporters and, most surprisingly, a man who had been at school with him and whom he hadn't clapped eyes on for twenty-six years. In the flurry of Customs examination, interviews, and the effort to sustain a reasonably intelligent flow of conversation with the Blochs, he was completely unable to recall the man's name; however it didn't matter, for after wringing his hand warmly, and standing by his side in silence for a few minutes, he disappeared into the crowd and Evan never saw him again.

Evan Lorrimer at the age of forty-three was, both in appearance and behaviour, a model of what an eminent Englishman of letters should be. He was five foot-ten, his figure was spare but well-proportioned, he had slim, expressive hands, dark hair greying slightly at the temples, deep-set grey eyes, a small, neat moustache and an urbane smile. Perhaps his greatest asset was his voice which was rich in tone and, at times, almost caressing, particularly when, with his slyly humorous gift of phrase, he was describing somebody a trifle maliciously. Lady Cynthia Cawthorne, who in Lowndes Square had achieved the nearest approach to a London salon since Lady Blessington, was wont to say, with her loud infectious laugh, that had she only been younger she'd have married Evan Lorrimer out of hand if only to hear him repeat over and over again his famous description of being taken, at the age of fifteen, to the Musée Grevin by Marcel Proust.

Evan, like so many people who have attained fame and fortune by their own unaided efforts, was a firm self-disciplinarian. He apportioned his time with meticulous care: so many hours for writing, so many for reading. He ate and drank in moderation and indulged in only enough exercise to keep himself fit. He contrived, although naturally of a highly strung, nervous temperament, to maintain an agreeable poise both physically and mentally and to derive a great deal of enjoyment from life, admittedly without often scaling the heights of rapture, but also without plumbing the depths of despair. This self-adjustment, this admirable balance, was dependent upon one absolute necessity and that necessity was sleep. Eight solid hours per night minimum, with a possible snooze during the day, was his deadline. Without that he was lost, his whole organism disintegrated. He became jumpy and irascible, unable to concentrate. In fact on one occasion, owing to an emotional upheaval when the pangs of not sufficiently requited love gnawed at his vitals for nearly four months, he became actively ill and had to retire to a nursing home. Realizing this one weakness, this Achilles heel, he arranged his life accordingly.

At home, in his small house in Chesham Place, his two servants had been trained to a mouselike efficiency. Until he was called in the morning the house was wrapped in the silence of death. The knocker had been taken off the front door, and both bells, front and back, muffled down to the merest tinkle; the telephone by his bed was switched off nightly and rang in the basement, and even there, after a series of dogged experiments by Albert his valet, it had been reduced to nothing more than a purr. Naturally, taking all this into consideration, the first few nights in New York were a torture to him. He had, of course, been warned that the sharpness of the climate and the champagne quality of the air would enable him to do with less sleep than he was accustomed to in the older, more stagnant atmosphere of England, and although he discovered this to be true to a certain extent, he was unable to repress a slight feeling of panic. If only, he reflected, he could get away into the country for two or three days, to relax, to give himself time to adjust himself, he might come to view the so much swifter tempo of American life with more equanimity.

It was on the fourth day after his arrival, towards the end of a strenuously literary cocktail party given in his honour by the Neuman Blochs, that he met Louise Steinhauser. He was introduced to her by his hostess and immediately taken out on to the terrace to look at the view. This had already happened to him five times, and although he had been deeply impressed by the view the first two times, it was now beginning to pall a little; however Louise was adamant. 'Look at it,' she said in a husky, rather intense voice. 'Isn't it horrible?'

Evan gave a slight start of surprise. Louise went on: 'Every time I look at New York from a height like this, I positively shudder. All those millions of people cooped up in those vast buildings give me such a feeling of claustrophobia that I think I'm going mad. If I didn't live out in the country most of the time I really should go mad. My husband, poor darling, comes in every day of course, and we have an apartment at the Pierre – you can just see it from here behind that tower that looks like a pencil with india-rubber on top – but really I hardly ever use it unless I happen to come in for a late party or an opening night or something, and even then I often drive down home afterwards, however late it is.'

'How far away is your home in the country?' enquired Evan.

'About an hour in the automobile; at night of course, it's much quicker and I can't begin to tell you how lovely it is to arrive at about two in the morning and smell the sea – my house is right on the sea – and just go to sleep in that wonderful silence – you'd think you were miles away from anywhere, and yet it's actually only a little way from New York. There are no houses near us, we're completely isolated –You really must come down for a weekend, except that I warn you there isn't a thing to do except lie about and relax. Bonwit, that's my husband, plays golf occasionally or a little tennis, but I don't play anything. I find at my age – I shall be forty-four next month, imagine!' – she laughed disarmingly, 'I never try to hide my age, it's so silly, after all what *does* it matter. Anyhow, as I was saying, at my age I find that all I want are my comforts, nice books, a few real friends, not just acquaintances, and good food. I'm afraid that's all I can offer you, peace and good food, but if you would like to slip away from all this,' she indicated the remainder of the cocktail party milling about inside with a wave of her hand, 'and really lead the simple life for a couple of days, you don't even have to bring dinner clothes if you don't want to. Please come, both Bonwit and I would be absolutely enchanted.'

Evan had been looking at her carefully while she was talking, carefully and critically. Being a writer, he was naturally observant, his mind was trained to perceive small indicative details. Being a celebrity he was also cautious. He noted Louise's clothes first: they were obviously expensive, the ruby and diamond clip in her small cloche hat could only have come from Cartier. Her pearls might or might not be real, but the clasp most certainly was. In addition to these external advantages he liked her. She was vivacious, humorous and friendly. She also seemed to have a sensible appreciation of the values of life.

'You're most kind,' he said. 'There's nothing I should like better.'

'Now isn't that lovely,' cried Louise. 'How long are you going to be here?'

'Alas, only until next Wednesday, then I have to lecture in Chicago.'

'I suppose you're booked up for this next weekend?'

Evan shook his head. He had been tentatively invited to the Neuman Blochs' house at Ossining, but he hadn't definitely accepted. 'I was supposed to go to the Blochs',' he said, 'but I can get out of it.'

'Then that's settled,' said Louise gaily. 'I'm coming in on Saturday to go to *Starlight*, that's a musical comedy that Lester Gaige is in. He's one of my greatest friends, you'll adore him. Why don't you dine with me and come too, and we'll all three drive down afterwards. He's the only person I've invited for this weekend. I daren't have a lot of people when he comes because he insists on being quiet. He says he gives out so much at every performance during the week that he's damned if he'll give a special performance on Sundays. He really is divine, and he certainly won't bother you because he does nothing but sleep.'

As they rejoined the cocktail party, Evan felt that the much-vaunted American hospitality was a very genuine and touching trait.

2

Lester Gaige was certainly amusing. At first, watching him on the stage, Evan had been unsure as to whether or not he was going to like him; he seemed to be too debonair, almost arrogant in the manner in which he moved through the bewildering intricacies of *Starlight*. True, he danced beautifully, sang, with no voice but compelling charm, and dominated by sheer force of personality every scene he was in; but there was something about him, a mocking veneer that made you a trifle uneasy as to what you might discover underneath. However, in the car driving down to the country, he was much more human. His clothes were inclined to be eccentric. He had on suede shoes, thin silk socks, very pale grey flannel trousers of exquisite cut, a *bois de rose* sweater with a turtle neck, a tweed sports jacket of extravagant heartiness and a fur-lined overcoat with an astrakhan collar. In addition he wore a small beret basque and a pair of the largest horn-rimmed glasses Evan had ever seen. The conversation between him and Louise was stimulating if a little local in allusion. They referred to so many people in such a short space of time that Evan became quite confused; but he sat back in the corner of the luxurious Packard and gave himself up to being agreeably soothed and entertained. It was obvious that Louise and Lester had been intimate friends for several years; their talk, generally in a gaily reminiscent vein, jumped from London to Paris, from Antibes back to New York, from New York to Venice and from Venice to California. 'That amazing party of Irene's when Broddie got blind and had that awful scene with Carola.' 'That terrible night in Salzburg when Nada refused to go home and finally disappeared into the mountains with Sonny Boy for three days.' Occasionally Evan, not wishing to appear out of it, ventured a question as to who So-and-so was, and was immediately rewarded by a vivid, if not always entirely kind, description of So-and-so's life, activities, and morals. On the whole he enjoyed himself very much. To begin with, they had all three had a Scotch Highball (ridiculous expression) in Lester's dressing room before they started and then another at Twenty-One, where they had had to stop for a moment because Lester had to give some message to Ed Bolingbroke, who had been apparently too drunk to understand it, then, not long after they had crossed the Fifty-ninth Street Bridge, Lester had produced a bottle of Scotch from his overcoat pocket, and they had all had a little extra swig to keep them warm. It was necessary to keep warm for the night was bitterly cold; there had been a blizzard the day before and the snow was several inches thick and freezing over.

When they finally reached the Steinhauser home Evan got out of the car, stretched his cramped legs and gave an exclamation of pleasure. It really was most attractive. A large low white house built on three sides of a square and looking out over Long Island Sound. It was a clear moonlight night and far away on the Connecticut coast lights twinkled across the water. Behind the house was nothing but snow, and a few bleak winter trees. Above all, there was silence, complete and soul-satisfying silence, broken only by the soft lap of the waves on the shore.

Inside, the house was the acme of comfort, a large fire was blazing away in a wide open fireplace in the main living room; before it was set a table laid for supper. A pleasant, coloured butler in a white coat met them at the front door. Evan sighed a deep sigh of relief. This was even better than he had imagined.

They sat up until very late over the fire talking. The supper had been delicious, a simple but tasty dish of spaghetti, tomatoes and eggs, a well-mixed green salad with cream cheese and Bar le Duc and further Scotch Highballs. Evan had had two since his arrival and although he was far from intoxicated he felt enjoyably mellow. Lester, who was really a great deal more intelligent than one would expect a musical comedy actor to be, displayed a flattering interest in Evan's work. He had read *A London Lady*, and been thrilled with it, he was also one of the few people who had read and enjoyed *My Steps Have Faltered*. Evan dismissed his praise of this with a deprecatory laugh, but he was pleased nonetheless. Louise was a good hostess and more than that, Evan decided, an extremely good sort. She talked with vivacity and her sense of humour was true and keen. She appeared to be one of those rare types, a rich woman who is completely unaffected by her wealth. She was downright, honest, and withal very attractive. She alluded to her husband frequently, and it was apparent that although they might not quite see eye to eye over certain things, she was deeply attached to him. They had a son at Harvard to whom they were both obviously devoted. Louise showed Evan a photograph of him dressed in the strange robotish armour of an American footballer. He was a husky, fine-looking lad. Lester was highly enthusiastic about him. 'That boy is fantastic,' he said, 'you'd never believe it to look at him, but he paints the most remarkable watercolours! He gave me one when I was playing Boston in *And So What*. It's a seascape, rather Japanesey in quality, almost like a Foujita.' Evan looked again at the photograph, slightly puzzled. Really Americans were most surprising. It was difficult to imagine that six feet of brawn and muscle painting demure seascapes, and even more difficult to understand how Lester Gaige playing in *And So What* in Boston could ever have heard of Foujita. Perhaps there was something to be said after all for that American culture that Europeans referred to with such disdain.

It wasn't until nearly four o'clock that Louise suddenly jumped up from the sofa on which she had been lying and cried, 'Really this is terrible – I bring you down here to rest and keep you up to all hours talking. We simply *must* go to bed.' She led the way through the hall and along a little passage. 'I've given you the quietest room in the house,' she said over her shoulder, 'it's on the ground floor and you'll have to share a bathroom with Lester. I would have given you a room upstairs with a bath to yourself but it isn't nearly so shut away and you might be disturbed by Bonwit getting up early or the servants or something.' She opened the door leading into a charmingly furnished bedroom. 'This is Lester's,' she said, 'you're along here.' They passed along another little passage and there was Evan's room. It was large, with two beds and decorated in a pale, restful green. In addition to the two beds there was a chaise-longue piled with cushions in front of the fire which, although it must have been lit hours ago, was still burning cosily. Evan smiled with pleasure. 'What a perfect room,' he said gratefully. Louise gave the fire a poke. 'I know how English people loathe central heating,' she said, 'and I've told them to have a fire for you all the time you're here, but if you'll take my advice you'll have the heat on a little bit as well, because the weather's really freezing.'

After Louise had said goodnight and gone up to bed, and Lester and Evan had smoked one more cigarette and exchanged the usual politenesses as to which of them should use the bathroom first, Evan, at last alone, opened the window, and, cold as it was, stood for a moment looking up at the stars and listening to the silence. He sniffed the icy air into his lungs, and with a sigh of utter contentment climbed into bed and was asleep in five minutes.

3

Evan woke at ten-thirty, which was rather early considering how late he had gone to bed. He counted up in his mind, four-thirty to ten-thirty, only six hours, but still it didn't matter, he could easily make up for it that night. He lay there idly looking at the reflection of the sea on the ceiling and contemplating, with a slight sinking of the heart, his lecture on Monday night. It was drawing very near and he was naturally nervous, but still he had certainly been wise to give himself this breathing space immediately before it. He planned to go over his notes sometime during the day. He was aware, of course, that he spoke well and that his subject 'History and the Modern Novel' was pretty certain to interest his American audience. He intended to start with the middle ages, the period of his first two novels, then jump to French eighteenth century, bringing in his *Porcelaine Courtesan, Madame Is Indisposed* and *The Sansculotte,* then to the Directoire and *Madame de Staël*, leaving the Restoration and *A London Lady* to the last. He was determined, in spite of the cautious advice of Neuman Bloch, to deliver a few well-deserved slaps at some of the more successful American writers who so impertinently twisted European history to their own ends. Evan detested slang and the use of present-day idiom in describing the past. Not that he was a believer in the 'Odd's Boddikins' 'Pish Tushery' school of historical writing; he himself eschewed that with the greatest contempt, but he did believe in being factually accurate insofar as was possible, and in using pure English. Had not the exquisite literacy of *A London Lady* been one of the principal reasons for its success with the Book Society? And not only the Book Society, with the reviewers of both continents and with the general public. One of Evan's most comforting convictions was that the general public had a good deal more discrimination and taste than it was given credit for, and that all this careless, slipshod, *soi-disant* modern style with its vulgarity of phrase and cheap Americanisms would, in a very little while, be consigned to the oblivion it so richly deserved.

At this point in his reflections he broke off to wonder whether or not he should ring for some fruit juice and coffee. He remembered from last night that the only entrance to his room was through Lester's and the bathroom and it would be inconsiderate to wake Lester if he were still sleeping. Evan, with a little sigh not entirely free from irritation, decided to go and see. He tiptoed out into the passage and into the bathroom and opened the door leading to Lester's room very quietly. Lester *was* still sleeping in a pair of pastel blue silk pyjamas with his head buried in the pillow. Evan stood there regarding him uncertainly for a moment. It would, of course, be unkind to wake him, and yet on the other hand he might possibly sleep until lunchtime and Evan would have to wait nearly three hours for his coffee. He retired into the bathroom, closing the door softly after him, and pondered the situation. Presently, renouncing indecision once and for all, he flushed the toilet and then listened carefully with his ear to the door. He was rewarded by hearing a few grunts and then the creaking of the bed. Quick as a flash he darted across to the lavatory basin and turned the tap on full, once embarked he intended taking no chances. After a few moments he opened the door again and peeped in. Lester was sitting up looking, he was glad to observe, quite amiable. Evan coughed apologetically. 'I'm awfully sorry,' he said, 'I'm afraid I woke you up. I'd no idea the tap would make such a row.'

'It wasn't the tap,' said Lester without rancour. 'It was the Lulu.'

'How does one get coffee, do you suppose?'

'Let's ring,' said Lester. 'We can either have it here or put on our dressing gowns and go into the sun porch – which do you prefer?'

'I don't mind a bit.' Evan, his plan having succeeded so easily, was feeling a little guilty and determined to be amenable at all costs.

'I think the sun porch is nicer.' Lester jumped out of bed, rang the bell and went into the bathroom to brush his teeth.

While they were breakfasting on the sun porch, an agreeable glass-enclosed room at the side of the house commanding a wide view of the sea and the drive, Bonwit Steinhauser appeared in elaborate plus-fours. He was a red-faced, rather dull-looking man, with a large body that had once been muscular but was now just fat. He said 'good morning' affably, and after a little desultory conversation went away. When he had gone Lester pushed his coffee cup out of his way and leant across the table almost furtively.

'You know I like Bonwit,' he whispered as though by such a confession he was straining credulity to the utmost. 'There's something really awfully kind about him. Of course everyone says he's a bore and I suppose he is in a way, but when he's had a few drinks, my dear!' He did one of his characteristic gestures of pawing the air with his right hand. 'He can be terribly, terribly funny! I shall never forget when I was up here one weekend with Ida Wesley, she's dead as a doornail now, poor sweet, and Bonwit, who shall be nameless, got so fried – ' Here he broke off abruptly and said: 'My God!' Evan turned round to see what had startled him and saw a car coming slowly up the drive. He jumped to his feet. Lester got up too, and, after looking out carefully a moment gave a laugh. 'It's all right,' he said, 'it's only Irene and Suki and Dwight and Luella – I thought for a minute it was strangers.'

'Are they coming for lunch?' asked Evan apprehensively.

'I expect so,' replied Lester, sitting down again. 'But you'll love Irene, she's divine, but divine – you've heard her sing, haven't you?'

Evan shook his head.

'You've never heard Irene Marlow sing!' Lester was horrified. 'You haven't lived, that's all, you just haven't lived! We'll make her sing after lunch. Suki's with her fortunately, he always plays for her. It really is the most lovely voice and there's somebody with an amazing sense of humour! I mean, she really gets herself, which is more than you can say for most prima donnas, and if you could hear her when she's in a real rage with Dwight – that's Dwight Macadoo who shall be nameless – my God! it's wonderful: bang goes the Italian accent and out pops Iowa!'

'We'd better go and dress, hadn't we?' suggested Evan, feeling unequal to greeting a famous Iowan prima donna in his pyjamas.

'You go and dress,' said Lester. 'And you might turn on a bath for me when you've finished. I'll go and deal with the visiting firemen.'

Evan retired to his room, shattered. It was really appalling luck that these people should have selected today of all days to come to lunch. How cross Louise would be. But still, he comforted himself, she'd be sure to get rid of them all as soon as possible.

When he emerged, bathed, shaved and dressed in perfectly cut English country clothes, he found everybody in the large living room. Apparently, while he had been dressing, some more people had arrived. Bonwit was mixing cocktails behind a little bar in the far corner of the room. There was no sign of Louise.

Seeing Evan come in, Lester, who was sitting on the sofa with a fattish little man and two women, jumped up. 'This is my friend,' he cried, 'I don't think you know my friend! who shall be nameless,' he added with a light laugh. Evan smiled sheepishly, he was unused to being nameless, but Lester came over and took him affectionately by the arm. 'I must introduce you to everybody,' he said. 'We'd better begin right here and work round the whole Goddamned circle.' He raised his voice. 'Listen, everybody – this is Evan Lorrimer, one of the greatest living English novelists, he's my friend and I'm mad about him!' He turned enquiringly to Evan. 'Aren't I, honey?'

Evan summoned up enough poise to give a little smile and say, 'I hope so,' whereupon Lester, holding him firmly by the arm, walked him round the room. A slight hush fell while this tour was in progress. Evan shook hands with everyone and responded pleasantly to their assurances of how glad they were to know him, but he was unable to catch more than a few names as he went along, and finally sat down feeling rather confused, in the place on the sofa that Lester had vacated. The fattish little man, he discovered, was Otis Meer, who wrote a famous gossip column for one of the daily papers, and the two women were Irene Marlow and Luella Rosen. Irene was flamboyant, but attractively so, she was dressed in a scarlet sports suit, with a vivid green scarf, her brown hair was done in clusters of curls and her hat – it couldn't have been anyone else's – was on the mantelpiece. Luella Rosen was sharp and black, like a little Jewish bird, she also was wearing sports clothes, but of a more sombre hue.

Irene smiled, generously exposing a lot of dazzlingly white teeth. 'Lester had been telling us all about you,' she said – her voice had a trace of a foreign accent – 'and you've no idea how thrilled we are to meet you. I haven't read your book yet, but I've got it.'

'Mr Lorrimer has written dozens of books, dear,' said Luella.

Irene sat back and closed her eyes in mock despair. 'Isn't Luella horrible?' she said. 'I'm never allowed to get away with a thing – anyway, I meant your last one, and I know it couldn't matter to you whether I've read it or not; but I really am longing to, particularly now that I've met you.' She winked at Evan, a gay, confiding little wink and nudged him with her elbow. Luella gave a staccato laugh. 'Irene's our pet moron,' she said. 'She's never read a book in her life except *Stories of the Operas*. She's just an Iowa girl who's made good, aren't you, darling?'

'Listen, lamb pie,' said Irene, 'you leave Iowa out of this. What's the matter with Iowa, anyway?'

'Nothing apart from Julia de Martineau,' said Otis Meer, and went into a gale of laughter. Irene and Luella laughed too. Evan was naturally unaware of the piquancy of the joke. At this point an exceedingly handsome man came up and handed him an 'old-fashioned'.

'This is my dream prince,' said Irene. 'Dwight, you know Mr Evan Lorrimer, don't you?'

'We've met already,' said Evan, nodding to Dwight who nodded back with a grin and sat down on the floor at their feet, balancing his own drink carefully in his right hand as he did so. 'Where the hell's Louise?' he asked.

'Louise has never been known to be on time for anything,' said Luella.

Irene turned to Evan. 'Isn't Louise a darling? You know she's one of the few really genuine people in the world. I can't bear people who aren't genuine, can you?' Evan made a gesture of agreement and she went on, 'Being a writer must be just as bad as being a singer in some ways, having to meet people all the time and look pleased when they say nice things about your books.'

'Tough,' said Luella. 'My heart goes out to you both.' She got up and went over to the bar.

'You mustn't pay any attention to Luella,' said Irene, comfortingly, observing that Evan looked a trifle nonplussed. 'She always goes on like that, she's actually got the kindest heart in the world, sometimes I really don't know what I'd do without her, she's one of our few really genuine friends, isn't she, Dwight?' Dwight looked up and nodded and then stared abstractedly into the fire. At this moment, Louise came into the room with a scream.

'I'm so terribly sorry, everybody – ' she wailed. 'I overslept.' While she was swamped with greetings, Evan looked at her in horror. She seemed to be a totally different person. Could this be the same woman whose friendly tranquillity and wise, philosophical outlook had so charmed him last night? Could she have known all these people were coming or was she merely masking her dismay at their appearance and trying to carry everything off with a high hand? If so, she was certainly doing it very convincingly. She seemed to be wholeheartedly delighted to see them. Her eye lighted on him and she came over with her arms round a red-haired women in black and a small fair man. 'My dear,' she said, 'you really must forgive me – I do hope you slept all right –' She broke off and turned to the red-haired woman. 'He's a sleep maniac just like me,' she said. Then to Evan again: 'You have met everyone, haven't you, and been given a drink and everything?' Evan held up his glass in silent acknowledgement, he was bereft of words, whereupon she snatched it out of his hand. 'You must have another at once,' she cried. 'That looks disgusting,' and led him vivaciously to the bar.

During the next half an hour, which Evan spent leaning against the bar, he managed to sort out people a little in his mind. The red-haired woman in black was the Countess Brancati, she had been a Chicago debutante a few years back and had married into the Italian aristocracy. The thin grey man by the window talking to Luella Rosen was her husband. The little fair man was Oswald Roach, commonly known as Ossie. Ossie was a cabaret artist whose speciality was to sing rather bawdy monologues to his own improvisations on the ukelele. The source of this information was Bonwit, who, although sweating copiously from the efforts of mixing different sorts of drinks for everybody, was willing, almost grateful, for an opportunity to talk. 'Who is the thin boy with the pale face?' Evan asked him. Bonwit shook the cocktail-shaker violently. 'That's Suki,' he said with obvious distaste. 'He's a Russian fairy who plays the piano for Irene, he's all right until he gets tight, then he goes cuckoo.'

Evan was regarding this phenomenon with interest, when there was a loud commotion in the hall, and two enormous Alsatians sprang into the room followed by a neatly-dressed girl in jodhpurs and a fur coat. 'I came just as I was,' she said, as Louise advanced to kiss her. 'I was riding this morning and Shirley wouldn't wait, she's gone into the kitchen to see about food for Chico and Zeppo.' She indicated the Alsatians who were running round the room wagging their tails and barking. 'I do hope you didn't mind us bringing them, but we couldn't leave them all alone in the apartment for the whole day.' Louise gaily assured her that she didn't mind a bit and brought her over to the bar. 'Here's someone who's been dying to meet you,' she said to Evan. 'Leonie Crane, she's written three plays herself, she's one of my closest friends and she's read everything you've ever written.' Leonie Crane blushed charmingly and wrung Evan's hand with considerable force. 'Not quite all,' she said in a well-modulated deep voice. 'Louise always exaggerates, but I think *A Lady of London* was swell. Shirley and I read it in Capri in the summer.'

'*A London Lady*,' Evan corrected her gently and she blushed again. 'That's typical of me,' she said. 'I'm so vague that Shirley says she wonders how I've lived as long as I have without being run over – Hallo, Bonny,' she leant over the bar and patted Bonwit's wet hand. 'What about a little hard liquor – I'm dying!'

Leonie was undeniably attractive, she radiated health and a sort of jolly schoolboyish vitality; her canary-coloured silk shirt was open at the neck and her curly brown hair was cut close to her head. She was a little shy and tried to conceal it with a certain lazy gaucherie. Evan found her most sympathetic, and they talked for several minutes and then Shirley appeared. Leonie presented her to Evan with brusque matter-of-fact despatch.

'This is Evan Lorrimer, Shirley – Shirley Benedict.' They shook hands. Shirley was on the same lines as Leonie but older and a little more heavily built. She had jet black hair, clear blue eyes, and was wearing a perfectly plain grey flannel coat and skirt. She wore no jewellery except a pair of pearl button earrings. Both girls were singularly free from trifling adornments.

Presently Lester reappeared dressed in an entirely new colour scheme so far as tie and sweater went, but with the same strong, garish sports coat that he had worn the night before. He kissed Leonie and Shirley affectionately, and told Evan that they were both angels and that when he'd got to know them a little better he'd worship them. They all four had an 'old-fashioned' on the strength of this prophecy and Evan began to feel a little drunk. It was not part of his usual routine to drink three tumblers of practically neat whisky in the middle of the day on an empty stomach, but he had now become sufficiently light-headed not to care. After all, there was no sense in just sitting about in corners looking sulky, just because some rather odd people had happened to come over for lunch. It would be both disagreeable and silly. Everyone seemed disposed to be most gay and friendly, why not relax and enjoy himself. Comforted by this successful disposal of his conscience, he agreed with cheerful resignation when Louise suggested that they should all go over to the Hughes-Hitchcocks for one more tiny drink before lunch. He had not the remotest idea who the Hughes-Hitchcocks were, but it was apparent from the enthusiastic assent of everyone present and from Lester's glowing description of them that they were an entrancing young married couple who lived only just down the road. Evan accepted an offer to go in Leonie's car and together with her and Shirley and Lester – the Alsatians were left behind – he went.

Lester's assurance that the Hughes-Hitchcocks lived only just down the road proved to be inaccurate. Evan, wedged between Shirley, who was driving, and Leonie in a small Dusenberg roadster, with Lester on his lap, suffered cramp and terror simultaneously for a full half an hour's fast going. Shirley drove well, there was no doubt about that. If she had not they would all have been dead within the first five minutes; but it was the sort of driving that is liable to react unfavourably on the nerves of anyone who happens to drive himself. Evan had driven for years. He owned a sedate Studebaker in faraway green England and frequently conveyed himself back and forth through the country in it, but not at a pace like this, not at seventy miles an hour over an ice-covered road that had frozen so hard that it was like glass. The fact that he was also unaccustomed to a right-hand drive added considerably to his agony. His instinct time and time again was to seize the wheel and swerve over to the left side to avoid what seemed to be imminent destruction. Fortunately, however, he restrained himself and sat in frozen misery until at last they turned into a large driveway under tall trees.

On the terrace outside the Hughes-Hitchcocks' house, which was a vast grey structure built on the lines of a French chateau, stood several cars. It was obviously quite a large party. Once inside, his legs felt so shaky after Lester's weight and the rigours of the drive, that he accepted with alacrity the first drink that was offered to him, which was a dry Martini in a glass larger than the cocktail glasses he was used to. After a little he relaxed sufficiently to look about him. There were at least twenty people in the room apart from his own party which was arriving in groups. His host, a good-looking hearty young man, brought up a fair girl whom he introduced as Mrs Martin. Evan, as he shook hands with her, was unable to avoid noticing that she was in an advanced stage of pregnancy. She seemed quite unembarrassed over the situation and looked at him with vague brown eyes. He observed that her fragile young hand was clasping a highball. 'Don't be frightened,' she said with a simper, 'it's not due until Wednesday, and if it doesn't come then I'm going to have a Caesarean.' Evan felt at a loss to know how to reply to such compelling candour, so he smiled wanly. She gave a slight hiccup and said, 'Excuse me.' Evan fidgeted awkwardly.

'Is that necessary?' he asked, and then flushed to the roots of his hair at the thought that she might imagine he was referring to the hiccup, but she either hadn't noticed or was too drunk to care. 'Not necessary,' she replied with a little difficulty, 'not exactly necessary, but nice work if you can get it,' then she drifted away. Presently Lester came up and they went over and sat down together in a window seat. 'It's always like this in this house,' he said. 'Thousands of people milling around – I can't think how they stand it. They're such simple people themselves too, and grand fun, you know, there's no chichi about them, that's what I like and Hughsie – ' here Lester chuckled – 'Hughsie's a riot, my dear, if you get Hughsie alone sometimes and get him to tell you some of his experiences in the Navy, he'll slay you; of course he's settled down now, and mind you he adores Sonia, and they've got two of the most enchanting children you've ever seen, but still what's bred in the bone comes out in the what have you ... '

At this moment Otis Meer joined them. 'Christ,' he whispered to Lester, 'Charlie Schofield's still trailing around with that bitch. I thought they were all washed up weeks ago.'

'You should know,' replied Lester, 'if anybody should.'

Evan asked for this interesting couple to be pointed out to him.

'That man over by the fireplace, the tall one with the blonde. He's Charlie Schofield, one of our richest playboys. She's Anita Hay, she used to be in "The Vanities". Otis hates her,' he added, Evan thought rather unnecessarily.

'She's one of these high-hatting dames,' said Otis. 'She'd high-hat her own father if she knew who he was.'

'Is she invited everywhere with Mr Schofield?' enquired Evan, who was puzzled by the social aspects of the situation.

'If she's not he just takes her,' replied Lester laconically. 'He's been crazy about her for years.'

Presently Louise came up with Luella Rosen. 'I must apologize for dragging you over here,' she said to Evan, 'but I absolutely promised we'd come, and they're such darlings really, but I'd no idea there was going to be this crowd – have another drink and we'll go in five minutes.'

'Can I drive back with you?' asked Evan wistfully.

'Of course,' said Louise. 'We'll meet in the hall in about five minutes.'

During the next hour Evan was forced to the conclusion that the time sense, in the wealthier strata of American society, was lacking. Louise showed no indication of wanting to leave. Almost immediately after she had promised to meet Evan in the hall in five minutes, she sat down with Mr Hughes-Hitchcock and began to play backgammon; her laugh rang out several times and Evan wondered bleakly if 'Hughsie' were retailing some of his experiences in the Navy.

Lester had disappeared. Otis Meer, Ossie and the Russian pianist were sitting in a corner engrossed in an intense conversation. Irene Marlow was entertaining a large group of people with a description or her first meeting with Geraldine Farrar – a few disjointed sentences came to Evan's ear – 'That vast empty stage – ' 'My clothes were dreadful, after all I was completely unknown then, just an ambitious little girl from Iowa –' 'She said with that lovely gracious smile or hers "My child" –' What Miss Farrar had said was lost to Evan for at that moment Charles Schofield came and spoke to him.

'We haven't been formally introduced,' he said amiably, 'but I think you know a great friend of mine, the Prince of Wales?' Evan, endeavouring not to betray surprise, nodded casually. 'Of course,' he said, 'although I fear I don't know him very well.' Actually he had met the Prince of Wales twice, once at a charity ball at Grosvenor House and once at a supper party at Lady Cynthia Cawthorne's. On both occasions he had been presented and the Prince had been charming, if a trifle vague; neither conversation could truthfully be said to have established any degree of intimacy.

'He's a grand guy,' went on Charlie Schofield, 'absolutely genuine. I've played polo with him a lot. Do you play polo?'

'No – I don't ride well enough.'

'It's a grand game,' said Charlie. 'I used to play on Boots Leavenworth's team – you know Boots Leavenworth, of course?'

Evan did not know the Earl of Leavenworth except by repute, but he felt it would sound churlish to go on denying everything. 'Rather,' he said, 'he's awfully nice.'

'I suppose you don't know what's happened about him and Daphne?'

'I think things are much the same,' hazarded Evan.

'You mean Rollo's still holding out?'

'When I left England,' said Evan boldly, 'Rollo was still holding out.'

'God!' said Charlie with vehemence. 'Aren't people extraordinary! You'd think after all that business at Cannes last summer he'd have the decency to face facts and come out into the open. As a matter of fact, I've always thought he was a bit of a bastard, outwardly amusing enough you know, but something shifty about him. As a matter of fact poor Tiger's the one I'm sorry for, aren't you?'

'Desperately,' said Evan.

'Where is Tiger now?'

'I don't know.' Evan wildly racked his brains for an appropriate place for Tiger to be. 'Africa, I think.'

'Jesus!' cried Charlie aghast. 'You don't mean to say he's thrown his hand in and left poor Iris to cope with everything?'

The strain was beginning to tell on Evan. He took refuge in evasion. 'Rumours,' he said weakly. 'One hears rumours, you know how people gossip.'

Fortunately at this moment Shirley and Leonie came up and asked him if he'd like to play table-tennis. 'We can't play at all,' said Shirley, 'we're terrible, but it's good exercise.' Evan smiled affably at Charlie and went with them into an enormous room glassed in on three sides, furnished only with the table, a few garden chairs and some large plants in pots. It was hotter than a Turkish bath. On the way he confided to them that he didn't play, but would be enchanted to watch them. He sat down, lit a cigarette and they started. They hadn't been playing a minute before he realized how wise he had been to refuse. They played like lightning, grimly, with an agility and concentration that was nothing short of ferocious. He watched them amazed. These two attractive young women, smashing and banging, occasionally muttering the score breathlessly through clenched teeth. Sometimes Leonie gave a savage grunt when she missed a shot, like a prizefighter receiving a blow in the solar plexus. Presently, they having finished one game and changed round and started another, Evan began to feel drowsy. The hypnotic effect of following the little white ball back and forth and the monotonous click of the wooden bats lulled him into a sort of coma. Vague thoughts drifted through his mind. He wondered who Rollo was and why he was probably holding out, and what Tiger might have left poor Iris to cope with – Poor Iris – Poor Tiger – Evan slept.

4

At ten minutes past four precisely the Steinhauser party rose from the lunch table and Evan went to his bedroom and shut the door. Lunch had not started until after three. There had been a certain amount of delay while Louise and Lester were rounding everybody up at the Hughes-Hitchcocks'. Then several arguments as to who should drive back with whom. Evan, with commendable tenacity, considering that he had just been awakened from a deep sleep, had clung to Louise like a leech despite all efforts of Shirley and Leonie to persuade him to go back with them, and finally succeeded in being brought home at a more reasonable speed in Louise's Packard. Lunch had been rather a scramble and consisted principally of clam chowder which he detested and veal cutlets which, not surprisingly, were so overdone as to be almost uneatable. Evan, whose head was splitting, took two aspirin, divested himself of his shoes, trousers and coat, put on his dressing gown and lay thankfully on the bed pulling the eiderdown up to his chin. If he could get a real sleep now, he reflected, not just a doze in a chair, and get up at about seven and bathe and change, everyone would have assuredly gone. They must all have dinner engagements in New York, and he would be able to dine peaceably with Louise and Bonwit and Lester, allow a polite hour or so for conversation, and go to bed firmly at ten-thirty. The warmth of the eiderdown stole round him, his legs began to congeal pleasantly with a prickling sensation, the throbbing of his head gradually diminished and he fell asleep.

About an hour later he felt himself being dragged to consciousness by somebody shaking him rhythmically. With intense reluctance he opened his eyes and beheld Lester bending over him. He moaned slightly and tried to evade that inexorable hand.

'You must wake up now, honey,' said Lester. 'You've had over an hour and Irene's going to sing.' Evan's mind, still webbed with sleep, tried unsuccessfully to grapple with this announcement. 'Who's Irene?' he muttered.

'Don't be silly,' said Lester. 'Irene Marlow; she's mad about you, she says she won't so much as open her trap unless you're there – we've been trying to persuade her for twenty minutes – she says she'll sing for you or not at all – come on.' He flicked the eiderdown off the bed and pulled Evan into a sitting posture. It was no use trying to go to sleep again now, even if Lester had allowed him to. Once wakened up like that he was done for. He went drearily into the bathroom and sponged his face, then came back and put on his trousers, coat and shoes. Lester, while he did so, lay on the chaise-longue and discoursed enthusiastically upon the quality of Irene's voice, her passion for Dwight Macadoo and the fact that leaving all her success and glamour aside she was really completely genuine. 'It's amazing about that boy,' he said apropos of Dwight. 'Really amazing – she's absolutely nuts about him and although he may be the biggest thing since *Ben Hur* I must say I think he's just plain dumb! Of course, you can't expect him to be anything else really, he was only a cowboy in Arizona when she met him, galloping about on a horse all day in "chaps" and rounding up all those Goddamned steers – who shall be name-less – well, anyway, she met him out on Grace Burton's ranch and gave her all if you know what I mean, and since that she's taken him everywhere – mind you, I'm not saying he isn't sweet, he is, but he just doesn't utter.'

Lester led the way into the living room. The party was sitting round expectantly. Irene was standing by the piano while Suki, with a cigarette dangling from his lips, was playing a few introductory chords. When Lester and Evan came in everybody said 'Shhh' loudly. They sank down on to the floor by the door, Irene flashed Evan a charming smile and started off on 'Vissi d' Arte'. She sang beautifully. Evan, whose understanding of music was superficial to say the best of it, recognized at once that the quality of her voice and the charm with which she exploited it was of a very high order indeed. When she had finished 'Tosca' everyone gave little groans and cries of pleasure, and someone called for 'Bohème'. Irene sang 'Bohème'; then Ossie implored her to sing the waltz from *The Countess Maritza*. She started this and forgot the words halfway through, so she stopped and sang three songs of Debussy in French, and then some Schumann in German. Evan, being by the door in a draught, wished that she'd stop, the floor was begin-ning to feel very hard and he was afraid of catching cold. Irene, blissfully unaware that even one of her audience wasn't enjoying her performance to the utmost, went on singing for over an hour. When she finally left the piano and sat down, amid ecstasies of admiration, Evan rose stiffly and went over to the bar. Otis was leaning against it with Shirley and Leonie, Bonwit was still behind it.

'Isn't that the most glorious voice you've ever heard?' cried Ossie. 'Frankly I'd rather listen to Irene than Jeritza, Ponselle and Flagstad all together in a lump.' Evan, repressing a shudder at the thought of Jeritza, Ponselle and Flagstad all together in a lump, agreed wholeheartedly and asked Bonwit for a drink.

'Martini, "old-fashioned", Daiquiri, rye and ginger ale, Scotch Highball, pay your dime and take your choice,' said Bonwit cheerfully. Evan decided on a highball, not that he wished to drink any more for the pleasure of it, but he was chilled by the draught from the door. Bonwit mixed him a strong one, and after a while he began to feel more cheerful. Louise came over. Evan noticed that she looked very flushed, and dragged Ossie away from the bar. 'Darling Ossie, you must,' she insisted, 'everybody's screaming for you – Lester's gone to get your ukelele, you left it in the hall.' Ossie, after some more persuasion, sat down in the middle of the room with his ukelele which Lester had handed to him, and began to tune it. Otis shouted out: 'Do "The Duchess",' and Irene cried, 'No, not "The Duchess", do "Mrs Rabbit".' Louise cried, 'No, not "Mrs Rabbit", do "Ella Goes to Court".' Several other people made several other suggestions, and there was pandemonium for a few moments. Shirley whispered to Evan, 'I do hope he does "Ella Goes to Court", you'll adore it, it's all about Queen Mary.'

Ossie silenced the clamour by striking some loud chords; then he sang 'Mrs, Rabbit'. 'Mrs Rabbit' was a description, half-sung and half-spoken, of the honeymoon night of an elderly lady from Pittsburgh. It was certainly amusing, while leaving little to the imagination. Ossie's rendering of it was expert. He paused, raised his eyebrows, lowered and raised his voice, and pointed every line with brilliantly professional technique. Everyone in the room shouted and wept with laughter. When he had finished with a vivid account of the death of Mrs Rabbit from sheer excitement, the clamour started again. This time he sang 'The Duchess'. It was rather on the same lines as 'Mrs Rabbit' although the locale was different. It described a widow from Detroit who married an English Duke and had an affair with a Gondolier during their honeymoon in Venice. Evan permitted himself to smile tolerantly at Ossie's somewhat stereotyped version of an English Duke. Finally, when he had sung several other songs, all of which varied only in the degree of their pornography, he consented to do 'Ella Goes to Court'. Evan, having finished his highball and noticing another close to his elbow, took it hurriedly and braced himself for the worst. 'Ella Goes to Court' was, if anything, bawdier than the others had been. It was a fanciful description of a middle-aged meat packer's wife from Chicago who, owing to the efforts of an impecunious English Countess, is taken to a Court at Buckingham Palace and becomes intimately attached to a Gentleman-in-Waiting on her way to the Throne Room. The whole song was inexpressibly vulgar, and to an Englishman shocking beyond words. Fortunately the references to the Royal Family were comparatively innocuous; if they had not been Evan would undoubtedly have left the room, but still, as it was, the whole thing with its sly implications, its frequent descents to bar-room crudeness, and above all the ignorance and inaccuracy with which Ossie endeavoured to create his atmosphere, irritated Evan profoundly. Aware that several people were covertly watching him to see how he would take this exhibition, he debated rapidly in his mind whether to look as disgusted as he really felt or to pretend to enjoy it. He took another gulp of his highball and forced an appreciative smile on to his face. 'Do you know,' said Leonie when Ossie had finished and the enthusiasm had died down, 'that's the favourite song of the Prince of Wales. Ossie had to sing it for him over and over again when he was at the Café de Paris in London.' Evan was about to reply with some tartness that that could only possibly be another imaginative flight of Ossie's when a diversion was caused by the noisy entrance of four newcomers. 'My God!' cried Lester. 'It's Carola!' There was a general surge towards a smartly dressed woman with bright eyes and still brighter hair who walked in a little ahead of the others. Lester kissed her, Louise kissed her, everybody kissed her except Evan, who was formally introduced a little later by Otis Meer.

Her name was Carola Binney and she was, according to Leonie and Shirley, the most famous and gifted comedienne on the New York stage. Evan vaguely remembered having heard of her at some time or other. She certainly possessed abundant vitality and seemed to be on the most intimate terms with everybody present. The people with her, Evan learned, were Bob and Gloria Hockbridge who were scenario writers from Hollywood, and Don Lucas. There was probably no one in the world, even Evan, who had not heard of Don Lucas. Evan looked at him and really experienced quite a thrill. He was even handsomer in real life than he was on the screen. His young finely modelled face healthily tanned by the sun; his wide shoulders and long curling lashes; his lazy, irresistible charm. There it all was. 'It was exactly,' thought Evan, 'as tho' some clear-eyed, vital young God from the wider spaces of Olympus had suddenly walked into a nightclub.' Lester brought him over. 'This is Don Lucas,' he said exultantly. 'He's just a struggling boy who's trying to make a name for himself and got sidetracked by somebody once saying he was good-looking.'

'Nuts, Les!' said the clear-eyed Olympian as he shook hands. 'Glad to know you, Mr Lorrimer.'

Lester, Don and Evan drifted over to the bar where Bonwit, after greeting Don, gave them each a highball. Evan tried to refuse but Lester insisted. 'Phooey!' he cried, placing his arm round Evan's shoulders. 'This is a party and life's just one big glorious adventure — which shall be nameless.'

Don, it appeared, was on a three weeks' vacation from Hollywood; he had just completed one picture, *The Loves of Cardinal Richelieu*, and was going back on Thursday to start another which was to be called *Tumult*, and was based on Tolstoy's *War and Peace*. The Hockbridges were writing it and had apparently done a swell job. Evan glanced across at the Hockbridges. Mr Hockbridge was a plump bald man in the early forties, while his wife was much younger, possibly not more than twenty-five, with enormous wide blue eyes and platinum blonde hair done in the style of Joan of Arc. Evan tried to imagine them sitting down together and writing the story of *War and Peace* and gave up. After three strong whiskies and sodas such fantasy was beyond him.

Don, within the first few minutes of their conversation, pressed him warmly to come and stay with him when he lectured in Los Angeles. 'It's a very simple house,' he said. 'None of that Spanish crap – all loggias and whatnot, but I can let you have a car and an English valet.' 'Simple house!' Lester gave a shriek. 'It's about as simple as Chartres Cathedral. It's the most gorgeous place in California.' He turned to Evan. 'You really must go,' he went on. 'Seriously, I mean it – it's an experience, if you know what I mean, and when I say experience, well! – ' He laughed and dug Don in the ribs.

'It would be grand to have you if you'd come,' he said. 'You mustn't pay any attention to the way Les goes on – we happened to have a party when he was there and oh boy!' He shook his handsome head and sighed as though shattered by the memory of it. 'But if you came you wouldn't be disturbed. I shall be working all day anyhow – you could do exactly as you liked.'

Evan thanked him very much, and said it sounded delightful. Lester went off into further eulogies about the magnificence of Don's house but was interrupted by Louise who came up and placed one arm round Don's waist and the other round Evan's.

'We're all going over to the Grouper Wendelmanns' for just ten minutes,' she said. 'Carola's longing to see their house; I must say it's unbelievable what they've done with it.' Evan gently disentangled himself. 'I don't think I'll come if you don't mind,' he said. 'I've got to go over my notes for my lecture tomorrow night.'

There was a shocked silence for a moment, then Louise gave a wail of distress. 'Oh my dear,' she cried, 'please come, just for a few minutes. The Grouper Wendelmanns will be so bitterly disappointed, they're pining to meet you and they're such darlings.'

Evan shook his head. 'I'd really rather not,' he said firmly.

'Then I won't go either,' said Lester.

'Neither will I,' said Louise. 'We'll none of us go.'

Don Lucas patted Evan's shoulder encouragingly. 'Come on,' he coaxed. 'Be a sport.'

'They're divine people,' said Lester. 'They really are, you'll love them, and old Bernadine's a riot; she's Jane Grouper Wendelmann's mother, you know; you can't go back to Europe without having seen Bernadine Grouper.'

'Only for just ten minutes,' said Louise. 'I shall really feel terribly badly if you don't go – it's quite near, just down the road and the house really is lovely, the most perfect taste, they've spent millions on it – '

'Don't worry him if he'd rather not,' said Don. 'Let's all have another drink.'

Evan, touched by the sympathy in Don's voice and embarrassed by Lester's and Louise's obvious disappointment, gave in. 'Very well,' he said, 'but I really must get back in time to go over my notes before dinner.'

Louise's face lit up with pleasure. 'Of course you shall,' she cried. 'You're an angel – the four of us shall go in my car – come on everybody.'

5

It was nearly an hour's drive to the Grouper Wendelmanns' house, and in the car Lester suggested playing a word game to pass the time. Evan didn't care for word games, but as he couldn't very well sit in morose silence he capitulated with as good a grace as possible. They played 'Who Am I?' and 'Twenty Questions' and 'Shedding Light'. Evan acquitted himself favourably and, owing to his superior knowledge of history, won reverent praise for his erudition in 'Twenty Questions'.

'Shedding Light' bewildered him, but he was glad to see that it bewildered Don Lucas even more. As a matter of fact everything bewildered Don Lucas; his contributions consisted mainly of the names of obscure baseball players and movie directors, but he persevered with naive charm in the face of the most waspish comments from Lester. Suddenly the games were interrupted by the chauffeur taking a wrong turning and arriving, after a few minutes of violent bumping, on to the edge of a swamp. Louise, who had been too occupied in trying to think of a Spanish seventeenth-century painter beginning with M to notice, leant forward, slid back the glass window and shouted a lot of instructions, most of which Lester contradicted. 'We ought to have turned to the left by the bridge, I know we ought,' she said.

'If we'd done that we should have arrived at the Witherspoons',' said Lester. 'And God forbid that we should do that.'

'Nonsense,' cried Louise. 'The Witherspoons are right over on the other side near the Caldicotts.'

'If,' said Lester with a trace of irritation, 'we had gone up that turning just past the Obermeyers' gate and then on over the hill we should have got into the highway and been able to turn right at the crossroads.'

'Left,' said Louise. 'If you turn right at the crossroads, you come straight to the golf course, and that's miles away, just next to the Schaeffers.'

'You'd better back,' said Lester to the chauffeur. 'And when you get into the main road again stop at the first petrol station and ask.'

Presently after some more bumping and a frightening moment when the frozen surface of the ground nearly caused the car to skid into a ditch, they emerged again on to the main road. About a quarter of an hour later, having followed the instructions of a Negro at a petrol station, and gone back the way they had come for a few miles, they turned up a small lane and arrived at the Grouper Wendelmanns'. The rest of their party had naturally arrived some time before and everybody was playing skittles in a luxurious skittle alley with a bathing pool on one side of it and a bar on the other. Mr and Mrs Grouper Wendelmann came forward to meet them both grasping large wooden balls. They were a good-looking young couple in bathing costume. 'This is wonderful,' cried Mrs Grouper Wendelmann. 'We thought you were dead, we're just going to finish this game, have one more drink and then go in the pool – go and talk to mother, she's stinking!'

Mr Grouper Wendelmann led them to the bar where the members of his own house party were sitting on high stools apparently having relinquished the joys of the alley and the pool to the invaders. Old Mrs Grouper, elaborately coiffed and wearing a maroon tea gown and a dog collar of pearls, greeted Evan warmly. 'You may or may not know it,' she said in a harsh, bass voice, 'but you're my favorite man!'

Evan bowed politely and tried to withdraw his hand, but she tightened her grasp and pulled him towards her. 'That book of yours,' she said portentously, and cast a furtive look over her shoulder as though she were about to impart some scurrilous secret, 'is great literature – No, it's no use saying it isn't because I know – Henry James used to be an intimate friend of mine and I knew poor Edith Wharton too, and believe me,' her voice sank to a hoarse whisper, 'I *know*.' She relaxed Evan's hand so suddenly that he nearly fell over backwards. At that moment his host gave him an 'old-fashioned' with one hand and piloted him with the other up to an emaciated dark woman in a flowered dinner dress.

'Alice,' he said, 'you English ought to get together – this is a countryman of yours – Mr Lorrimer – Lady Kettering.' Lady Kettering shook hands with him wearily and gave an absent smile. 'How do you do,' she said. The sound of an English voice comforted Evan, he hoisted himself on to a vacant stool next to her. Mr Grouper Wendelmann, having done his duty as a host, left them. 'What a lovely house,' said Evan. Lady Kettering looked at him in surprise and then glanced round as though she were seeing it all for the first time. 'I suppose it is,' she replied, 'if you like this sort of thing.'

Evan felt a little crushed. 'Of course I haven't seen much of it. I've only just arrived.'

'I've been here for three months,' said Lady Kettering, 'and I must say it's beginning to get me down. I'm going to Palm Beach next week. I think Palm Beach is bloody, don't you?'

'I've never been there,' said Evan.

'Well, take my advice and don't go. It's filled with the most frightening people.'

'I shan't be able to anyhow,' said Evan. 'I'm over here to do a lecture tour.'

'How horrible,' said Lady Kettering. 'Whatever for?'

'My publishers were very insistent that I should.' Evan was slightly nettled. 'And after all I think it will be interesting to see something of America. This is my first visit.'

'You ought to go to Mexico,' said Lady Kettering. 'That's where you ought to go.'

'I'm afraid I shan't have time.'

'That's the one thing you don't need in Mexico – Time doesn't exist – it's heaven.'

'Why don't you go to Mexico instead of Palm Beach?'

'I've promised to join the Edelstons' yacht and go on a cruise in the Bahamas,' said Lady Kettering. 'Do you know the Edelstons?'

'No,' replied Evan.

'Well take my advice,' she said, 'and give them a wide berth. They're bloody.'

At this moment Don Lucas came and prised Evan gently off his stool. 'Come and swim,' he said.

The idea of swimming on a Sunday evening in mid-February seemed fantastic to Evan. 'I don't think I will.'

'Come on, be a sport.'

'I'd rather watch you.'

'Nuts to that,' cried Don. 'Everybody's going to swim, it'll be swell.'

Evan allowed himself to be led over to the pool, inwardly vowing that no power on earth would get him into the water. Leonie and Shirley were giving an exhibition of fancy diving from the highest board, while Louise, Lester, Carola Binney, Irene Marlow and Ossie, who were already in bathing suits, sat around the edge and applauded. 'Isn't that amazing?' cried Lester as Leonie did a spectacular jackknife. 'I'd give anything in the world to be able to dive like that, but everything, if you know what I mean!'

Don took Evan firmly into a richly appointed men's dressing room and handed him a pair of trunks. 'Now undress,' he ordered.

Once more Evan protested. 'Really I'd rather not – '

'What the hell – ' said Don. 'The water's warm and we'll all have fun – come on, be a pal – '

'Honestly – ' began Evan.

'Now listen here,' Don sat down on a bench and looked at Evan reproachfully, 'this is a party and we're all having a good time and you're just bent on spoiling the whole shooting match.'

'Why should you be so anxious for me to swim?' asked Evan almost petulantly.

'Because I like you,' said Don with a disarming smile. 'I liked you from the word go and you like me too, don't you? Come on, be frank and admit it.'

'Of course I like you,' said Evan. 'I like you very much.'

'Very well then,' said Don triumphantly. 'Do we swim or don't we?'

'You do and I don't.'

'You wouldn't like me to get tough now, would you?' said Don in a wheedling voice, but with an undertone of menace. 'I could, you know!'

'I'm sure you could, but I fail to see – '

'Come on now, quit stalling.' Don advanced towards him and forcibly removed his coat. For one moment Evan contemplated screaming for help, but visualizing the ridiculous scene that would ensue he contented himself with struggling silently in Don's grasp. 'Please let me go,' he muttered breathlessly, 'and don't be so silly.'

Don had succeeded in slipping Evan's braces off and was endeavouring to unbutton his shirt when Lester came in. 'Boys, boys,' he cried admonishingly, 'do try to remember that this is Sunday – which shall be nameless,' and went into gales of laughter. Don released Evan immediately.

'This guy's a big sissy,' he said. 'He won't swim.'

'I don't blame him,' said Lester. 'The water's like bouillabaisse. It's got more things in it than Macy's window.'

'To hell with that. I'm going to swim if it kills me.'

'It probably will on top of all that liquor.' Lester went over and took a packet of cigarettes out of the pocket of his coat which was hanging on a peg. Then he came and sat on the bench next to Evan who, with a flushed face, was adjusting his clothes. 'Relax, honey,' he said, 'Don always goes on like this when he's had a few drinks. Have a Camel?'

Evan took a cigarette, meanwhile Don was tearing off his clothes with ferocious speed. When he was completely naked he stood over Lester and

Evan with arms folded and regarded them with scorn. Lester looked up at him. 'It's all right, Puss,' he said, 'we've seen all that and it's gorgeous, now go jump in the pool and sober up.'

'I don't know what's the matter with you guys,' he grumbled, and went towards the door.

'You'd better put on some trunks,' said Lester, 'or have I gone too far?'

Don came slowly back and put on a pair of trunks. 'Funny, hey?' he said bitterly and went out. A moment later they heard a loud splash and a shriek of laughter.

'What about another little drinkie?' said Lester.

6

About an hour later Evan found himself in a car sitting between Carola Binney and Luella Rosen whom he hadn't spoken to since before lunch. Don and Lester were squeezed together in the front seat next to Dwight Macadoo who was driving. The car apparently belonged to Irene Marlow. Evan had had two more 'old-fashioneds' since his struggle with Don and was drunk, but in a detached sort of way. He had lost all capacity for resistance. From now on, he decided, he would drink when he was told to, eat when he was told to and go where he was taken. There was no sense in fighting against overwhelming odds. He lay back, quite contentedly, with his head on Luella's shoulder and listened to Carola describing a man called Benny Schultz who had directed a play she had tried out in Boston last September.

'Never again − ' she was saying vehemently, 'would I let that rat come within three blocks of me − My God − you've no idea what I went through − he comes prancing into my dressing room on the opening night after the first Act − the first Act! believe it or not, and starts giving me notes − "Listen, Benny," I said, "you may have directed *Crazy Quilt* and *Mother's Day* and *The Wings of a Dove,* and you may have made Martha Cadman the actress she is, and Claudia Biltmore the actress she certainly isn't, but you're not coming to my room on an opening night and start telling me that my tempo was too fast and that I struck a wrong note by taking my hat off at my first entrance. To begin with I had to take that Godawful hat off which I never wanted to wear anyway because the elastic band at the back was slipping, and if I hadn't it would have shot up into the air and got a laugh in the middle of my scene with Edgar; in the second place if you had engaged a supporting company for me who could act and a leading man who had some idea of playing comedy, and at least knew his lines, I wouldn't have had to rush through like a fire engine in order to carry that bunch of art-theatre hams and put the play over, and in the third place I should like to remind you that I was a star on Broadway when you were selling papers on the East Side, and I knew more about acting than you when I was five, playing the fit-ups with *The Two Orphans*. And what's more, if you think I'm going to tear myself to shreds trying to get laughs in the supper scene in the pitch dark – well, you're crazy – "' She paused for a moment. Luella gave a barely audible grunt.

'You've got to have light to play comedy,' she went on, 'and all the phoney highbrow directors in the world won't convince me otherwise.'

'For all that I think Benny's pretty good,' said Luella.

'He's all right with Shakespeare. I give you that,' said Carola.

'His *Macbeth* was fine, what you could see of it, but comedy never – look at the flop he had with *Some Take It Straight*.'

'*Some Take It Straight* was the worst play I ever sat through,' Luella admitted.

'It needn't have been,' cried Carola. 'I read the original script. They wanted me to do it with Will Farrow, it really wasn't bad apart from needing a little fixing here and there – then that rat got hold of it and bitched it entirely.'

Lester let the window down. 'What's Carola yelling about?' he enquired.

'Benny Schultz,' said Luella.

'I wouldn't trust him an inch, not an inch,' said Lester. 'Look what he did to *Macbeth*.'

'Are we nearly home?' asked Evan.

'We're not going home – we're going to Maisie's.'

Evan lifted his head from Luella's shoulder. 'Who's she?' he asked sleepily.

'She's divine,' replied Lester. 'You'll worship her – I mean she's a real person, isn't she, Luella?'

'It depends what you call real,' said Luella. 'Personally she drives me mad.'

At this point the car turned into a gateway and drew up before a low, rather rambling white-walled house. Everyone got out and stamped their feet on the frozen snow to keep warm, while they waited for the door to be opened, which it presently was by a large forbidding-looking Swedish woman who regarded them suspiciously. Lester embraced her. 'It's all right, Hilda,' he said, 'it's only us.'

She stood aside and they all trooped in, shedding their coats in the hall. Lester led the way into a sort of studio panelled in pitch pine with wide bow windows and an immense log fire. The room was luxuriously furnished in a style that Evan supposed was early American. Anyhow in spite of its being extremely overheated, its simplicity was a relief after the other houses he had visited. He felt as though he had been going from house to house all his life.

A grizzled woman with fine eyes and wearing a riding habit greeted them brusquely and introduced the other people in the room. There were two girls called Peggy and Althea, one fat and the other thin, a very pale young man in green Chinese pyjamas called George Tremlett, and a statuesque French-woman with raven hair who appeared to be dressed as a Bavarian peasant. The only two members of their own party present were Leonie and Shirley who were lying on the floor playing with a Siamese cat. There was a large table of drinks along one of the windows. Don Lucas made a beeline for it. 'Donny wants some fire water,' he said. 'Donny wants to get stinking.'

'You were stinking at the Grouper Wendelmanns',' said Luella.

'Isn't he beautiful,' said the Frenchwoman.

When everyone had helped themselves to drinks Evan found himself sitting on a small upright sofa with George Tremlett.

'You arrived in the middle of a blazing row,' whispered George with a giggle. 'Suzanne and Shirley haven't spoken for two years and suddenly in she walked with Leonie – '

'Which is Suzanne?'

'The dark woman, Suzanne Closanges. She writes poetry either in French or English, she doesn't care which, and she lives here with Maisie.'

'Maisie who?' asked Evan.

'Maisie Todd, of course,' said George with slight irritation. 'This is Maisie Todd's house – I did it.'

'How do you mean "did it"?'

'Designed it,' George almost squealed. 'I'm George Tremlett.'

'How do you do?' said Evan.

'It was lovely doing this house,' went on George, 'because I had an abso-lutely free hand – Maisie's like that – we had the grandest time driving all over New England and finding bits and pieces here and there. I found this very sofa we're sitting on tucked away in a fisherman's bedroom at Cape Cod.'

'How extraordinary,' said Evan – he felt overpoweringly sleepy.

Leonie came over with the Siamese cat and placed it on Evan's lap. 'Isn't he adorable?' she said. 'I gave him to Maisie for a Christmas present in 1933 and he's grown out of all knowledge.'

The cat arched its back, dug its claws into Evan's leg and with a loud snarl hurled itself to the floor. 'They're very fierce,' went on Leonie picking it up again by the nape of its neck so that it hung spitting and kicking in the air. 'And the older they grow the fiercer they get, but Dante isn't fierce though he's older than hell – are you, my darling?' she added affectionately, kissing it on the side of the head. The cat gave a sharp wriggle and scratched her cheek, from her eye, which it missed by a fraction, to her chin. She screamed with pain and dropped it on to a table where it knocked over and smashed a photograph of a lady in fencing costume framed in glass, jumped down and disappeared behind a writing desk. Evan started to his feet, everyone came crowding over.

'The son of a bitch,' wailed Leonie. 'He's maimed me for life.' With that she burst into tears. Maisie Todd took charge with fine efficiency. She produced a large white handkerchief to staunch the blood, dispatched George to fetch some iodine from her bathroom. Shirley flung her arms round Leonie and kissed her wildly. 'Don't darling, don't cry,' she besought her. 'For God's sake don't cry, you know I can't bear it.'

'There's nothing to cry about,' said Maisie, 'it's only a scratch.'

'It may only be a scratch,' cried Shirley, 'but it's terribly deep and it's bleeding.'

'Don't fuss,' said Maisie.

'It's all very fine for you to say don't fuss,' Shirley said furiously, 'but it might very easily have blinded her – you oughtn't to keep an animal like that in the house, it should be destroyed.'

'Leonie gave it to Maisie herself before she knew you,' put in Suzanne with a little laugh.

'Mind your own business,' snapped Shirley.

Leonie dabbed her eyes and her cheeks alternately with the blood-stained handkerchief.

'For God's sake shut up, everybody. I'm all right now, it was only the shock.'

'Drink this, darling,' said Lester, handing her his glass.

'We should never have come – I knew something awful would happen,' said Shirley.

'There is nothing to prevent you going,' Suzanne spoke with icy dignity. There was a horrified silence for a moment. Shirley left Leonie and went very close to Suzanne.

'How dare you,' she said softly. Evan noticed that she was trembling with passion. 'How dare you speak to me like that – '

Maisie intervened. 'Now listen, Shirley,' she began. Shirley pushed her aside. 'I've always disliked you, Suzanne, from the first moment I set eyes on you, and I wish to say here and now that you're nothing but a fifth-rate gold-digger sponging on Maisie the way you do and making her pay to publish your lousy French poems, and you're not even French at that – you're Belgian!'

Suzanne gave a gasp of fury, slapped Shirley hard in the face and rushed from the room, cannoning into George Tremlett who was coming in with the iodine and knocking the bottle out of his hand on to the floor. 'Oh, dear!' he cried sinking on to his knees. 'All over the best Hook rug in the house!'

From then onwards everybody talked at once. Maisie dashed out of the room after Suzanne; Leonie started to cry again. The two girls, Althea and Peggy, who had been watching the whole scene from a corner, decided after a rapid conversation to follow Maisie and Suzanne, which they did, slamming the door after them. George was moaning over the Hook rug and trying to rub out the iodine stains with a silk scarf. Lester joined Luella and Carola by the fireplace. Carola was protesting violently at Suzanne's behaviour, while Luella smiled cynically. Lester, genuinely distressed, was sympathizing with Shirley and Leonie, while Don added to the din by strolling over to the piano with Dwight Macadoo and playing 'Smoke Gets in Your Eyes' with one hand. Presently he desisted. 'This piano stinks,' he said. 'No tone – where's the radio?' Before he could find it Luella, to Evan's intense relief, suggested that they should all go, and led the way firmly into the hall. While they were struggling into their coats and wraps the large Swedish woman watched them silently with a baleful expression. The freezing night air struck Evan like a blow between the eyes; he staggered slightly. Don quickly lifted him off the ground and deposited him in the car with infinite tenderness.

'You were wrong about that swim,' he said affectionately. 'It was swell, made me feel like a million dollars. Now we'll go home and have a little drinkie.'

7

They had no sooner got inside the Steinhausers' front door when Irene came rushing out of the living room. 'Where the hell have you been?' she cried angrily to Dwight. 'I looked for you all over and when I came out you'd gone off in my car.'

'Now don't be mad at me, darling – ' began Dwight.

'Mad at you! I've never been madder in my life – come in here.' She dragged him into the library and banged the door.

'Well,' said Lester, 'isn't she the cutest thing – My dear!' He waved his hand benevolently after them. 'These prima donnas – who shall be nameless – '

Louise appeared with a great cry and flung her arms round Evan. He was dimly aware that she had changed into a long flowing tea gown. '*There* you are,' she said. 'I couldn't think what had happened to you – you must be starving.' Still holding him tightly she pulled him into the living room which had undergone a startling change. All the furniture had been pushed out on to the sun porch with the exception of the chairs which were arranged round the walls. An enormous buffet loaded with hams, turkeys, salads, bowls of fruit, bowls of cream, two large cakes and piles of plates, stood along one side of the room. Another smaller table for drinks was joined on to the bar behind which Bonwit was still officiating, assisted by a Japanese in a white coat. There were at least fifty people in the room and the noise was deafening. Evan, dazed as he was, distinguished the Grouper Wendelmanns, Lady Kettering, and several of the people he had seen at the Hughes-Hitchcocks', including the young expectant mother who was sitting on the floor with her back against one of the piano legs, and a large plate of variegated food on her lap, apparently in a stupor, while Suki played an unending series of complicated syncopation in her ear.

Louise led Evan to the table and gave him a plate on which she piled, with professional speed, a turkey leg, Virginia ham, baked beans, a fish cake, potato salad, lettuce, a wedge of Camembert cheese and a large slice of strange-looking brown bread. 'There,' she said, 'now sit down quietly, and eat, you poor dear.' With that she whisked away from him and rushed across to Carola and Luella. He looked round for a vacant chair but there wasn't one, so he stayed where he was and ate standing against the table. The food was certainly good although there was far too much of it on his plate. He was about to slide the cheese and one of the slices of ham into an empty bowl that had held salad when he was arrested by Charlie Schofield putting his hand on his shoulder. He jumped guiltily as though he'd been caught in the act of doing something nefarious.

'I told Alice Kettering what you said about Tiger being in Africa,' said Charlie, 'and she's in an awful state – she was crazy about him for years you know.'

Before Evan could reply Don came up and forced a glass into his hand. 'I promised you a little drinkie,' he said genially, 'and a little drinkie you're going to have.'

A big woman in yellow put her arm through Charlie Schofield's and led him away. Evan saw out of the corner of his eye that Lady Kettering was drifting towards him. He retreated on to the sun porch followed by Don looking very puzzled.

'What's the idea?'

'Just somebody I don't want to talk to,' said Evan with as much non-chalance as he could muster.

'Listen, Pal,' said Don. 'If there's anyone you don't like just you tip me off and I'll sock 'em.'

Evan, shuddering inwardly at the thought of Don socking Lady Kettering, muttered that it was of no importance really, and leant against the window.

Outside the moon had come up and the sea shone eerily in its light like grey silk; far away in the distance a lighthouse flashed. It all looked so remote and quiet that Evan felt inclined to weep. Don squeezed his arm reassuringly. 'You know I like you,' he said, 'I like you better than any Englishman I've ever met. Most Englishmen are high-hat, you know, kind of snooty, but you're not high-hat at all, you're a good sport.'

'Thank you,' said Evan dimly.

'I hope you weren't sore at me for trying to make you go in the pool,' Don went on. 'I wouldn't like to have you sore at me. It isn't often I get a chance to talk to anyone really intelligent – not that you're only just intelligent, you're brilliant, otherwise you wouldn't be able to write all those Goddamned books, would you now?'

'Well,' began Evan, feeling that some reply was demanded.

'Now don't argue.' Don's voice was fierce. 'Of course you're brilliant and you know you are, don't you?'

Evan smiled. 'I wouldn't exactly say – '

Don patted his hand tolerantly. 'Of course you do – everybody knows when they're brilliant, they'd be damned fools if they didn't. Jesus, the way you played that question game in the car – if that wasn't brilliant I should like to know what is. But what I mean to say is this. I'm just a simple sort of guy, really, without any brains at all – I've got looks, I grant you that, otherwise I shouldn't be where I am today should I? But no brains, not a one. Why, the idea of sitting down and writing a letter drives me crazy let alone a book. Sometimes when I look at something beautiful like all that,' he indicated the view, 'or when I run across someone really brilliant like you are I feel low – honest to God I do – '

'Why?' said Evan.

'Because I'm such a damn fool of course. I couldn't write down what that looks like to me, not if you paid me a million dollars I couldn't. I couldn't paint it either, I couldn't even talk about it. What do I get out of life I ask you? Money, yes – I make a lot of dough and so what – Happiness, no – I'm one of the unhappiest sons of bitches in the whole world,' he broke off.

'Cheer up,' said Evan as cheerfully as he could. He was feeling depressed himself.

'It gets me down,' murmured Don, pressing his forehead against the glass of the window. 'It just gets me down.'

Evan was pained and embarrassed to observe that he was crying. A concerted scream of laughter came from the living room. Evan peeped in. Everyone was grouped round Carola who, with a man's Homburg hat perched on her head, was doing an imitation of somebody. Evan glanced back at Don, who was still staring out into the night; his shoulders were heaving. Now was the moment to escape, everyone was far too occupied to notice whether he was there or not; if he could get into the hall without Louise seeing him, the rest was easy; he could get into his room, lock the door and go to bed. He crept along behind the buffet, avoiding Mr Hockbridge, who was asleep on a chair, and reached the hall in safety. From behind the closed door of the library came sounds of strife, apparently Irene's fury at Dwight had in no way abated. Evan paused long enough to hear her scream angrily – 'It was Luella's fault, was it – we'll see about that!' – then he darted down the passage, through Lester's room and the bathroom and reached his own room with a sigh of relief. He switched on the lights by the door and started back in horror. Stretched out on his bed was a woman in a heavy sleep. On closer examination he recognized the Countess Brancati. Her black dress was rumpled and her hair was spread over the pillow like pink hay.

A great rage shook Evan to the core. He seized her by the shoulder and pushed her backwards, and forwards, violently; she continued to sleep undisturbed. He knelt down on the floor by the bed and shouted 'Wake up – please wake up' in her face to which she replied with a low moan. He shook her again and one of her earrings fell off; he picked it up and put it on the bed table and stood there looking at her, his whole body trembling with fury and frustration. He gave her one more despairing shove but she paid no attention. Then, with an expression of set determination, he marched back to the living room. On his way he met Bonwit emerging from the library. 'My God,' Bonwit said, 'there's all hell breaking loose in there,' and then, noticing Evan's face, 'what's happened to you?'

'There's a woman on my bed,' Evan almost shouted.

'I'll bet it's Mary Lou Brancati,' said Bonwit. 'She always passes out somewhere – come on – we'll get her out.'

They went back together. The countess had turned over on to her face. Bonwit slapped her behind; she wriggled slightly and he did it again harder. Presently, after several more whacks, she turned over and muttered, 'G'way and leave me alone – ' Bonwit whereupon hoisted her up on to the side of the bed and shook her. She opened her eyes and looked at him malevolently. 'Get the hell away from me,' she said. 'What d'you think you're doing!'

'Come on, baby,' said Bonwit, 'you're missing everything. There's a party going on.'

'To hell with it,' she replied. 'G'way and leave me alone.'

'Take her other arm,' ordered Bonwit. Evan obeyed and they hauled her struggling and protesting into the bathroom. There Bonwit dabbed her face with a wet sponge; she gave a scream and tried to hit him. Finally they got her into the hall and deposited her in a chair. Bonwit slapped his hands together as though he had just felled a tree and said, 'Now you're okay, fellar.'

At that moment the hall suddenly filled with people, Louise came out of the library with her arms around Irene who was sobbing. Dwight followed them miserably. Unfortunately Luella and Otis Meer came out of the living room at the same instant followed by Lester, Lady Kettering and the Grouper Wendelmanns. Irene, catching sight of Luella, wrested herself from Louise's arms. 'So you're still here,' she said harshly. 'I'm surprised you have the nerve!'

Luella looked at her coolly. 'You're tight, Irene,' she said. 'You'd better go home.'

'You're a snake,' cried Irene, breathing heavily. 'A double-faced, rotten snake!'

Lester tried to calm her. 'Look here, honey,' he said, 'there's no cause in getting yourself all worked up.'

Irene pushed him aside. 'You shut up – you're as bad as she is – you're all of you jealous of Dwight and me and always have been – Luella's been trying to get him for years, and if you think I'm so dumb that I haven't seen what's been going on you're crazy.'

'Really,' murmured Lady Kettering. 'This is too bloody – we'd better go – '

'Go and be damned to you!' said Irene.

Louise gave a cry of distress. Lady Kettering turned and tried to make a dignified exit into the living room, but was prevented by Ossie, Suki, the Hughes-Hitchcocks and Mrs Hockbridge, who had crowded into the doorway to see what was happening.

Luella seized Irene by the arm in a grip of steel. 'Behave yourself,' she hissed. 'What do you mean by making a disgusting scene like this about nothing?'

'Nothing!' Irene screamed and writhed in Luella's grasp. Otis Meer gave a cackle of shrill laughter. Dwight tried to coax Irene back into the library. Louise wept loudly and was comforted by Lester and Ossie. Lady Kettering struggled valiantly through the crowd to try to find her cloak. Carola, who had joined the group with Shirley and Leonie, announced in ringing tones that in her opinion the possession of an adequate singing voice was hardly sufficient excuse for behaving like a Broadway floozie. Lester turned on her and told her to shut up and not make everything worse, and in the indescribable pandemonium that ensued, Evan fled.

8

About an hour later, Evan, sitting up rigidly in his bed, began to relax. He had brushed his teeth, taken three aspirins, undressed, tried to lock the door but discovered there was no key, and read four chapters of *Sense and Sensibility* which he always travelled with as a gentle soporific. He had left no stone unturned in his efforts to drag his aching mind away from the horrors he had endured. He had turned out the light twice and attempted to sleep but to no avail. Incidents of the day, people's names, unrelated scraps of conversation crowded into his brain, making even the possibility of lying still out of the question let alone sleep. Sleep was eons away, he felt that it was well within the bounds of probability that he would never sleep again. The thought of the lecture he had to give that very night, it was now three a.m., tortured him. He felt incapable of uttering one coherent phrase and as for talking for an hour, his mind reeled at the very idea of it. The continual noise, the endless arrivals and departures, the impact of so many different atmospheres and personalities, the unleashing of vulgar passion he had witnessed to say nothing of the incredible amount of alcohol he had drunk, had lacerated his nerves beyond bearing. He was outraged, shamed, exhausted and bitterly angry.

Now at last he was beginning to feel calmer. The three aspirins he had taken had made his heart thump rather, his maximum dose as a rule being two, but it was apparently taking effect. He glanced at his watch, ten minutes past three, if he could manage to sleep until eleven he would have had nearly his eight hours and probably be able to get in an extra hour at his hotel before his lecture if he wasn't too nervous. 'I'll give myself another ten minutes,' he reflected, 'and then turn out the light, by that time it ought to be all right.'

He lay there still as a mouse, resolutely emptying his mind and concentrating on gentle, peaceful things, the waves of the sea, a vast four-poster bed in some remote English country house, the cool, soft lavender-scented sheets, the soughing of the wind outside in the elms – At this moment the door opened and Bonwit came in on tiptoe. He was in his pyjamas and carrying a pillow and an eiderdown. He looked relieved when he saw that Evan wasn't asleep.

'I'm awfully sorry, fellar,' he said, 'but I've got to come and use your other bed – there's been all hell going on. Irene drove off in her car with Dwight, leaving Suki and Luella behind, the Brancatis went too, leaving Ossie and Otis, and we've only just found Don Lucas – he's in the living room on the sofa. Ossie and Otis are in with Lester, Luella's in with Louise and Suki's in my room. I've got to get up at seven to go into town but don't be afraid I'll disturb you – I've left my clothes in the bathroom so I can dress in there.'

'Oh,' said Evan hopelessly, the blackness of despair made further utterance impossible.

Bonwit clambered into bed and switched off his light. 'I'm all in,' he said. 'Goodnight, fellar.'

Evan switched off his light too, and lay staring into the darkness.

In a remarkably short space of time Bonwit began to snore. Evan groaned and tried to fold the pillow over his ears, but it was no good, the snores grew louder. They rose rhythmically to a certain pitch and then died away. Occasionally the rhythm would be broken by a grunt, then there would be silence for a moment, then they'd start again. Evan, after a half an hour of it, suddenly leapt up on an impulse of pure blinding rage, switched on the light and went over to Bonwit's bed and stood looking at him. Bonwit was lying on his back with his mouth wide open – the noise issuing from it was incredible. Evan, flinging all gentleness and consideration to the winds, seized him violently by the shoulders and turned him over. Bonwit gave a terrific snort, turned back again almost immediately and went on snoring louder than ever. Evan began to cry, tears coursed down his cheeks and fell on to his pyjamas – panic assailed him – if this went on he would definitely go mad. He walked up and down the room fighting to prevent himself from losing control utterly and shrieking the house down. He went over to the window and looked out. The night was crystal clear, there wasn't a cloud in the sky. Suddenly he knew what he was going to do, the idea came to him in a flash. He was going away, that's what he was going to do. He was going to dress, telephone for a taxi and leave that horrible house for ever. It was idiotic not to have thought of it before. He would leave a note for Louise in the hall asking her to bring his suitcase into New York with her. He tore off his pyjamas and began to dress. Bonwit stopped snoring and turned over. Evan switched off the light and stood still hardly daring to breathe. If Bonwit woke up and caught him trying to escape, he'd obviously try to prevent him – there would be arguments and persuasions and protests, probably ending in the whole house being roused.

Bonwit started to snore again and Evan, with a sigh of relief, finished dressing. Holding his shoes in his hand he crept down the passage, through the bathroom and into Lester's room. He could dimly make out two forms in one bed and one in the other. He banged against a chair on his way to the door and immediately lay down flat on the floor. Lester moved in his sleep but didn't wake; finally, on hands and knees, Evan crawled out into the other passage and into the hall. Once there, he put on his shoes and went cautiously in search of the telephone; just as he was about to go into the library he remembered that it was in the bar, he had heard Bonwit using it before lunch. He went into the living room. The curtains were not drawn and moonlight was flooding through the windows. Don was sleeping soundly on a sofa, he looked rather debauched but extraordinarily handsome. Poor Don. Evan shook his head at him sorrowfully and went over to the bar. There was a shutter down over it which was padlocked. This was a terrible blow. Evan thought for a moment of going back and waking Bonwit; but decided against it. If there was no taxi he'd walk and if he didn't know the way he'd find it, at all events he knew he would rather die in the snow than spend one more hour in that house. He scribbled a note to Louise in the library. 'Dear Mrs Steinhauser – ' He debated for a moment whether or not to address her as Louise, she had certainly kissed him several times during the day and called him Darling frequently, also he knew her to be a kindly, well-intentioned woman, although at the moment he could cheerfully have strangled her. On the whole he felt that 'Mrs Steinhauser' better expressed the manner in which he was leaving her house. 'Dear Mrs Steinhauser – Finding myself unable to sleep I have decided to go back to New York. Please forgive this unconventional departure, but it is essential, if I am to lecture with any degree of success, that I relax for several hours beforehand. Please don't worry about me, I am sure I shall find my way to the station quite easily, but if you would be so kind as to have my suitcase packed and bring it in with you tomorrow, I should be more than grateful. With many thanks for your delightful hospitality I am, yours sincerely, Evan Lorrimer.' He signed his name with a flourish. 'She can stick that in her damned visitors' book,' he said to himself. He left the note in a prominent position on a table in the hall, found his hat and coat in a cupboard and let himself quietly out of the front door. The cold air exhilarated him. It was odd, he reflected, how the excitement of escape had completely banished his nervous hysteria. He felt surprisingly well, all things considered. The snow shone in the moonlight and the country lay around him white and still. He noticed a glow in the sky behind a hill. That must be a village, he thought, and set off jauntily down the drive.

About an hour later, when he had walked several miles and his adventurous spirit had begun to wilt a trifle, he was picked up by a milk van. The driver was rugged and friendly and agreed to take him to the nearest station. They had some coffee together in an all-night lunchroom when they got there; the next train for New York wasn't due for three-quarters of an hour, and the driver talked freely about his home and domestic affairs with an accent that Evan found, at moments, extremely difficult to understand. Finally he drove away in his van, having allowed Evan to pay for the coffee, but refused to accept two dollars.

'Nuts to that,' he said with a laugh. 'I like you – you're not high-hat and kind of snooty like most Englishmen – So long, buddy.'

Buddy, warmed by this tribute, went to the platform and waited for the train.

When he arrived in New York it was daylight. The night porter at his hotel greeted him in some surprise and handed him a pile of telephone messages and a letter. When he got to his room he opened the letter first. 'Dear Mr Lorrimer,' he read. 'Although we have never met, your books have given me so much pleasure that I am taking this opportunity of welcoming you to Chicago, where I understand you are going to talk to us next week on "History and the Modern Novel". My husband and I would be so pleased if you would come out to us for the weekend after your lecture. Our home is on the edge of the lake and we flatter ourselves it is the nearest approach to an English country house that you could find in the whole of the Middle West. It is peaceful and quiet, and no one would disturb you, you could just rest. If you have anyone with you we should, of course, be delighted to receive them, too. My husband joins me in the hope that you will honour us by accepting. Yours very sincerely, Irma Weinkopf.' Evan undressed thoughtfully and got into bed.

THE NOVEL

Noël wrote several novels or parts of novels, though only one was published.

Enthused by the prolific literary output of his childhood actress friend, Esmé Wynne, he was determined to try his hand at a novel of his own. Called Cats and Dogs *(1918), it was the story of a brother and sister, who talk brightly and incessantly for some 80,000 words before inspiration deserted him — and he deserted them. It bore more than a passing relationship to Shaw's* You Never Can Tell *and in 1921 Noël was to return to it in his play* The Young Idea.

Meanwhile — also in 1918 — there was Cherry Pan . . .

'Cherry Pan, I regret to tell you, was the daughter of the Great God Pan and was garrulous and tiresome to the point of nausea. Having materialized suddenly on a summer evening in Sussex, she proceeded with excruciating pagan archness to wreak havoc in a country parsonage before returning winsomely to her woodland glades and elfin grots. I remember being bitterly offended by a friend who suggested that the title should be changed to *Bedpan*.'

In 1929, after the success of Bitter-Sweet, *Noël set off on a long trip to the Far East. On the boat between Honolulu and Yokohama he started work on* Julian Kane, *the story of a man who committed suicide because he was bored.*

'I worked hard on my novel . . . but became increasingly discouraged by its obvious dullness, until I finally decided that, if it continued as it was going, the future readers of it would commit suicide from boredom long before the hero ever reached that point of defeat.'

Julian Kane *lived but* Julian Kane *died on the journey. And Noël became understandably wary of the form — as well as being overly committed elsewhere — for many years to come.*

'I am getting on steadily with my novel, and reading, in between whiles, a lot of Henry James. This is very good for me and, at moments, very hard going. He really was the king of exquisitely phrased verbosity. It is good for me technically because I am inclined to over-simplify my descriptive passages and reduce them to staccato interludes rather than letting them be part of the general structure. This is the natural result of years of dialogue writing. It is only when I have done a couple of pages of – to my mind – elaborate and drawn-out description that, on reading it over, I discover to my astonishment that it is neither elaborate nor drawn-out. On the contrary, it is usually on the skimpy side. This, I suppose, is the reason that so few playwrights write good novels and vice versa. Particularly vice versa. Most novelists overload their plays with masses of words.

'Personally, I am quite determined to be good at both. I am not sure yet, judging from my short stories and autobiographies, that I have evolved a personal style. It is not a thing to pursue consciously. I expect that, on the whole, I have, up to a point. But up to date I haven't really written enough fiction and prose to be able to judge clearly.'

Diary, 3 March 1957

★

Then in 1960 came Pomp and Circumstance. *Set in Noël's imaginary South Sea island of Samolo, one of the few remaining outposts of the Empire, it tells of the impact on the locals at the prospect of a royal visit. 'My novel is so light,' he wrote to his American publishers, 'that you will have difficulty capturing it between hard covers.'*

'It is gay and irreverent and with little sentiment and no significance . . . I know that my greatest gift is comedy and this gives me wonderful opportunities for all sorts of irrelevancies, because my heroine has a light mind and through her I can have a lot of fun with all the colonial types.'

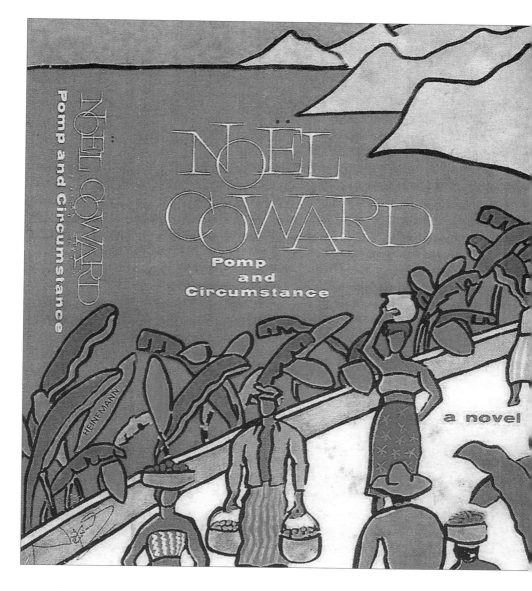

The story is narrated by Griselda ('Grizel'), the wife of a local planter
and old friend of Lady Sandra Shotter, the Governor's wife. Naturally,
everyone on the island who considers themselves part of the elite –
which is everyone – is determined to take part in a suitably
magnificent event in honour of their visitors.

And, naturally, there must be a committee meeting to decide who does
what . . .

POMP AND CIRCUMSTANCE

The meeting of the Samolan Amateur Dramatic Society (or SADS) took place in the back room of the Art Institute. I arrived a few minutes late, having had the usual difficulty of finding somewhere to park the car. Everybody was standing about gossiping, and a long table was impressively set out with pads and pencils and individual ash trays. I greeted Buddha and Dusty and Cuckoo Honey, who was wearing a tiny hat with a knob on the top, like the lid of a jar of preserved ginger. Alma Peacock, impressive in a flowing print with an eye-searing pattern of white pineapples on a pink background, took the chair and we all arranged ourselves round the table. Alma is an admirable character in many respects. She is kindly, resolute, enthusiastic, and industrious. Under her ebullient leadership the SADS, which she started from scratch many years ago, has certainly achieved some creditable if occasionally overambitious productions. There is, however, something about her personality, a certain incongruous schoolgirlishness, which always makes me want to laugh whenever I look at her. On the other hand Ivy Poland, who runs a dancing school in Queen Street and has achieved local fame with her 'Ivy Poland Dancers', without whose ardent modern posturing no annual pantomime is complete, retains no endearing aura of long-ago School Theatrics. She is professional to the core, sharp as a needle, and is reputed, when unduly irritated, to fly into ungovernable rages. Her mouth droops a trifle at the corners, and it is not difficult to envisage her whacking the shins of the I. P. Dancers with a cane when their jetés and coupés are clumsily executed. It *is* difficult however, looking at her now, a small grey woman in her middle forties, to imagine her in her far-off heyday as a ballroom dancer floating glamorously into the Palm Court of the Grand Hotel, Folkestone, on the arm of some agile and suitably betailed male partner, and more difficult still to picture her in even earlier years flitting through the enchanted forest of *Where the Rainbow Ends* as a will-o'-the-wisp. Nevertheless that, we are led to believe, is her authentic background and it would ill become any of us in our distant colonial isolation to question it. It is scarcely necessary to add that there exists between her and Alma a state of decently veiled hostility which only on very rare occasions has been permitted to blaze into open warfare. The rest of the committee, apart from Buddha, Dusty, Cuckoo, and myself, consists of Peter Glades and Esmond Templar, who landed hand in hand on the island in 1949 and set up an antiques shop, Michael Tremlett, Brinsley Martin, and Keela Alioa. Brinsley Martin is our main character actor and is chiefly remarkable for his prowess at elaborate make-up. He has seldom appeared in any production, wigged, padded, lined, and crêpe-haired, without a spontaneous round of applause at his first entrance. On one or two occasions, however, his passion for visual characterization has led to disaster as on the famous night when he was playing the inquisitor to Letty Togstone's St Joan and his entire nose fell with a soft thud into her outstretched hands. Michael Tremlett, although lacking any outstanding histrionic ability, is an efficient stage manager; Peter Glades and Esmond Templar are enthusiastic but occasionally petulant artistic supervisors, and Keela Alioa, our star turn as an actor, is on the committee in an honorary capacity as representative of Samolan interests. He is in his mid-twenties and extremely handsome, and his performance of Hamlet in modern dress was the talk of the island. It was an all-Samolan production, and as their idea of modern dress consisted mostly of brilliantly coloured sarongs the visual effect was quite enchanting.

When we were all seated and the buzz of conversation and the scraping of chairs had died down, Alma whacked the table with a little hammer and embarked on a lengthy speech which glowed with royalist enthusiasm and was peppered with splendid phrases such as 'Allegiance to the Crown' and 'Our Imperial Visitors' and 'Showing the Flag', etc. When she had finished and sat down amid a few grunts of assent and muttered 'hear hears' everyone began talking at once until she had to whack the table again for silence.

There is something about well-intentioned, amateur committee meetings that induces in me a feeling of claustrophobia, I feel trapped and hopeless and quite incapable of constructive thought or concentration, and this one was no exception to the rule. It droned on for two solid hours, during which time I drew hideous faces on the piece of paper in front of me. Hot sunlight filtered through the slats of the venetian blind, and outside in the street the noise of gears changing and dogs barking and klaxons hooting made it difficult at moments to catch what anyone was saying, and everyone, as usual, was saying a great deal. It was finally decided after many impracticable suggestions had been put forward and discarded that an ordinary theatrical production in the local Playhouse would be inadequate and that what was needed was something on a much larger scale. At this point Cuckoo Honey sprang to her feet and delivered a stirring eulogy of a military tattoo she had seen in Darjeeling when she was a little girl – 'It really was magnificent,' she said, her nose growing quite pink with remembered emotion. 'The Cavalry came charging through a gap in the hills and all the people who had been besieged in a fort for weeks cheered and cried and then the fort went up in flames and everyone sang "Abide with Me".'

'A curious moment to choose,' said Buddha in a loud whisper, but Cuckoo ignored this and went on. 'What I really mean is,' she said, 'that it made a tremendous impression on the natives, and I do honestly think that we should try to do something on those lines. After all we *are* a British colony and we have got the Royal Shropshires.'

'We have also got several gaps in the hills,' said Dusty, 'but I still don't think a military tattoo is quite the answer.'

'Speaking as the only "native" present,' said Keela with gentle acidity, 'I cannot feel that my brother Samolans at this present time would be so easily impressed by sudden chargings and flames and a great display of British militancy. It would puzzle them, and when Samolans are puzzled they laugh.'

'It was only an idea.' Cuckoo sat down rather crossly.

'What about a lovely medieval pageant?' suggested Esmond Templar. 'With the Knights of the Round Table and everybody in armour and wimples and that sort of thing.'

'I should think that would puzzle the Samolans into hysterics!' said Dusty.

Alma rose to her feet authoritatively. 'Our main object,' she said sternly, 'is not only to entertain the inhabitants of our island but to give pleasure to our royal visitors.'

'Hear hear,' murmured Peter Glades and giggled. Alma shot him a disapproving look and continued, 'I have, as you know, given this matter a lot of thought and I am aware that we have very little time at our disposal, but I am convinced that what we really should do is to present Her Majesty with something that she could see nowhere else, something indigenous to our island and entirely Samolan. Ivy is in complete agreement with me over this . . .' She smiled at Ivy Poland, who nodded austerely. 'We discussed it yesterday after the Bleekers' cocktail party, and as the idea was originally hers I now take pleasure in asking her to explain it to the committee.' Alma sat down and there was a slight pause while Ivy blew her nose delicately and rose to her feet.

'The idea is this,' she said modestly. 'An historical water pageant.' She paused, unfortunately long enough to allow Buddha to mutter 'Good God!' and then went on. 'We thought of telling the story of the island beginning with the legend of FumFumBolo in which my girls could do a ballet as water sprites. Then the landing of Captain Cobb and the missionaries and so on right up to the present day. We also' – she smiled encouragingly at Cuckoo – 'thought of enlisting the aid of the Royal Shropshires, in fact I have already telephoned Colonel Shelton warning him that we might call on him to help us. They are a fine body of men and would do splendidly for pirates in the earlier scenes . . .'

'Where on earth do you propose to do all this?' interrupted Buddha.

'Cobb's Cove,' replied Ivy triumphantly. 'It would make an ideal setting. We have it planned in our minds. We could have grandstands built round the semicircular beach and the two headlands would provide wonderful wings for entrances and exits. The Samolan Electrical Company and the Royal Shropshires between them could organize the floodlighting. We also propose to ask Kerry Stirling to write the libretto, probably in blank verse, and persuade dear Inky Blumenthal to compose a score based on traditional Samolan folk music – you all know how brilliant he is at that sort of thing – and we thought, as a grand finale, that the church choir, which we've got to use anyway, could come sailing in on a barge singing, while the Royal Shropshires, having changed back into their uniforms, would march down that path from behind the Turlings' bungalow and assemble on the beach and do a sort of trooping of the colours!' She paused, smiling expectantly, and then rather abruptly sat down. There was silence for a moment or two, which was broken by Esmond Templar clapping his hands and crying enthusiastically that it was a marvellous idea.

'It's not "trooping *of* the *colours*",' said Buddha. 'It's "trooping the colour".'

'I remember being taken to see it for the first time when I was a tiny little girl,' said Cuckoo. 'Daddy had six months' leave and we stayed at the Hyde Park Hotel and I cried my eyes out!'

'The Hyde Park Hotel can be depressing,' murmured Dusty.

'Come, come,' cried Alma firmly, 'to our muttons!'

From then on everyone began talking at once and the noise was deafening.

Eventually, inevitably, the day of the dress rehearsal arrives.

Presently, when the excitement had died down a little, the band of the Royal Shropshires, which was huddled, a trifle insecurely I thought, on a wooden rostrum under an umbrella of wild almond trees, began to tune up with little irrelevant trills and glissandi on the trumpets and wood winds and intermittent bangings on the drums. Ever since I was taken to my first pantomime at the age of nine this particular sound has enchanted me. It evokes nostalgic memories of warmth and plush and gold: of squeezing sixpences into slots to release tiny pairs of opera glasses: of sudden, thrilling darkness followed by footlights glowing on red velvet curtains: of feverish anticipation, excited wriggling, and chocolates in silver paper. I have never outgrown this special joy, although the present-day theatres of our welfare state with either no music at all or a panatrope scratching away in an empty orchestra pit concealed by dusty greenery have dampened it considerably and provide little prelude to glamour. However, I managed to recapture a small whiff of it sitting there looking out over the dark sea with the band tuning up and the lights glimmering in the trees.

The audience reseated themselves on their chairs and benches amid a babble of conversation which was drowned out by the band embarking briskly on a selection from *The Pirates of Penzance*.

'The dear Royal Shropshires,' said Sandra. 'They're always right up-to-the-minute, aren't they?'

'Inky Blumenthal's overture isn't orchestrated yet,' I said, leaning forward. 'The only alternatives to this were *The Indian Love Lyrics*, *The Gondoliers*, and *William Tell*.'

'We shall probably get the lot before the evening's over.' Sandra produced her glasses from her bag and studied the programme. 'I'm afraid it's going to be a long job.'

At the end of the overture the lights in the trees went out all except one which stayed on, resolutely pinpointing Mrs Innes-Glendower, who was sitting in the front row wearing a multi-coloured Chinese coat and a glittering Spanish comb embedded in her bright blue hair. She fidgeted unhappily in the glare and shaded her eyes with her hand. There were some muffled shouts, and Alma's voice rang out authoritatively from the darkness. 'If it won't go out by itself somebody must climb up and *turn* it out!' There was a short pause and the sound of further argument until a small boy dashed out on to the sand, shinnied up the tree like a monkey, and wrestled valiantly with the lamp. He managed to shift it slowly round so that it illuminated each of the occupants of the front row in turn, including old Sir Albert, who shrank back in his seat and placed a handkerchief over his head. Finally the poor boy, obviously in the grip of mounting panic, shook the lamp violently with the result that it broke away from its moorings and fell with a dull thud on to the beach where it was pounced upon by two policemen who staggered away with it into the shadows. The little boy slid down the tree to vociferous applause and the band struck up the opening bars of Inky Blumenthal's water music.

While this was going on, Captain Gedge and Lieutenant Proctor of the Royal Shropshires, both of whom had had previous experience of Military Tattoos at Aldershot, switched on two searchlights from each side of the cove and Keela Alioa was discovered standing facing the sea with his back to us with his arms outstretched to the stars. The small waves were breaking over his feet and he turned slowly, with exquisite grace, and walked out of the sea towards us. He was wearing a short silver tunic, and in the bright light his dark skin shone like polished mahogany. He began to speak, but his first words were lost in a spontaneous burst of applause. We were all well used to Keela's good looks, but the picture of this handsome young Samolan standing there against the night was suddenly breathtaking.

'Well,' said Sandra, clapping vigorously. 'It's started with a nice sexy bang at any rate, hasn't it?'

Keela certainly spoke the prologue resonantly and well but alas, the lines themselves fell a good way below his rendering of them. Kerry Stirling, although he was Samolo's literary lion and had written a number of successful novels reeking with local atmosphere, obviously had no more than a nodding acquaintance with the poetic muse. His verse, hovering uneasily between Scott, Macaulay, and Ella Wheeler Wilcox, was at its best merely serviceable and at its worst almost excruciatingly banal. There was a great deal of heavy-handed allegory interspersed with flowery rhyming couplets such as:

> 'Long long ago in Time's primaeval dawn
> This island paradise, in fire, was born
> And fire and water, striving hand in hand
> Wrought, on this desolate, small coral strand
> Strange music where, as yet, no birds had sung
> And whilst the ancient universe, still young,
> Gazed down upon a sea of azure blue
> Amazed to see a miracle come true,
> Far out, beyond the breaker's thundrous boom,
> Other small islets born of Neptune's womb
> Rose up like jewels from the deeps below
> Thus to create our archipelago.'

'Fancy Neptune having a womb!' whispered Sandra. 'I always saw him as rather a hearty type.'

When the prologue ended, Keela, with his arms still raised in a gesture of invocation, turned slowly, walked into the sea, and with a graceful dive disappeared from view. The lights went out, and in a silence after the applause had died away we distinctly heard Alma's voice say 'Now!' in a piercing whisper. There was the sound of whispering and scuffling in the darkness; the lights came on again, and from down the gangways on each side of the grandstand Ivy Poland's sprites bounded on to the beach where they arranged themselves, a little breathlessly, into a stylized tableau. They were dressed in diaphanous sea-green chiffon, long flowing green wigs to represent seaweed, and necklaces of coral-pink shells. They held the tableau gallantly for a long time, occasionally shooting anxious glances at the band, which remained discouragingly mute. Finally, after some audible hissing in the direction of the bandstand, the music began and they started their dance. It was a pretty enough dance although not startlingly original and they executed it charmingly, but it didn't really come to life until Tauhua Tali suddenly appeared from the outer darkness glittering like a dragonfly in peacock blue and did a quite enchanting *pas de deux* partnered by Kokoano, Juanita's head beach boy, who wore nothing but gilded bathing trunks and looked like a dusky Greek god who had been touched up by Gauguin. This brought forth storms of applause and they were recalled over and over again.

One of the principal difficulties in the original planning of the pageant was the almost monotonous tranquillity of Samolan history. Whereas other Pacific islands had had their full quota of wars, invasions, human sacrifices, and bloodshed, the Samolan archipelago had basked peacefully and cheerfully in its eternal sunshine for centuries. True, there had been a gentle whisper of incipient revolution in 1791 when it had been considered advisable to ask King Kopalalua III to abdicate, but this had been swiftly hushed by the willing co-operation of Kopalalua himself, who after a feast lasting for three days and nights, made a public announcement to his subjects. This announcement stated candidly and with dignity that, as he found no personal satisfaction in intercourse with the opposite sex and could therefore contribute little to the future of the dynasty, he thought it wiser to retire with his private entourage to the island of Tunaike and leave the ruling of Samolo to his nephew, young Prince Kefumalani, who, although still in his teens, had already proved that his procreative capabilities were beyond question. Esmond Templar and Peter Glades had enthusiastically voted that this historical incident should be included in the pageant but had been sharply overruled by the rest of the committee.

As it was, the pageant had been divided into two parts, the first of which dealt mainly with fantasy and the ancient legends, including the famous eruption of FumFumBolo. This, although technically complicated, went smoothly and was most effective. Tauhua Tali and Kokoano played FumFum the goddess of fire and Bolo the god of water, respectively. An enormous raft with the volcano built on to it was towed, under cover of darkness, from behind the left headland and, when suddenly illuminated by searchlights, erupted entirely satisfactorily. When the applause for this had died away the lights were swivelled back on to the beach again and the Royal Shropshires, dressed picturesquely as pirates, came whooping and shrieking down the two side gangways and engaged each other in a tremendous battle with pikes and cutlasses, eventually, as the lights faded, leaving many of each other for dead. This was enjoyed, not only by the audience, but very much indeed by the Royal Shropshires.

The finale of the first half was the historic landing of Captain Evangelus Cobb with his cargo of missionaries and their reception on the beach by King Kefumalani and his retinue. It had originally been intended to show the actual shipwreck with *The Good Samaritan* breaking up on the rocks. But this idea had been abandoned when Peter Glades had pointed out that for a ship to break up on rocks in perfectly calm water would not only be expensive and difficult to do, but would inevitably cast a slur on the heroic Captain Cobb's skill as a navigator. It had therefore been decided that the wreck must be *presumed* to have taken place out of sight behind the headland and that the survivors, battered and and exhausted by a *presumed* tempest, should appear out of the darkness in one of the ship's boats.

All this went according to plan except that poor Letty Togstone, who had made a striking success last season as Mrs Alving in *Ghosts,* was stricken down by malignant fate in what should have been her moment of triumph. As Mrs Brunstock, the chief evangelist missionary, she had to spring on to the prow of the boat when it was only a few yards from shore, clad in a long white shift with a blood-stained bandage round her head, and declaim exultantly with arms outstretched:

> 'Land – Land! The Blessed Land at last.
> The storm is over and the tempest past.
> Thanks be to Thee, dear Lord, our faith sufficed
> To carry to these isles the Word of Christ!'

This dramatic moment had been meticulously directed by Alma Peacock and, at the last few rehearsals with the band playing 'Nearer My God to Thee' in the minor and Letty Togstone giving the full force of her voice, many onlookers, including Madame Alice and the Fumbasi brothers, had been reduced to tears. Tonight however, owing to nerves, perhaps, she miscalculated her leap on to the prow and teetered dangerously on the edge. Michael Tremlett, who was navigating the boat slowly from the stern with a muffled outboard motor, perceiving poor Letty's plight, suddenly, in a misguided effort to help, slammed the engine into reverse, whereupon she tumbled head foremost into the sea. Even then the situation might have been saved if she hadn't unfortunately repeated the word 'Christ!' as she struck the water.

There was a horrified gasp from the audience and then, as she surfaced, an uncontrollable roar of laughter. She disregarded this with magnificent presence of mind, waded ashore, and sank gracefully at the feet of King Kefumalani, who, bending forward to lift her up, struck her sharply on the head as he did so. With a loud cry of pain she fell back on to the sand again and from that moment on the scene went to pieces. Michael Tremlett, unnerved by his previous error, switched the engine to full speed ahead and the boat shot forward and grounded on the beach with such force that Captain Cobb and the missionaries fell into a heap. The audience's laughter rose to a hysterical pitch, the band played a crashing chord, and all the lights went out. Unhappily they came on again a moment or two later disclosing the missionaries clambering out of the boat, Letty Togstone in floods of tears, and Alma Peacock in a gold lamé dress, up to her knees in water, gesticulating furiously at Michael Tremlett.

After this debacle there was a twenty minutes' interval during which we retired to the Anteroom behind the royal box.

★

Presently the lights flickered on and off, there was a long roll of drums from the band, and we all returned to our seats.

'Hold on to your hats,' said Sandra. 'We're off again.'

The lights dimmed and went out and suddenly, from the two headlands, the little bay was brilliantly illuminated. In the middle of it, a few yards from shore, was moored the raft that earlier on had held the erupting volcano. It now held the Ladies' Church Choir in full strength. The singers were arranged in three tiers and stood immobile, staring fixedly at their leader, Mrs Lamont, who, vast in black satin, was standing, baton raised, in a small flat-bottomed dinghy just below their eye line. The dinghy was kept in position by two Samolan boys, one in the bow and one in the stern, each clasping an oar.

Owing to a slight miscalculation the Royal Shropshires hadn't quite finished playing the *William Tell* 'Overture' when the lights came on. Realizing this, the band leader, Sergeant Major Brocklehurst, increased the tempo violently, but there was still an appreciable time lag before the music crashed to an untidy conclusion, during which Mrs Lamont shot baleful looks over her shoulder at the bandstand.

To Mrs Lamont the Ladies' Church Choir was the be-all and end-all of existence, the sum total of her dreams and the golden apple of her eye. She rehearsed it interminably year in year out; fought tigerishly in defence of its rights and monotonously insisted on its appearance at any and every public function where it could conceivably be appropriate. For this occasion Alma

Peacock had suggested that the choir's routine costumes of plain white Mother Hubbards banded with red, blue, and violet ribbons to distinguish the sopranos, mezzos, and contraltos, should be abandoned in favour of native dress. But Mrs Lamont, deaf to all entreaty, had stood firm. Vainly had Alma and Ivy pleaded that as the scene represented the first burgeoning of Christianity on the island which took place early in the nineteenth century, the coloured sarongs and gay brassières of the period would not only be effective but a great deal more accurate from the pomt of view of atmosphere, but Mrs Lamont had remained obdurate. The Ladies' Church Choir was primarily a religious body, she argued, and as such could not be expected to jettison the insignia by which it was so justly famed and impair its high dignity by romping about in the wanton apparel of a pagan age. Finally, after much heated discussion and a lot of acrimonious correspondence, Alma and Ivy were forced to give in and Mrs Lamont won the day. So here they were, those serried ranks of white-covered bosoms and exalted brown faces, looking as they had always looked and standing as they had always stood, except that on this occasion a slightly ambulant raft had been substituted for the more familiar terra firma of the Town Hall.

At the long-awaited end of the overture there was a short pause. Mrs Lamont raised her baton still higher, Sandra gave an audible groan, and the Ladies' Church Choir burst forth.

The oratorio, 'Blessed the Hearts That Suddenly See' was, in Inky Blumenthal's opinion at least, the high spot of his musical score. He had worked over it laboriously for weeks, and poor Kerry Stirling had been driven to the verge of a nervous breakdown by having to rewrite the verses no less than eleven times. Not that he need have bothered, because the Ladies' Church Choir in all their years of triumph had never been known to enunciate a single word that was even remotely comprehensible. However, the sounds they made were generally considered to be of high quality, and when they all opened their mouths together and let fly, as they were required to do in the opening bars of Inky's opus, the impact was considerable.

There was no escaping the fact that 'Blessed the Hearts That Suddenly See', musically speaking, was a pretentious hash-up of Handel, Elgar, and Verdi with, alas, none of the melodic quality of any of them. It was also far far too long. We sat there battered into a state of hypnotic resignation watching glumly the rows of bosoms rising and falling, the numberless mouths opening and shutting, and Mrs Lamont flailing the air with her arms and rocking the dinghy dangerously with her feet. After a while I closed my eyes and tried to shut my ears and my mind to what was going on and concentrate on something entirely different. Suddenly, however, I became conscious of an extra sound over and above the incessant booming and trilling. A queer, metallic whining noise that seemed to be growing in volume. I opened my eyes again and saw that the raft was rocking alarmingly. At this moment, with a shriek and a roar, the storm struck. There were a few screams from the audience and a panic-stricken rush for the exits. The skies opened and a curtain of rain, shining like glass spears in the searchlights, crashed down on to the sea obliterating completely the raft, the choir, Mrs Lamont, and even the palm trees a few feet away from us. We all instinctively rose from our seats and crowded up into the back of the grandstand to get as much cover as we could, but it was of little avail because the wind was blowing straight into the cove and within a few seconds we were all drenched to the bone.

'This,' said Sandra through chattering teeth, 'comes under the heading of "An Act of God", and I must say I'm on His side.' . . .

There we stood, huddled into a sodden little group waiting for the first violence of the storm to die down. After what seemed an age there was indeed a slight lull. The force of the wind lessened and the density of the rain thinned out.

'Oh Lord!' cried Sandra. 'Look at the church choir!'

We all looked, and the sight that met our eyes will be emblazoned on my memory for ever and a day. On the first impact of the storm the raft had broken loose from its moorings and begun to drift away towards the open sea. At the same moment, apparently, the dinghy had capsized and was now floating upside down with Mrs Lamont lying across it like a large black seal supported on each side by the two fisher boys. The choir itself, Samolan-born and bred from the biggest contralto to the smallest soprano and therefore as at home in the water as on dry land, appeared, at the same moment to arrive at a unanimous decision. In almost perfect unison they tore off their coloured ribbons, whipped their white robes over their heads, and in varying states of nudity dived into the turbulent waves and struck out firmly for the shore. At this moment the wind struck again with a renewed shriek, and a fresh deluge of rain blotted the scene from view.

'If only they'd done that in the first place,' said Sandra, 'it would have brought the house down.'

THE FILMS

'Films are not an offshoot of the stage.
They are a totally different medium.'

Noël in an interview with *Picturegoer*, August 1927

★

'I'm not very keen on Hollywood . . .
I'd rather have a nice cup of cocoa, really.'

Noël in a letter to his mother, *c.* 1930

'ALL MY PLAYS EXCEPTING CAVALCADE HAVE BEEN
VULGARIZED DISTORTED AND RUINED BY MOVIE MINDS
STOP AM NOW MIDDLE AGED AND PRESTIGE AND
QUALITY OF MY WORK ARE MY ONLY ASSETS FOR THE
FUTURE STOP THEREFORE HAVE DECIDED HENCE-
FORWARD NEVER TO SELL FILM RIGHTS UNLESS I HAVE
ABSOLUTE CONTROL OF SCRIPT DIALOGUE CAST TREAT-
MENT DIRECTOR CAMERAMAN CUTTER AND PUBLICITY
STOP CONVINCED PRESENT UNAVOIDABLE LOSS IS
FUTURE INEVITABLE GAIN STOP'

Cable from Noël to his US Manager, Jack Wilson, 1942

There was something more than a little surrealistic about the early efforts to put Noël's work on film.

His play The Vortex *put him on the theatrical map in 1924 and, after due time for reflection, the fledgling British film industry – specifically Michael Balcon at Gainsborough Studios – decided Coward was the stuff movies were made of. In 1927–28 Gainsborough made films of* The Queen Was in the Parlour, Easy Virtue *and* The Vortex.

There was just one problem. The silver screen was still silent and a Coward play without the Coward dialogue was thin stuff. The director had to compensate with title cards – and Noël didn't even write them!

In fact, there were other problems. Competitive ego was one. Easy Virtue *was an early outing for Alfred Hitchcock and he reorganized the material significantly. It might have ended up better cinematically but it was not Coward – and that was a problem Noël would continue to suffer from, even when sound came in at the end of the decade.*

Another was the film censor. Balcon sent an assistant to the censor's office with a tentative script for The Vortex. *He returned bearing glad tidings. The script was fine – with a few changes. The mother could not have a lover and, of course, the son could not take drugs . . .*

Noël's work fared a little better in the early sound era. He found the Hollywood Private Lives *of 1931 'passable' but the* Tonight Is Ours *(based on* The Queen Was in the Parlour) *in the following year an experience that left him 'exhausted from the strain of trying to disentangle my own dialogue from the utter mediocrity that the Paramount screen writers had added to it'.*

Cavalcade *in the same year was in a different class altogether and won the Oscar as Best Film. Ten years later he would write: 'Of all my plays,* Cavalcade *had been filmed with taste and integrity.' It was, he felt, 'superior in every way than if I personally had been connected with the actual production'.*

However, Design for Living *(1933) not only had its ménage à trois storyline eviscerated, but scriptwriter Ben Hecht boasted that he had removed every line but one of Noël's original dialogue.*

*In that same year there was a respectable British production of his
musical* Bitter-Sweet *with Anna Neagle in the lead, but Hollywood
did its best to do its worst with its Technicolor version of 1940, starring
Jeanette MacDonald and Nelson Eddy. Noël wrote to his secretary,
Lorn Loraine:*

'It is, on all counts, far and away the worst picture I have ever
seen. MacDonald and Eddy sing relentlessly from beginning to
end looking like a rawhide suitcase and a rocking horse
respectively . . . Miss M's hair gets redder and redder until you
want to scream. Oh, dear, money or no money, I wish we'd
hung on to that veto.'

★

It took the Second World War to change things for the better. In Future
Indefinite *Noël tells of how, in mid-1941,*

'a deputation of three gentlemen . . . called on me at the Savoy
Hotel. I received them warily because I knew that the object of
their visit was to persuade me to make a film, and I had no
intention of making a film then or at any other time . . . I had
convinced myself, with easy sophistry, that [film-making] was a
soul-destroying industry in which actors of mediocre talent
were publicized and idolized beyond their deserts, and authors,
talented or otherwise, were automatically massacred.'

*By when the 'deputation' left, they had Noël's promise at least to
consider the proposition. The following day he happened to be having
dinner with his old friend, Louis Mountbatten, who was serving with
the Royal Navy. Mountbatten told him how his command, the
destroyer HMS* Kelly, *had recently been sunk off the coast of Crete.
Noël knew at once that he had his story.*

*Inspiration had come quickly but implementation was infinitely harder.
It took influence from Mountbatten and even King George VI himself
to overcome bureaucratic resistance. One problem was that Noël intended
to play the leading role of Captain Kinross − a character based almost
too closely on Mountbatten − himself. Another was that his command,
the HMS Torrin (a.k.a. Kelly) is also lost − a fact that was considered
to be negative propaganda for the war effort. It took the King to point
out that 'although the ship is lost, the spirit which animates the Royal*

Navy is clearly brought out in the men and the procession of ships coming along to take its place at the end and demonstrates the power of the Navy'.

The film In Which We Serve *went ahead – its title being taken from a Naval 'prayer to be used at sea'. ('Be pleased to receive into thy Almighty and most Gracious protection the persons of us thy servants, and the Fleet in which we serve.')*

What set the film apart was not so much the battle scenes as the use of 'thy servants'. Noël – having been advised by co-director David Lean to study Orson Welles's acclaimed Citizen Kane *– borrowed the flashback technique to create a deeper human context. We see the ship torpedoed and the survivors floating in the water, clinging to a life raft, watching her slowly sink. Then, one by one, we see something of each man's personal story.*

The film was an immediate and lasting success. The critic C. A. Lejeune concluded: 'His heart has sneaked up on Mr Coward. In Which We Serve *never gushes, but there is a subtle warmth in the old astringency. For the first time he seems to be speaking, not to the select but to the simple.'*

The casting was considered to be impeccable. John Mills, Celia Johnson (as Mrs Kinross), Bernard Miles, Joyce Carey, Michael Wilding, Kay Walsh, Kathleen Harrison – and Richard Attenborough in his first film role.

★

IN WHICH WE SERVE

(1942)

CAPT. 'D' KINROSS	Noël Coward
SHORTY BLAKE	John Mills
WALTER HARDY	Bernard Miles
ALIX (MRS KINROSS)	Celia Johnson
FLAGS	Michael Wilding
NUMBER ONE	Derek Elphinstone
NARRATOR	Leslie Howard

Produced by Two Cities, directed by Noël Coward and David Lean
Released 27 September 1942

NARRATOR   This is the story of a ship . . .

*In early sequences we see the HMS Torrin being built. Now it is
fully commissioned and Captain Kinross addresses his new crew:*

STUDIO EXT. PLYMOUTH QUAYSIDE. DAY.

>*Close shot,* CAPTAIN *and* NUMBER ONE.

NUMBER ONE   Ship's company present, sir.

CAPTAIN   (*acknowledging salute*) Thank you – stand them at ease, please.

NUMBER ONE   Aye, aye, sir. (*To ship's company.*) Ship's company – stand at – ease.

>*The* CAPTAIN *advances and climbs on to a bollard. He stands for a moment looking over the troops.*

CAPTAIN   Break ranks and gather round me.

STUDIO EXT. PLYMOUTH QUAYSIDE. DAY.

>*Long shot with* CAPTAIN 'D' *in the foreground and the* MEN *breaking ranks. The* CAPTAIN *beckons them nearer.*

CAPTAIN   Come a bit nearer – I don't want to have to shout. Can you hear me all right in the back row?

SAILOR   (*in back row*) Yes, sir – we can hear you fine.

STUDIO EXT. PLYMOUTH QUAYSIDE. DAY.

>*Long shot, different angle, with the* MEN *in foreground, and* CAPTAIN *in the background.*

CAPTAIN   Good. You all know that it is the custom of the Service for the Captain to address the ship's company on commissioning day to give them his policy and tell them the ship's programme. Now my policy is easy and if there are any here who have served with me before, they will know what it is. Are there any old shipmates of mine here?

>*About half a dozen hands go up eagerly in different parts of the crowd.*

STUDIO EXT. PLYMOUTH QUAYSIDE. DAY.

>*Close shot,* CAPTAIN 'D' *as he recognizes them one by one.*

CAPTAIN   Glad to see you again, Johnson.

STUDIO EXT. PLYMOUTH QUAYSIDE. DAY.

Medium shot, JOHNSON *in the crowd. The camera zip-pans to a group which includes* COOMBE.

CAPTAIN   (*off*) . . . and Coombe . . .

Zip-pan to ADAMS.

CAPTAIN   (*off*) . . . and Adams . . .

Zip-pan to REYNOLDS.

CAPTAIN   (*off*) . . . and Reynolds . . .

The camera zip-pans to another group. We see a hand sticking up behind the heftily built CHIEF STOKER.

STUDIO EXT. PLYMOUTH QUAYSIDE. DAY.

Close shot, the CAPTAIN.

CAPTAIN   Who's that small fellow hiding his face behind the Chief Stoker?

STUDIO EXT. PLYMOUTH QUAYSIDE. DAY.

Medium shot, the CROWD. *There is a general murmur of laughter as* PARKINSON *steps clear.*

PARKINSON   Parkinson, sir.

STUDIO EXT. PLYMOUTH QUAYSIDE. DAY.

Close up, the CAPTAIN.

CAPTAIN   You were Cox'n of the 'All Comers' whaler in the Valletta, weren't you?

STUDIO EXT. PLYMOUTH QUAYSIDE. DAY.

Close up, PARKINSON.

PARKINSON   I was that, sir, when we won the 'All Comers' cup in the 1936 regatta.

STUDIO EXT. PLYMOUTH QUAYSIDE. DAY.

Close up, the CAPTAIN.

CAPTAIN   Yes, and fell into the ditch when you got back to the ship.

STUDIO EXT. PLYMOUTH QUAYSIDE. DAY.

Long shot, over the CAPTAIN's *shoulder. There is loud laughter. The tension of the new ship's company is lightened, and a friendly, more free and easy air comes over them.*

CAPTAIN   Well, there are enough old shipmates to tell the others what my policy has always been. Johnson, Coombe, Adams, Reynolds, Parkinson – what sort of a ship do I want the *Torrin* to be? (*There is a slight pause.*) Come on, Reynolds?

STUDIO EXT. PLYMOUTH QUAYSIDE. DAY.

Close up, REYNOLDS.

REYNOLDS   A happy ship, sir.

STUDIO EXT. PLYMOUTH QUAYSIDE. DAY.

Close up, CAPTAIN.

CAPTAIN   That's right.

STUDIO EXT. PLYMOUTH QUAYSIDE. DAY.

Close up, COOMBE.

COOMBE   An efficient ship, sir.

STUDIO EXT. PLYMOUTH QUAYSIDE. DAY.

Medium shot, the CAPTAIN.

CAPTAIN   Correct. A happy and efficient ship. A very happy and a very efficient ship. Some of you might think I am a bit ambitious wanting both but, in my experience you can't have one without the other. A ship can't be happy unless she's efficient, and she certainly won't be efficient unless she's happy. Now for our programme. You've most of you seen the commissioning programme of the *Torrin* published in Plymouth General Orders, and you will have noted that this allows the customary three weeks. In peace-time it takes all of three weeks to get a new ship's company together, to let them sling their hammocks and teach them their stations and various duties, to get all the cordite and shells and oil fuel and stores on board and so on and so forth. Well, you've read your papers and you know that Ribbentrop signed a non-aggression pact with Stalin yesterday. As I see it, that means war next week, so I will give you not three *weeks* but exactly three *days* to get this ship ready to sail. None of us will take off our clothes or sling our hammocks or turn in for the next three days and nights until the job is finished, then we'll send Hitler a telegram saying 'The *Torrin's* ready – you can start your war!'

The film experienced its normal quota of technical problems but Noël himself encountered one he had never expected – his own voice. West End audiences had attuned their ears to the clipped Coward delivery but not so the Denham Studios sound technicians, and after the 'happy ship is an efficient ship' speech a sound man was heard to ask if someone would please tell Mr Coward to watch his enunciation during that 'fish and chips speech'.

Before the ship sails there is a party in the Wardroom for the immediate families of the senior crew. One of them, 'Flags', has just become engaged and Kinross (Captain 'D') persuaded his wife, Alix, to toast the happy couple . . .

INT. WARDROOM. NIGHT.

            Close up, ALIX.

ALIX   (*to* 'FLAGS' *and his fiancée,* MAUREEN) Stop whispering, you two – Number One, you ought never to have put them next to each other.

INT. WARDROOM. NIGHT.

> *Close up,* CAPTAIN 'D'.

CAPTAIN We ought to drink to them. Come on, everybody – to the 'newly betrothed'.

INT. WARDROOM. NIGHT.

> *Long shot, the table as seen between* 'FLAGS' *and* MAUREEN.

EVERYBODY To the 'newly betrothed'.

> *They all drink.*

BOBBY What's 'betrothed', Daddy?

CAPTAIN The beginning of the end, my boy.

'FLAGS' On behalf of my fiancée and myself – thank you very kindly.

INT. WARDROOM. NIGHT.

> *Close up,* CAPTAIN 'D'.

CAPTAIN Alix, as 'Flags' and Maureen are so bashful – I think it only right and proper that you should make a speech.

INT. WARDROOM. NIGHT.

> *Medium shot: the* GROUP *around* ALIX.

ALIX No – no – I can't – honestly I can't . . .

NUMBER ONE Come on, Mrs Kinross – I'll support you.

MRS MACADOO Hear, hear – speech.

> EVERYBODY *calls for speech. Finally, still protesting,* ALIX *rises to her feet.*

ALIX Teddy, I swear I'll never forgive you for this. Oh dear – what am I to say?

CAPTAIN (*laughing*) Happy Christmas!

ALIX Just you wait.

CAPTAIN Come on now – silence, everybody – Her Worship the Lady Mayoress is about to declare the bazaar open . . .

NUMBER ONE Don't let him get you down, Mrs Kinross.

ALIX   Ladies and gentlemen – I'll begin by taking my husband's
            advice . . .

CAPTAIN   Hurray!

ALIX   . . . and wish you all a very, very happy Christmas. I'm sure
            that Mrs Farrell and Mrs Macadoo will back me up when
            I say I am going to deliver a word of warning – on behalf
            of all wretched naval wives – to Maureen, who has been
            unwise enough to decide on joining our ranks . . .

            General laughter and murmurs of 'hear-hear' from MRS
            FARRELL *and* MRS MACADOO.

INT. WARDROOM. NIGHT.

            Close two shot, MAUREEN *and* 'FLAGS'.

ALIX   (*off*) Dear Maureen – we all wish you every possible
            happiness but it's only fair to tell you in advance what
            you're in for . . .

'TORPS':   (*off*) Shame – shame!

INT. WARDROOM. NIGHT.

            Close up, ALIX.

ALIX   Speaking from bitter experience I can only say that the
            wife of a sailor is most profoundly to be pitied. To begin
            with her home life – what there is of it – has no stability
            whatever. She can never really settle down – she moves
            through a succession of other people's houses, flats and
            furnished rooms. She finds herself grappling with domestic
            problems in Hong Kong, Bermuda, Malta, or Weymouth –
            we will not deal with the question of pay! That is
            altogether too painful, but what we will deal with is the
            most important disillusionment of all and that is . . .

INT. WARDROOM. NIGHT.

            Close up, CAPTAIN 'D'.

CAPTAIN   Stop her, somebody – this is rank mutiny.

INT. WARDROOM. NIGHT.

> *Close up,* ALIX.

ALIX (*firmly*) That is, that wherever she goes, there is always in her life a permanent and undefeated rival – her husband's ship! Whether it be a sloop or a battleship, or a submarine or a destroyer . . . it holds first place in his heart – it comes before home, wife, children, everything. Some of us fight this and get badly mauled in the process – others, like myself, resign themselves to the inevitable. That is what you will have to do, my poor Maureen – that is what we all have to do if we want any peace of mind at all. Ladies and gentlemen, I give you my rival – it is extraordinary that anyone could be so fond and proud of their most implacable enemy – this ship – God bless this ship and all who sail in her.

> *She drinks as the scene dissolves.*

One of the film's most moving scenes takes place below decks between Walter Hardy and Shorty Blake.

INT. PETTY OFFICERS' MESS. DAY.

> *In the foreground of the picture is* WALTER, *writing a letter. In the background are* BRODIE, STEVENS, HOOPER *and* RIDGEWAY. BRODIE *and* STEVENS *are reading.* HOOPER *is doing his accounts.* WALTER *dips his pen in the ink and starts to write again.*

INT. PETTY OFFICERS' MESS. DAY.

> *Close up, Walter's letter.*

> 'My dear wife – well, here we are, old darling, in port again for a bit – so near and yet so far – as you might say.'

INT. PETTY OFFICERS' MESS. DAY.

> *Medium shot,* WALTER. *In the background* SHORTY *can be seen coming into the mess.*

WALTER	(*looking up and seeing* SHORTY) Hello, Shorty . . . come in.
	SHORTY *takes off his cap and comes up to* WALTER.
SHORTY	(*rather haltingly*) I – er – I just popped along to see if you'd had any news from home –
WALTER	Not so much as a PC . . . That's Kath all over – in all the years we've been married she's never got a post right yet. Have you heard from Freda?
SHORTY	Yes.
WALTER	How's she doing?
SHORTY	She's all right.
WALTER	(*noticing something strained in* SHORTY*'s manner*) What's the matter?
SHORTY	It's Kath, Walter . . . she and Mrs Lemmon . . . you see, they was all in the house together and – and it got blitzed . . .
WALTER	What do you mean?
SHORTY	(*miserably*) Kath got killed . . . both of them did – Freda was all right – she was under the stairs . . .
WALTER	(*after a pause*) Oh – oh, I see.
SHORTY	I thought I'd better tell you, seeing that – well – I mean . . .
WALTER	Thanks, son, I'm much obliged – thanks very much. (*He rises.*) I think I'll go out on deck for a bit . . .
SHORTY	Righto.
WALTER	(*as he moves away, he stops*) I'm glad Freda's all right.
SHORTY	(*with an attempt at a smile*) Yes – she's fine. (*Almost apologetically.*) We got a son.
WALTER	(*coming back and giving* SHORTY *a pat on the shoulder*) That's good . . . Congratulations.
	WALTER *walks away from camera into a long shot and goes out of the mess.*
	Dissolve to:

STUDIO EXT. QUARTER DECK. DAY. (B.P.)

> *Medium shot,* WALTER. *He reaches the extreme aft of the quarterdeck and looks towards the shore. He suddenly discovers that his unfinished letter to Kath is in his hand. He looks at it almost unseeingly for a moment, then crumples it up and throws it over the side.*

STUDIO EXT. (SMALL TANK.) DAY. (INSERT)

> *Close shot, the water, from above. The crumpled letter falls into the water and drifts away out of picture.*

Before – and indeed all the way through – production Noël and his colleagues were totally dependent on the support of the top naval brass. Mountbatten recommended that Noël invite the Second Sea Lord – the Admiralty Head of Personnel – to come along and see some of the rushes, since the Admiralty had lent the production an entire ship's company.

He was shown the scene above and Mountbatten recalled:

'The Admiral was very emotional. "By Jove, Coward," he said – "that convinces me you were right to ask for a proper ship's company, real sailors. No actors could possibly have done that."'

The Torrin *is sunk and most of her crew has perished with her. The survivors are taken to Alexandria to be reassigned to other ships. Kinross addresses them for the last time. It was perhaps the most difficult scene in the film as far as Noël was concerned.*

'I had to say goodbye, stand still and say goodbye to each one of them. I had written some things in and I tore up my script and said – "Please, chaps, say what you think you would have said in this situation." And this I could hardly take. Each of them said their own line, like "Good luck, sir!" or "Chin up, sir" – all these perfectly trite, ordinary phrases, spoken from the heart. Talk about improvisation. It was nothing to do with "acting". They were *being*.'

INT. LARGE SHED, ALEXANDRIA. DAY. (MATTE.)

> *Long shot. Five* OFFICERS *and ninety* MEN *are gathered. They are dressed in a variety of borrowed tropical clothing — vest, singlets, shirts, shorts or trousers, white or khaki. Not hats or caps. Several men are bandaged. The* RNVR SUB-LIEUTENANT *calls out:*

SUB-LIEUT   Ship's company — *'shun!*

INT. LARGE SHED. ALEXANDRIA. DAY.

> *Medium shot.* CAPTAIN 'D' *and the* SUB-LIEUTENANT. *The latter comes to attention, but does not salute as he has no cap.*

At the end of the film Captain 'D' says goodbye to the survivors of HMS *Torrin*.

SUB–LIEUT	Ship's company present, sir.
CAPTAIN	Thank you – stand easy, please.
SUB–LIEUT	Ship's company – stand – *easy*!
CAPTAIN	I have come to say goodbye to the few of you who are left. We have had so many talks but this is our last . . . I have always tried to crack a joke or two before and you have all been friendly and laughed at them. But today I am afraid I have run out of jokes, and I don't suppose any of us feels much like laughing. The *Torrin* has been in one scrap after another – but even when we have had men killed, the majority survived and brought the old ship back. Now she lies in fifteen hundred fathoms and with her more than half our shipmates. If they had to die, what a grand way to go, for now they lie all together with the ship we loved, and they are in very good company. We have lost her but they are still with her. There may be less than half the *Torrin* left but I feel that each of us will take up the battle with even stronger heart. Each of us knows twice as much about fighting and each of us has twice as good a reason to fight. You will all be sent to replace men who have been killed in other ships, and the next time you are in action, remember the *Torrin*. As you ram each shell home into the gun, shout *Torrin*, and so her spirit will go on inspiring us until victory is won. I should like to add that there isn't one of you that I wouldn't be proud and honoured to serve with again. Goodbye, good luck and thank you all from the bottom of my heart.

INT. LARGE SHED, ALEXANDRIA. DAY.

Close shot. CAPTAIN 'D'. *The* MEN *file past and he shakes hands with each one.*

MEN	(*mumbling*) Good luck, sir . . .
	Thank you, sir . . .
	Etc., etc.
SHORTY	Goodbye, sir . . . (*He shakes hands with the* CAPTAIN.)
WALTER	(*shaking hands*) Goodbye, sir.

Camera tracks closer and closer to the CAPTAIN*'s face. The music swells and the scene fades out.*

Fade in:

The music swells and the voice of the NARRATOR, *who spoke the Prologue to the film, says:*

NARRATOR   Here ends the story of a ship, but there will always be *other* ships, for we are an island race. Through all our centuries the sea has ruled our destiny. There will always be other ships and men to sail in them. It is these men, in peace or war, to whom we owe so much. Above all victories, beyond all loss, in spite of changing values in a changing world, they give, to us their countrymen, eternal and indomitable pride. God bless our ships and all who sail in them.

As he speaks, we see a series of shots of minelayers, sloops, destroyers, trawlers, aircraft carriers, submarines, cruisers, tugs, converted liners, tankers, motor torpedo boats and battleships . . . all sailing purposefully into the future.

STILL LIFE

(from *Tonight at 8:30*, 1936)

LAURA JESSON   Gertrude Lawrence
ALEC HARVEY   Noël Coward

Phoenix Theatre, London, 18 May 1936

Tonight at 8:30 (1936) *consisted of nine one-act plays that were produced in repertory — three plays a night on three successive nights. One of them was* Still Life.

The scene is the station buffet at Milford Junction. Laura Jesson (Gertrude Lawrence), a suburban housewife with children, comes into Milford every week on a shopping trip, which is almost certainly the highlight of her very predictable week. One day she accidentally meets the equally respectable Alec Harvey (Noël), a married doctor who practises in Milford one day a week. Laura gets a piece of grit in her eye from a passing express train, Alec removes it and they strike up a conversation. They meet again the following week . . . and then the next . . . and the next. Neither is prepared to acknowledge what is obvious — that they are falling in love.

They are again in the buffet. Alec brings some dubious-looking buns over to the table . . .

ALEC: You must eat one of these — fresh this morning.

LAURA: Very fattening.

ALEC: I don't hold with such foolishness.

LAURA: They do look good, I must say.

ALEC: One of my earliest passions — I've never outgrown it.

LAURA: Do you like milk in your tea?

ALEC: Yes, don't you?

LAURA: Yes — fortunately.

ALEC: Station refreshments are generally a wee bit arbitrary, you know.

LAURA: I wasn't grumbling.

ALEC (*smiling*): Do you ever grumble – are you ever sullen and cross and bad-tempered?

LAURA: Of course I am – at least not sullen exactly – but I sometimes get into rages.

ALEC: I can't visualize you in a rage.

LAURA: I really don't see why you should.

ALEC: Oh, I don't know – there are signs you know – one can usually tell –

LAURA: Long upper lips and jaw lines and eyes close together?

ALEC: You haven't any of those things.

LAURA: Do you feel guilty at all? I do.

ALEC (*smiling*): Guilty?

LAURA: You ought to more than me, really – you neglected your work this afternoon.

ALEC: I worked this morning – a little relaxation never did anyone any harm. Why should either of us feel guilty?

LAURA: I don't know – a sort of instinct – as though we were letting something happen that oughtn't to happen.

ALEC: How awfully nice you are!

LAURA: When I was a child in Cornwall – we lived in Cornwall, you know – May, that's my sister, and I used to climb out of our bedroom window on summer nights and go down to the cove and bathe. It was dreadfully cold but we felt very adventurous. I'd never have dared do it by myself, but sharing the danger made it all right – that's how I feel now, really.

ALEC: Have a bun – it's awfully bad for you.

LAURA: You're laughing at me!

ALEC: Yes, a little, but I'm laughing at myself, too.

LAURA: Why?

ALEC: For feeling a small pang when you said about being guilty.

LAURA: There you are, you see!

ALEC: We haven't done anything wrong.

LAURA: Of course we haven't.

ALEC: An accidental meeting – then another accidental meeting – then a little lunch – then the movies – what could be more ordinary? More natural?

LAURA: We're adults, after all.

ALEC: I never see myself as an adult, do you?

LAURA (*firmly*): Yes, I do. I'm a respectable married woman with a husband and a home and three children.

ALEC: But there must be a part of you, deep down inside, that doesn't feel like that at all – some little spirit that still wants to climb out of the window – that still longs to splash about a bit in the dangerous sea.

LAURA: Perhaps we none of us ever grow up entirely.

ALEC: How awfully nice you are!

LAURA: You said that before.

ALEC: I thought perhaps you hadn't heard.

LAURA: I heard all right.

Dolly Messiter (Everley Gregg) interrupts Alec Harvey (Noël) and Laura Jesson (Gertrude Lawrence) at an emotional moment in *Still Life* (1936).

In adapting Still Life *for the screen, Noël profited again from the lesson of* Citizen Kane.

Whereas the stage and theatre audiences of the day traditionally expected narrative continuity, film could play with time and – with a little necessary guidance – expect its audience to follow.

In addition, you expected to look at what was going on on that stage objectively – a spectator seeing through the fourth wall of the set. With film you could take a point of view and be inside the head of one of the characters.

This is what Noël chose to do with his screenplay. Instead of simply observing Laura Jesson, the film audience could see events from Laura's perspective. Brief Encounter *was to be her story. As a device it would prove much more emotionally involving.*

BRIEF ENCOUNTER

(1945)

LAURA JESSON	Celia Johnson
ALEC HARVEY	Trevor Howard
MYRTLE BAGOT	Joyce Carey
ALBERT GODBY	Stanley Holloway
BERYL	Margaret Barton
DOLLY MESSITER	Everley Gregg
FRED JESSON	Cyril Raymond

Produced by Cineguild, directed by David Lean
Released 26 November 1945

The film begins with the story's ending. Social conventions have dogged Laura and Alec's relationship from the start. Now, about to say goodbye in the railway buffet where they first met, suburbia intrudes yet again in the shape of a casual acquaintance of Laura's, Dolly Messiter . . .

In the far end of the refreshment room, seated at a table, are ALEC HARVEY *and* LAURA JESSON. *They are in earnest conversation, but we do not hear what they are saying.*

DOLLY *is seen at the counter. Forgetting her tea, she hurries across the room to join* LAURA *and* ALEC.

DOLLY: Laura! What a lovely surprise!

LAURA (*dazed*): Oh, Dolly!

DOLLY: My dear, I've shopped until I'm dropping! My feet are nearly falling off, and my throat's parched. I thought of having tea in Spindle's but I was terrified of losing the train. I'm always missing trains, and being late for meals, and Bob gets disagreeable for days at a time – he's been getting those dreadful headaches you know – I've been trying to make him see a doctor, but he won't. (*Flopping down at their table.*) Oh, dear.

LAURA: This is Doctor Harvey.

ALEC (*rising*): How do you do!

DOLLY (*shaking hands*): How do you do. Would you be a perfect dear and get me my cup of tea? I don't think I could drag my poor old bones back to the counter again. I must get some chocolates for Tony, too, but I can do that afterwards.

She offers him money.

ALEC (*waving it away*): No, please . . .

He goes drearily out of frame towards the counter. Close shot of DOLLY *and* LAURA.

DOLLY: My dear — what a nice-looking man. Who on earth is he? Really, you're quite a dark horse. I shall telephone Fred in the morning and make mischief — this is a bit of luck. I haven't seen you for ages, and I've been meaning to pop in, but Tony's had measles, you know, and I had all that awful fuss about Phyllis —

LAURA(*with an effort*): Oh, how dreadful!

At the counter, ALEC *is standing next to* ALBERT, *who is finishing his cup of tea.* ALBERT *leaves and* MYRTLE *hands* ALEC *the change for* DOLLY*'s cup of tea.*

DOLLY (*off*): Mind you, I never cared for her much, but still Tony did. Tony adored her, and — but never mind, I'll tell you all about that in the train.

ALEC *picks up* DOLLY*'s tea and moves back to the table. He sits down again.*

DOLLY: Thank you so very much. They've certainly put enough milk in it — but still, it'll be refreshing. (*She sips it.*) Oh, dear — no sugar.

ALEC: It's in the spoon.

DOLLY: Oh, of course — what a fool I am — Laura, you look frightfully well. I do wish I'd known you were coming in today, we could have come together and lunched and had a good gossip. I loathe shopping by myself anyway.

There is the sound of a bell on the platform, and a loudspeaker voice announces the arrival of the Churley train.

LAURA: There's your train.

ALEC: Yes, I know.

DOLLY: Aren't you coming with us?

ALEC: No, I go in the opposite direction. My practice is in Churley.

DOLLY: Oh, I see.

ALEC: I'm a general practitioner at the moment.

LAURA (*dully*): Doctor Harvey is going out to Africa next week.

DOLLY: Oh, how thrilling.

There is the sound of ALEC's *train approaching.*

ALEC: I must go.

LAURA: Yes, you must.

ALEC: Goodbye.

DOLLY: Goodbye.

ALEC shakes hands with DOLLY, *looks at* LAURA *swiftly once, and gives her shoulder a little squeeze. The train is heard rumbling into the station. He goes over to the door and out on to the platform.*

LAURA is gazing at the door through which ALEC *has just passed. She seems unaware of the chattering* DOLLY *at her side.*

Then, as she sits on the train with the garrulous Dolly, we hear her thought voice . . .

LAURA'S VOICE: This can't last – the misery can't last – I must remember that and try to control myself. Nothing lasts really – neither happiness nor despair – not even life lasts very long – there will come a time in the future when I shan't mind about this any more – when I can look back and say quite peacefully and cheerfully 'How silly I was' – No, no – I don't want that time to come ever – I want to remember every minute – always – always – to the end of my days.

And even when she reaches the safety of home and family and looks at her safe, predictable husband, we continue to hear what she is thinking.

LAURA'S VOICE: Fred – Fred – dear Fred. There's so much that I want to say to you. You are the only one in the world with enough wisdom and gentleness to understand – if only it were somebody else's story and not mine. As it is you are the only one in the world that I can never tell –

never – never – because even if I waited until we were old, old people, and told you then, you would be bound to look back over the years . . . and be hurt and oh, my dear, I don't want you to be hurt. You see, we are a happily married couple, and must never forget that. This is my home . . .

A shot of FRED *over* LAURA'*s shoulder. He is engrossed in his crossword puzzle.*

LAURA'S VOICE: . . . You are my husband – and my children are upstairs in bed. I am a happily married woman – or rather I was, until a few weeks ago. This is my whole world and it is enough – or rather, it was, until a few weeks ago.

Close shot of LAURA.

LAURA'S VOICE: But, oh, Fred, I've been so foolish. I've fallen in love! I'm an ordinary woman – I didn't think such violent things could happen to ordinary people.

Again a shot of FRED *over* LAURA'*s shoulder.*

It all started on an ordinary day, in the most ordinary place in the world, the refreshment room at Milford Junction. I was having a cup of tea and reading a book that I'd got that morning from Boots – my train wasn't due for ten minutes . . . I looked up and saw a man come in from the platform. He had on an ordinary mac with a belt. His hat was turned down, and I didn't even see his face. He got his tea at the counter and turned – then I did see his face. It was rather a nice face. He passed my table on the way to his . . .

> *Then – the series of accidental meetings. The following week they run into each other in the street . . . The next week he happens to come into the tea shop where Laura is having lunch and, since the place is crowded, he has to share her table . . . Laura always goes to see a film after lunch as part of her regular routine ('What exciting lives we lead, don't we?'). On this occasion Alec asks if he may join her.*
>
> *And so it goes. All perfectly innocent – or so they believe.*
>
> *For the first time they talk about themselves. Or, at least, Alec does . . .*

Close shot of LAURA *and* ALEC.

LAURA: Is tea bad for one? Worse than coffee, I mean?

Laura (Celia Johnson) reflects on how her humdrum suburban life has changed.

ALEC: If this is a professional interview my fee is a guinea.

LAURA: Why did you become a doctor?

ALEC: That's a long story. Perhaps because I'm a bit of an idealist.

LAURA: I suppose all doctors ought to have ideals, really – otherwise I
   should think their work would be unbearable.

ALEC: Surely you're not encouraging me to talk shop?

LAURA: Why shouldn't you talk shop? It's what interests you most, isn't it?

ALEC: Yes – it is. I'm terribly ambitious really – not ambitious for myself
   so much as for my special pigeon.

LAURA: What is your special pigeon?

ALEC: Preventative medicine.

LAURA: Oh, I see.

ALEC (*laughing*): I'm afraid you don't.

LAURA: I was trying to be intelligent.

ALEC: Most good doctors, especially when they're young, have private dreams – that's the best part of them; sometimes, though, those get over-professionalized and strangulated and – am I boring you?

LAURA: No – I don't quite understand – but you're not boring me.

ALEC: What I mean is this – all good doctors must be primarily enthusiastic. They must have, like writers and painters and priests, a sense of vocation – a deep-rooted, unsentimental desire to do good.

LAURA: Yes – I see that.

ALEC: Well, obviously one way of preventing disease is worth fifty ways of curing it – that's where my ideal comes in – preventative medicine isn't anything to do with medicine at all, really – it's concerned with conditions, living conditions and common sense and hygiene. For instance, my speciality is pneumoconiosis.

LAURA: Oh, dear!

ALEC: Don't be alarmed, it's simpler than it sounds – it's nothing but a slow process of fibrosis of the lung due to the inhalation of particles of dust. In the hospital here there are splendid opportunities for observing cures and making notes, because of the coal mines.

LAURA: You suddenly look much younger.

ALEC (*brought up short*): Do I?

LAURA: Almost like a little boy.

ALEC: What made you say that?

LAURA (*staring at him*): I don't know – yes, I do.

ALEC (*gently*): Tell me.

LAURA (*with panic in her voice*): Oh, no – I couldn't really. You were saying about the coal mines.

ALEC (*looking into her eyes*): Yes – the inhalation of coal dust – that's one specific form of the disease – it's called anthracosis.

LAURA (*hypnotized*): What are the others?

ALEC: Chalicosis – that comes from metal dust – steelworks, you know . . .

LAURA: Yes, of course. Steelworks.

ALEC: And silicosis – stone dust – that's gold mines.

LAURA (*almost in a whisper*): I see.

There is the sound of a bell.

LAURA: That's your train.

ALEC (*looking down*): Yes.

LAURA: You mustn't miss it.

ALEC: No.

LAURA (*again with panic in her voice*): What's the matter?

ALEC (*with an effort*): Nothing – nothing at all.

LAURA (*socially*): It's been so very nice – I've enjoyed my afternoon enormously.

ALEC: I'm so glad – so have I. I apologize for boring you with those long medical words.

LAURA: I feel dull and stupid, not to be able to understand more.

ALEC: Shall I see you again?

There is the sound of a train approaching.

LAURA: It's the other platform, isn't it? You'll have to run. Don't worry about me – mine's due in a few minutes.

ALEC: Shall I see you again?

LAURA: Of course – perhaps you could come over to Ketchworth one Sunday. It's rather far, I know, but we should be delighted to see you.

ALEC (*intensely*): Please – please . . .

The train is heard drawing to a standstill . . .

LAURA: What is it?

ALEC: Next Thursday – the same time.

LAURA: No – I can't possibly – I . . .

ALEC: Please – I ask you most humbly . . .

LAURA: You'll miss your train!

ALEC: All right.

He gets up.

LAURA: Run . . .

ALEC (*taking her hand*): Goodbye.

LAURA (*breathlessly*): I'll be there.

ALEC: Thank you, my dear.

He leaves LAURA, *and the camera tracks into a big close shot to hold her, smiling with joy.*

LAURA *collects her shopping basket and goes towards the door to Number 3 platform.*

She comes out of the refreshment room on to the platform. She looks up past camera at ALEC's *train, which can be heard pulling out of the station.*

A shot of ALEC, *from* LAURA's *viewpoint. He is leaning out of a carriage window and waves to her as the train starts to pull out of the station.*

Close-up of LAURA. *She waves back, and her eyes follow the departing train.*

LAURA'S VOICE: I stood there and watched his train draw out of the station. I stared after it until its little red tail light had vanished into the darkness. I imagined him arriving at Churley and giving up his ticket and walking through the streets, and letting himself into his house with his latchkey. Madeleine, his wife, would probably be in the hall to meet him – or perhaps upstairs in her room – not feeling very well – small, dark and rather delicate – I wondered if he'd say 'I met such a nice woman in the Kardomah – we had lunch and went to the pictures' – then suddenly I knew that he wouldn't – I knew beyond a shadow of doubt that he wouldn't say a word, and at that moment the first awful feeling of danger swept over me.

Their affair is never to be consummated and Alec makes the decision to take a job in Africa. They return to the refreshment room for the last time and now the film replays the opening scene – except that it now carries a very different meaning . . .

ALEC (*quietly*): You know what's happened, don't you?

LAURA: Yes – yes, I do.

ALEC: I've fallen in love with you . . .

LAURA: Yes – I know.

ALEC: Tell me honestly – my dear – please tell me honestly if what I believe is true . . .

LAURA (*in a whisper*): What do you believe?

ALEC: That it's the same with you – that you've fallen in love too.

LAURA (*near tears*): It sounds so silly.

ALEC: Why?

LAURA: I know you so little.

ALEC: It is true, though – isn't it?

LAURA (*with a sigh*): Yes – it's true.

ALEC (*making a slight movement towards her*): Laura . . .

LAURA: No please . . . we must be sensible – please help me to be sensible – we mustn't behave like this – we must forget that we've said what we've just said.

ALEC: Not yet – not quite yet.

LAURA (*panic in her voice*): But we must – don't you see!

ALEC (*leaning forward and taking her hand*): Listen – it's too late now to be as sensible as all that – it's too late to forget what we've said – and anyway, whether we'd said it or not couldn't have mattered – we know – we've both of us known for a long time.

LAURA: How can you say that – I've only known you for four weeks – we only talked for the first time last Thursday week.

ALEC: Last Thursday week. Hadn't it been a long time since then for you? Answer me truly.

LAURA: Yes.

ALEC: How often did you decide that you were never going to see me again?

LAURA: Several times a day.

ALEC: So did I.

LAURA: Oh, Alec.

ALEC: I love you – I love your wide eyes and the way you smile and your shyness, and the way you laugh at my jokes.

LAURA: Please don't . . .

ALEC: I love you – I love you – you love me too – it's no use pretending that it hasn't happened because it has.

LAURA (*with tremendous effort*): Yes it has. I don't want to pretend anything either to you or to anyone else . . . but from now on I shall have to. That's what's wrong – don't you see? That's what spoils everything. That's why we must stop here and now talking like this. We are neither of us free to love each other, there is too much in the way. There's still time, if we control ourselves and behave like sensible human beings, there's still time to – to . . .

She puts her head down and bursts into tears.

ALEC: There's no time at all.

We are now back to their final moments together. Again, the station refreshment room.

ALEC: Are you all right, darling?

LAURA: Yes, I'm all right.

ALEC: I wish I could think of something to say.

LAURA: It doesn't matter – not saying anything, I mean.

ALEC: I'll miss my train and wait to see you into yours.

LAURA: No – no – please don't. I'll come over to your platform with you – I'd rather.

ALEC: Very well.

LAURA: Do you think we shall ever see each other again?

ALEC: I don't know. (*His voice breaks.*) Not for years anyway.

LAURA: The children will all be grown up – I wonder if they'll ever meet and know each other.

ALEC: Couldn't I write to you – just once in a while?

LAURA: No – please not – we promised we wouldn't.

ALEC: Laura, dear, I do love you so very much. I love you with all my heart and soul.

LAURA (*without emotion*): I want to die – if only I could die.

ALEC: If you died you'd forget me – I want to be remembered.

LAURA: Yes, I know – I do too.

ALEC (*glancing at the clock*): We've still got a few minutes.

DOLLY (*off*): Laura! What a lovely surprise!

LAURA (*dazed*): Oh, Dolly!

DOLLY *joins* LAURA *and* ALEC.

DOLLY: My dear, I've been shopping till I'm dropping. My feet are nearly falling off, and my throat's parched, I thought of having tea in Spindle's, but I was terrified of losing the train.

LAURA'S VOICE: It was cruel of Fate to be against us right up to the last minute. Dolly Messiter – poor, well-meaning, irritating Dolly Messiter . . .

The camera is slowly tracking in to a close-up of LAURA.

DOLLY: I'm always missing trains and being late for meals, and Bob gets disagreeable for days at a time. (*Her voice is fading away.*) He's been getting those dreadful headaches, you know. I've tried to make him see a doctor but he won't.

Her voice fades out.

LAURA'S VOICE: ... crashing into those last few precious minutes we had together. She chattered and fussed, but I didn't hear what she said. I was dazed and bewildered. Alec behaved so beautifully with such perfect politeness. Nobody could have guessed what he was really feeling – then the bell went for his train.

The platform bell rings.

LAURA: There's your train.

ALEC: Yes, I know.

DOLLY: Aren't you coming with us?

ALEC: No, I go in the opposite direction. My practice is in Churley.

DOLLY: Oh, I see.

ALEC: I am a general practitioner at the moment.

LAURA (*dully*): Doctor Harvey is going out to Africa, next week.

DOLLY: Oh, how thrilling.

There is the sound of ALEC's *train approaching.*

ALEC: I must go.

LAURA: Yes, you must.

ALEC: Goodbye.

DOLLY: Goodbye.

He shakes hands with DOLLY, *and looks swiftly once only at* LAURA.

Close-up of LAURA. ALEC's *hand comes into the shot and gives her shoulder a little squeeze.*

LAURA'S VOICE: I felt the touch of his hand for a moment and then he walked away ...

ALEC *is seen from* LAURA's *viewpoint. He crosses the refreshment room and goes out of the door on to the platform.*

LAURA'S VOICE: ... away – out of my life for ever.

Fortunately the film has stayed in our lives for ever, and consistently rates highly on almost every critic's top-ten list.

In 2007 it was turned into a successful stage play, and in 2009 into an opera. A brief encounter has turned into a long run.

ENVOI

'Really, my life has been one long extravaganza.'
Noël on rereading his journals

'Some day, I suspect, when Jesus has definitely got me
for a sunbeam, my works may be adequately assessed.'
Diaries, 1956

Noël left behind a manuscript for an unfinished novel, Beyond These Voices, *which he began in 1956. Like several of his plays and stories it is set in his mythical South Sea island, Samolo — his synonym for Jamaica.*

It sounds almost as though both the author and the narrator, Kerry Stirling, were taking their leave. It begins . . .

'I have come home again, this time, I suspect, for good. The years that are left to me I intend to pass here on the island where the winds are soft and the climate temperate and where, except for a few weeks twice a year in the rainy season, there is always sunshine.

'This thought fills me with gentle pleasure for I am tired. Not physically tired, for I am in the best of health and look and feel a great deal younger than I am, but spiritually a little under the weather. This is not a disagreeable sensation; on the contrary it is rather pleasant, for there is space around me and time ahead of me, time enough at least to enable me to give myself up to my quiet *malaise* and wait, without agitation, until the unhurried days smooth it away.'

By the time he arrived in Jamaica that last time, there were, as it turned out, only days left to Noël. He died peacefully in the early morning of 26 March 1973.

And, indeed, the winds that day were soft . . .

THE PARTY'S OVER NOW

The Party's over now,
The dawn is drawing very nigh,
The candles gutter,
The starlight leaves the sky.
It's time for little boys and girls
To hurry home to bed
For there's a new day
Waiting just ahead.
Life is sweet
But time is fleet,
Beneath the magic of the moon,
Dancing time
May seem sublime
But it is ended all too soon,
The thrill has gone,
To linger on
Would spoil it anyhow,
Let's creep away from the day
For the Party's over now.

Words and Music (1932)

ACKNOWLEDGEMENTS

Coward Estate Archives: 17, 18, 24, 27, 28, 29, 30, 31, 33, 35, 42, 44, 46, 58, 71, 74, 86, 137, 138, 174, 184, 201, 315, 334, 344, 350, 355

From the collection of Geoffrey Johnson: 41, 43, 364

Mander and Mitchenson Archive: 51 (by Sasha), 349

Faber Music: 180, 187, 192, 198, 206, 211, 214, 218, 220, 231, 235, 245, 248

The Executor of Lady Lancaster: 178, 179

Methuen Drama: 250

INDEX

ALSO BY BARRY DAY

GROWING UP AT GOVERNMENT HOUSE

GROWING UP AT GOVERNMENT HOUSE

Rosemary Harmar

ANGUS
& ROBERTSON
PUBLISHERS

Page 2: *The portico of
Government House.*

ANGUS & ROBERTSON PUBLISHERS

Unit 4, Eden Park, 31 Waterloo Road,
North Ryde, NSW, Australia 2113;
14 Newton Road, Auckland 1, New Zealand; and
16 Golden Square, London W1R 4BN, United Kingdom

Created, designed and produced by
Mead & Beckett Publishing
25 Surrey Street, Darlinghurst
NSW, Australia 2011

Designed by Kate Finnie
Typeset by Asco Trade Typesetting Ltd., Hong Kong
Printed by Kyodo-Shing Loong, Singapore

First published in Australia by Angus & Robertson Publishers in 1989
First published in New Zealand by Angus & Robertson NZ Ltd in 1989
First published in the United Kingdom by Angus & Robertson (UK) in 1989

National Library of Australia Cataloguing-in-publication data.

Harmar, Rosemary.
Growing up at Government House.

ISBN 0 207 16347 2

1. Harmar, Rosemary—Childhood and youth. 2. Government House
(Sydney, N.S.W.)—Biography. 3. New South Wales—Governors—
Children—Biography. 4. Sydney (N.S.W.)—Social life and customs—
1929–1939. I. Title.

994.4'1042'0924

Contents

Tell me, tell me, smiling child
What the past is like to thee.
ROBERT BRIDGES

To the memory of my father

*Doing homework in Mother's
upstairs sitting room at
Government House.*

Preface

I FELT compelled to write this book so that my grandchildren might be able to read a story which I hope shows the kind of character their great-grandfather possessed and that they might perhaps be inspired by his modesty and integrity.

I am greatly indebted to Mr L.J. Rose for sending me his book, *The Framework of Government*, which I have found invaluable. I would also like to thank Mrs Bethia Foott for allowing me to use her book, *The Dismissal of a Premier*, which was most helpful, and my brother Bill (Philip Malcolm Game), who helped in countless ways and provided valuable material—letters, press cuttings, etc. Also I am most grateful to all who helped in various other ways: Mrs Goddard and Mrs Roberts, who kindly typed my manuscript, Mrs Elizabeth Fabri, Mrs Helen Rutledge, Mrs Caroline Simpson for her untiring help, my cousin Iris Gibb, who spurred me on, and my husband, Nigel D'Oyly Harmar, for his unfailing patience and help.

1 Life at Home in England

MORE than fifty years have passed, over half a century, and yet I remember that dreary November afternoon as though it were yesterday. The leaves mushy underfoot, the woods still and dank with no sound. Lifeless and chilly. It was the kind of afternoon to sit by a glowing fire and forget the outside world, which was just what my mother and I were doing when the telephone rang.

My father had recently retired and bought a house in the village of Cricket Malherbie. It was more a hamlet than a village, there being only the church, vicarage and farm besides ourselves and a few farm labourers' cottages. We were in the depth of the country, with similar villages around us and everywhere a labyrinth of lanes, their banks strewn with wildflowers in summer and thick with snow in winter.

The church was tiny, which was, perhaps, a blessing, for the farmer had quarrelled with the vicar so that the congregation on Sundays consisted almost entirely of the vicar's family and us. The singing, practically non-existent, was never loud enough to drown the rhythmical thud of the organ hand pump. *Bang-bang-bang!* it went, usually just out of time with the music. Father always turned towards a pillar when he sang; he said he felt that it was kinder to us, as he was so unmusical. My mother, though she loved music, could never keep in tune, and my two brothers and I only added to the singing when we liked the hymns. It was left to the vicar's wife to keep things going.

Cricket, as the house was called, lay in the lee of a hill, sheltered from the wind and with a fine view of the Taunton Vale below. On a clear day the wireless masts of Bristol were just visible from the terrace. In between lay woods, fields and farms clad with that soft beauty found only in England. I cannot pretend that it was the view that appealed to my brothers, Bill and David, and me; it was the garden, so intriguingly wild as to invite constant exploration and provide us with hours of enjoyment.

Somerset was a friendly county. In a short time we had plenty of companions who were as happy as we were to bicycle in the lanes, climb the trees, or investigate the stretch of water some two hundred yards from the house which we referred to as the moat. Some of the trees in the garden were magnificent cedars of Lebanon with fine horizontal branches perfect for climbing. The moat gave us inexhaustible pleasure. We spent weeks in the summer making a raft. It was not very seaworthy, for it was only a few planks of wood roughly joined together and supported in the water by an empty petrol tin at each corner. I can still see Bill's fair hair and blue eyes bobbing above the water as he swam ashore with a friend, the raft having sunk.

Below the terrace was a sunken garden enclosed by a curious horseshoe-shaped wall for which there seemed to be no particular explanation, but as the house was supposed to have been built by an Italian madman, we merely considered it one of his follies. Only years later, long after our time, was an entrance to a large stone underground room discovered in that wall. The room was thought to have been used by smugglers to hide their illicit cargo brought from the sea, only seventeen miles away.

The house was built of yellowing sandstone in an elegant Georgian style. The Italian architect had embellished it with attractive wrought-iron balconies. A wide flight of steps led up to the front door. Underneath the steps was the entrance to the cellars. These were extensive, and there were stories of an underground passage leading from them to the church, but although we often searched for this, we never found it.

Inside the front door was a large square hall, beautifully light, for it extended right up to a glass roof. A fine sweeping oak staircase led up to my brothers' rooms and then on to the spare room and library. The library was our playroom. It was circular, with deep Georgian windows reaching from floor to ceiling separated by bookshelves. Here and there, in irregular fashion, were false wooden books glued into place on the shelves. To the right of the library was a large gallery which gave a view down to the hall and front door. There was also a smaller gallery above the main staircase. As children we found these vantage points very useful, for we could watch for visitors and, if we did not care for the look of them, make our escape by the back stairs to the garden.

The architect certainly had had eccentric ideas. Visitors who came to stay would open the door of the spare-room cupboard and find, to their amazement, a folding staircase which when unfolded led up to my parents' bedroom. My room had no less than seven small cupboards in the thick walls, which were only just large enough for trinkets and toys. The back stairs were spiral and were built just as in old castles, inside a cylindrical column. At each floor there were openings leading to different parts of the house. It was all ideal for children, and at the weekends and in the holidays it echoed with noisy games of hide-and-seek. The two Christmases we spent there were two of the gayest that I ever remember, with plenty of parties and all the traditional things that are so much a part of Christmas.

My mother and I were alone in the house that autumn afternoon. My father and brothers had gone hunting. She went into the study to answer the telephone and came rushing out into the hall, her blue eyes shining, her soft brown hair framing her face—so pretty in her excitement—and took me in her arms.

'It's a call for Daddy,' she cried, 'from the Dominions Office. They say it's a matter of national importance. What *do* you think they want?' I could not begin to imagine. I was very young and had not the remotest idea of what the mysterious words 'Dominions Office' meant, but my mother was clearly very excited and her excitement communicated itself to me.

My mother's mind was not on the games she played with me after that. She was busy thinking about the telephone call and what it could mean.

My parents on the stone terrace at their home at Cricket Malherbie, Somerset. There was reputedly a secret tunnel between the house and the church, but we could never find it even after extensive searches of the cellars.

What *could* it mean? What did 'a matter of national importance' imply? She *must* try to be patient. However, her thoughts kept returning to that extraordinary statement. She was also thinking about my father. He had looked so nice that day as she had waved him goodbye. He was such a good horseman, and breeches and tweeds suited him well with his lean figure. It was sad that he walked with a slight limp. The memory of that skating accident some years before still caused her distress; but what was the use of going back to all that, to the day when he had insisted (for undoubtedly he had a streak of obstinacy) on playing ice hockey with his skates screwed to his *shoes* and to the terrible moment when he had fallen, fracturing his femur so badly that he had been forced to lie on his back for almost a year. He had never complained.

'Life is so dull if you never take risks' was all he had said. All that was over now, and here they were, settled in Somerset. She must try and push away the uncomfortable thoughts that would keep coming into her mind: that her husband had retired too early, that he was wasting his talents. There had been that letter to him from Air Commodore A.D. Cunningham which had said, 'I hope that your house and garden in Somerset will, for some time, provide an outlet for that feverish energy of yours of which the Royal Air Force took such advantage.' The words were disturbing. She knew that he had never been a man with personal ambition, had never sought the top of the tree or the limelight, and that all he had ever wanted was a job in which he was fully stretched and to which he could give himself heart and soul. Even so, would gardening ever be enough to satisfy him? She could not help having grave doubts.

My father, Philip Woolcott Game, was born in Streatham, London, on 30 March 1876 to Clara and George Beale Game. His early childhood was spent at Harrow Weald, but in 1902 the family moved to Barn House, Broadway,

Round the corner from the terrace (middle left of picture) was the main garden, planned and worked in by both my parents. The bay window is the dining room; above it, their bedroom. The drawing room leads out onto the terrace.

Worcester, and this is where he grew up. He was the second of eight children. One girl died in infancy, and another, a twin, died at birth. My father was educated first at Hillside Preparatory School, Surrey, and then at Charterhouse, also in Surrey. He was unhappy at school and as far as I know showed no particular brilliance. It was at the Royal Military Academy, Woolwich, that he began to make his mark, passing out as top gunner. From then on he never looked back.

On 11 August 1908 he married Gwendolen Hughes-Gibb, daughter of Francis Hughes-Gibb and his wife, Eleanor Mary (née Wigram), of the Manor House, Tarrant Gunville, in Dorset. My grandmother, who was widowed in 1917, continued to live at Tarrant Gunville until a few years before her death in 1947, and it was there that we spent our holidays when we were in England. A very happy relationship grew up between my father and his mother-in-law; it was to her that he wrote for kindly advice when he was perplexed and distressed some twenty-five years later.

One man who was watching Philip Game during his early military career, observing his progress and his character with a deep scrutiny, was Sir Hugh Trenchard (later Lord Trenchard). In 1916 Trenchard was in command of the Royal Flying Corps in France and asked for Philip Game to join him, together with the two Salmond brothers, Geoffrey and John, both later knighted. My father became Trenchard's Chief of Staff. He proved to be exactly the right choice. Trenchard later referred to him as 'the best staff officer I have ever had or ever seen'. By 1918 he had become part of the newly formed Royal Air Force and had learned to fly. In 1923 he was sent to India as Air Officer Commanding. This was a three-year appointment, and my parents had to face up to the heart-rending decision to leave their two little boys behind them to be educated in England. I was still in the 'tender' years and able to be taken with them. They had been away less than a year when a peremptory telegram arrived in Delhi from the forceful and ever-persistent Trenchard: 'COME HOME AT ONCE, WE NEED YOU HERE.'

I do not remember much of that short time in India except for certain small details. My English nanny used to take me along the Ladies' Mile at Simla. When we reached a certain spot she would sit on a seat next to a gentleman called Mr Green. Most conveniently, Mr Green always seemed to be waiting for us. Neither Nanny nor I ever mentioned Mr Green to my mother. We somehow had a tacit understanding between us about this.

Sometimes Nanny took me to the Governor of the Punjab's Residence. We would stand by the great wrought-iron gates, which, if we were lucky, would be open. Then he would drive out in his carriage while I waved to him, shouting; 'The Punjab, the Punjab!'

With the arrival of the telegram, my father and mother left their gay life and pleasant house, Nanny left Mr Green, and I left 'the Punjab'. We all came back to England, where my father took up his post as Air Member for Personnel on the Air Council at the Air Ministry. It was only when it was intimated, in 1929, that he was to be promoted to Chief of Air Staff, over the heads of the Salmond brothers, which he considered grossly unfair to them, that he promptly retired from the Royal Air Force at his own request. He was

My father at work on a rockery. He almost always made rockeries in each house he lived in.

Above: *My parents' wedding.*
Back row (left to right): *my
father's sister Beatrix, the
bridegroom, Isabel Crowdy;*
front row: *my mother's sister
Dorothy, the bride, an unknown bridesmaid.*

Opposite page: *My mother
at her writing desk. She loved
to write letters and always said
a desk made her mouth water.*

only fifty-two, and it is small wonder that my mother worried herself and felt
that her husband was far from ready for retirement.

On the particular afternoon of which I am writing, she was still pondering
on this and the telephone message from London when my father arrived
home. He telephoned Whitehall immediately and was told to be at the
Dominions Office early next morning. It was not until the following afternoon when he arrived back from London that he was able to tell us that he
had been asked to go out to Australia as Governor of New South Wales.

'Go out to Australia as Governor of New South Wales.' My mother repeated the words after him as though she were learning them by heart.

'You can't possibly want to go out *there*,' said Bill. 'It's all flat and brown
and bare.' David, always gentle, murmured that he did like his school and
that he would not really want to leave. My geography did not allow me to say
anything, so I just sat and stared at everyone else.

Then quite suddenly we were all talking at once.

'What's it like?'

'When are we going?'

'Can we ride?'

'How long will it take to get there?'

My mother's voice trickled through. 'I suppose I'll need a new dress or
two.'

The Governor's lady in evening dress complete with ostrich fan and pearl tiara. The string of pearls was a wedding present from one of her aunts.

The old house became very much alive during the next few weeks. The telephone rang continually, maps were spread over tables—for our geography was appalling—and my father made innumerable journeys to London. It was to be a five-year appointment, and there were many problems to sort out. He was still in great doubt about accepting the offer; he even went so far as to ask to have his name withdrawn but was begged by the Dominions Office not to do this. He had quite decided that he would not go unless he could take all his family with him. The main difficulties were the interruption of our education and doubts about whether my grandmother could or should be left for five years. She settled this herself by persuading him that she really wanted him to accept. 'It will be a great challenge, and I should like to see you tackle it,' she said. Little did she know then how her words would come back to him later on.

Our education was eventually arranged to my father's satisfaction after he had made several long telephone calls to Sydney.

And so it was, then, that during the dark, cold months of the winter of 1929/30, all the preparations for our journey to Australia were begun.

My mother made mysterious visits to London, and a few weeks later huge exciting parcels began to arrive by post. These were full of clothes for her 'trousseau'. As the parcels arrived, they were unpacked and her dresses were hung up in a spare-room cupboard. When her friends came to tea, directly the business of eating and drinking was over they would all vanish upstairs to be shown the collection. Their oohs and ahs and ecstatic expressions of approval floated downstairs. They sounded to me like people watching a high trapeze act at a circus, with their little high-pitched screams of delight intermingled with low notes of awe. After a time they would emerge, chattering furiously all down the stairs like a flock of parrots, to pat me on the head or tweak my chin, making such remarks as 'What a lucky little girl!', 'Aren't you excited?', 'What a *lovely* time you're going to have' and then 'What *dream* clothes you've got, my dear!' to my mother as they finally departed throught the hall to the front door.

I did not think much of some of the day clothes my mother bought. Beige was the 'in' colour. I considered this drab and dull. I was not too keen on cloche hats either; her face seemed to alter when she had them on and was not really 'Mummy'. But her evening dresses I adored.

There was a pale pink chiffon embossed with tiny matching pink velvet flowers. It had a gently swathed top and the skirt fell in soft folds. The little flowers danced and glowed as my mother moved in it. The apricot satin was totally different, being close-fitting and slinky. It was more beautiful than the pink chiffon but not so pretty, rather as some women have striking features but a severe expression. All the same, it certainly did justice to my mother's slim figure. There was a black evening dress too, covered with yellow flowers. I hated that one, but I was told that Arthur—the couturier who designed all these dresses—considered that it suited Her Ladyship to *perfection*. I did not agree but kept my opinions to myself. The one I liked best of all was a quite delicious pale eau-de-nil silk. I thought it was a dress fit for a queen. It looked to me like moonlight, and it might have been in just such a dress that Maud stole away into the garden to meet her lover. The dress my mother considered her best for really formal occasions was gold. It was cut with a straight, narrow skirt. The material was lacy and radiated light. Worn with a pearl tiara, it won instant approval in Sydney.

To be worn over these as evening wraps for visits to theatres, balls and dinners were two evening coats that I remember in particular. One was a black velvet cape with a large white fur collar and cuffs, the other a perfectly delicious white fur jacket. The pile was deep and luxurious, and burying my face in it was like being enveloped by a pedigree Persian cat. My cheeks disappeared into the depths of the fur and I was transported to a kind of Alice-in-Wonderland world where the fur became larger and larger and I became smaller and smaller.

Lina Arnold, a Swiss au pair girl, was living with us at the time. My parents invited her to come with us to Sydney. She would have to look after my mother's clothes and continue teaching me French conversation. Lina was very keen to travel, and her parents very sensibly throught it a wonderful opportunity for her. She went home to Switzerland to say goodbye to them and to have a few lessons in hairdressing so that she could keep my mother's hair in order during the voyage.

The next few months for my father may well have been as hectic as any he had yet experienced. His personal life became one of incessant telephone calls, visits from and interviews with the press, hurried visits to London to order clothes and to see people who would be helpful in giving him their advice. He also had to make time to say goodbye to relations and friends. As well as all this, of course, he was being briefed about the job he was to do.

As his personal aide-de-camp, the Air Ministry recommended a young man who had started his career in the navy but had been transferred to the air force. Charles Gifford (who still retained his rank as lieutenant-commander) not only was to become one of our greatest friends and a companion to all the family but was to capture the hearts of nearly the whole of Sydney. He was at the one time carefree and light-hearted, impulsive and kind, comic and serious. His laugh was almost unbelievable. It started as a little tinkling stream, then rushed along at ever-increasing speed until it was in full spate, carrying with it by this time the entire room. Its volume was colossal. When he was in good form, Charles could silence a whole stage full of actors and actresses, partly because they could not be heard, but mostly because they too were being carried away on the tidal wave of his laughter. His face, round and red like the setting sun, was usually wreathed in smiles. We loved him from the moment we met him.

One of my mother's oldest friends, Isabel Crowdy, also travelled out with us as my mother's personal secretary. Izzy, as we affectionately called her, taught me to play the piano and, in my mother's words, 'led all the family into the world of music'. This was not strictly accurate, for my father remained totally unmusical right to the end of his life. Isabel was a dear, kind person, and she too became very much loved.

On the morning of 23 April 1930, eight excited people met at Victoria Station to catch the boat train to Dover. They discovered to their utter astonishment that a crowd of relations and friends, including Sir Hugh Trenchard and Sir Geoffrey Salmond, representing the Royal Air Force, had gathered together to bid them farewell. My mother was so overwhelmed and talked so long and so hard that she almost missed the train. She was pushed in by friends and pulled in by us after it had started to leave the platform.

Above: *Isabel Crowdy, my mother's private secretary and one of her oldest friends.*

Right: *My father and his aide-de camp, Commander Charles Gifford, in full dress Royal Air Force uniform.*

2 Voyage to Australia

WE travelled overland to Marseilles because my mother was such a bad sailor. We had an enormous amount of luggage, a great deal of which must have gone round by sea. My parents had been advised to take some small pieces of furniture, books and pictures to fill the 'blank walls of Government House'. At the back of our minds was an odd feeling that we were off to a bare, far distant land where modern amenities and the comforts of life were hard to come by. What a surprise was in store for us!

Really, the English in those days were appallingly insular; the Empire in many people's minds was decidedly uncivilised besides being far flung. We were no exception.

At Marseilles we joined SS *Moldavia* of the P & O Line. Captain Allen had a kindly, weather-beaten face. He had taken tremendous trouble to make us comfortable. Two cabins amidships had been converted into a private sitting-room; as well as this, the small piece of deck directly outside them was reserved for our own personal use. This overlooked the bows of the ship, so that from it we had an almost uninterrupted view of the sea ahead. Besides the sitting-room, my mother and father had a bedroom and dressing-room, and each of us three children had a cabin to ourselves.

To me the whole voyage was sheer joy from beginning to end. A few days after we got on board we were able to use the swimming pool. The ship was full, and as there seemed to be plenty of young people, we were soon one large and gloriously happy band of youth.

I sometimes wonder if the older folk enjoyed that voyage quite as much as we did. We spent hours swimming. Plenty of games were provided—deck quoits, rings to throw on to hooks, sandbags to lob into squares, and nets for deck tennis—but our energy seemed inexhaustible. Bill invented his own game, gathering together the younger members of the ship for a new version of French and English. 'Divide yourselves into two teams,' he said. 'Team A is to straddle itself across the ship at all levels. Team B will go to the stern and at a given signal from me will storm the enemy lines and reach the bows without being caught.'

We set off with screams and shouts of joy. Each day the teams would change sides. Only the bridge and engine-room were out of bounds, and we were not too fussy about people who were resting or wanting to read. We did, however, try to choose a convenient time for this gleeful romp, partly because of a few pesonal requests from the less youthful passengers but also because by teatime we had exhausted all other entertainment. We started

Bill, my mother, myself and David on board the Moldavia.

promptly at 5 p.m. I lived for five o'clock. To me it was a most exhilarating moment when we could tear along the deck at high speed or wait behind a convenient door to seize the enemy. Occasionally accidents occurred when the enemy turned out to be an elderly lady or gentleman disappearing to the lavatory.

Father was an excellent sailor. He loved the sea and was never happier than when in a ship. He and I got up very early as the voyage went on and the weather became hot. Sometimes we were on deck as early as 5 a.m., he in his white flannel trousers and I in my pyjamas rolled up to the knee, paddling together while the sailors washed down the decks.

'Like to help clean the brass?' they would say to me, and they let me help (or hinder) them whenever I felt inclined. Those early mornings were lovely. We would stand for ages gazing out over the ocean and watch the gulls wheeling in the wake of the ship. Every now and then a box of rubbish would be tipped over the side and the gulls would dive down to snatch a titbit before it sank into the waves. The pearly skies, blue sea and the sun suddenly bursting up over the horizon had an appeal for me which in a different way was every bit as enjoyable as the riotous games of the evening before.

The first excitement after we left Marseilles was seeing Stromboli belching fire and smoke and behaving very attractively for us. On we went through the Strait of Messina, very close to the Sicilian shore with its tiny white houses huddled together looking like model villages, until we reached our first port of call, Port Said.

To the experienced traveller Port Said is dull, dirty, noisy and flat. But to us children it was tremendously thrilling. Never before had we seen anything like it. The little boats that came crowding round the *Moldavia*, the shouting natives and the intriguing souks, where exotic wares were for sale, amazed us. The tourist shop Simon Artz and the stalls outside it seemed to me to be filled with treasures to delight the eye. Perhaps I felt on familiar ground as we swung slowly from the quayside and began our journey down through the Suez Canal, for had I not been this way before, to visit the 'Punjab' in his castle? There were no troubles or disputes over the canal in those days, and we sailed on most peacefully past little native dhows and into the Bitter Lakes. By the time we reached Suez we were into May and it was becoming very warm.

Although my geography was poor, I was beginning to discover things: I soon learnt that Suez was the great gateway to that most entrancing of waterways, the Red Sea. Both its shape and its name spelt romance. I had been well grounded in the doings of the Children of Israel. We must be getting near to the place where the Egyptians in their fine chariots were engulfed by this long, narrow stretch of water.

Captain Allen was most understanding and kind. 'Come up on the bridge whenever you like,' he said. 'No need to ask, just find your way up.' Looking back, I realise that in the heedless way of youth I took so much for granted, never really realising how lucky I was to be given such a privilege. But I have at least remembered the joy of seeing the ship pounding through the waves from high up above her bows. I tried to imagine the sea being divided into two parts and huge walls of water rising up on either side, leaving a dry pathway. Moses would have been standing over on the left bank, his hand raised imperiously to dominate those great waters, waiting for the moment to command them to crash down with all their fury and swallow up the enemy. His domination of that powerful sea and his complete mastery of the situation made me shiver a little, even though it had all happened so long ago. Perhaps even now those people and their chariots were still lying below the ship in which we were being borne southward.

It was almost night when we reached Aden, the time when for a moment the earth seems to stand still. We were just in time to see the red rocky hills behind the little town glowing in the last of the sunset. Gradually lights began to twinkle, first a sprinkling of them, then more and more thickly, until Aden became like a jewel on the edge of the dark water. Little rowing-boats, each with its own coloured lantern, came towards the ship, bringing out their wares to sell. Baskets filled with beads and bangles were held up in the light of the ship, and the sea round the *Moldavia* was alive with dark, eager faces and the sparkle of their merchandise. To me it was like Aladdin's cave.

We awoke in the morning to a blue sea and a heaving swell. The jewels of Aden were a dream that had vanished in the night.

A sailor knocked on our sitting-room door that morning. 'A wireless message for you,' he said. It had been sent by a passing ship. 'Respectful greetings and good wishes for term of office,' it read, and was signed by the Bishop of Grafton. My mother later recorded 'This was the first time that we were to hear those pregnant words "term of office" which I have ever since associated with extremes of enjoyment and happiness, but also with the opposite.'

It evidently came home to her that this was no ordinary voyage, that we were on our way to the unknown, to a job that was to be both taxing and rewarding, and she knew, I think, that the ultimate result depended largely upon her husband and herself.

Approaching Ceylon we were greeted by pale, sandy beaches and waving palm trees. It was a good foretaste of the beauty of the island. Forest-covered hills, tropical fruits and flowers, women clad in the rich colours of the East, and the hot air filled with the scent of spices—all combined together to reveal something of the appeal of the tropics. Small wonder that we were sad to have only one day on this sunlit island. Indeed, the sun was tremendously hot, and we were glad of the shade from the umbrella-like banyan trees, their aerial roots ornamented with great hanging tassels. We visited a Buddhist temple. It was cool inside, cool and dark. On a high platform, Buddha lay on his back looking heavenward, an immense figure seventy feet long and painted yellow. I gazed up at him in wonder. There were no angels round his throne, and he gave me no sense of strength or awe. I was puzzled at having to remove our shoes as a token of respect before entering his house, for the atmosphere was more of curiosity than of mystery. Our feet were scrubbed with disinfectant that night, as Buddha's floor in my mother's opinion was none too clean. The sun was sinking red into the Indian Ocean as we left on our long sea voyage towards Australia.

Jan Kubelik, the world-famous Czech violinist and father of the conductor Rafael Kubelik. Even my father, who was not musical, loved to listen to him playing.

There were some interesting passengers on board. The Czech violinist Jan Kubelik was one. He was kindly and unassuming, but with great pride he told us that he had a son who would one day be a world-famous conductor. It still seemed a little unreal to be sitting on board a ship in mid-ocean listening to Kubelik playing his violin, when such a short time before I had been bicycling down the lanes of Somerset. Another evening two comedians, Madge Elliott and Hindel Edgar, who were on their way to play in *Mr Cinders* at Her Majesty's Theatre in Sydney, entertained the passengers with short skits. Everyone enjoyed that evening. Then of course there was our Charles Gifford who, as usual, was the life and soul of the party, particularly at the ceremony of Crossing the Line. My chief memories of this are round the swimming pool, where Charles picked up a middle-aged woman (who was considered rather fast because she wore pale pink beach pyjamas) and threw her into the water fully clad, to the delighted cheers of the spectators.

By this time my mother had got her sea legs and was living and eating like a normal human being. She realised that while I was enjoying myself hugely I was doing no school work at all. She produced a geography textbook, and we started off with the capes of England. This bored me to tears. I was just not interested in the North Foreland, Selsey Bill or even Land's End, and I said so.

'All right,' she said, 'but we'll go on with geography for the moment because although we are travelling right across the world I don't think you've any idea of England and its geographical relationship to Europe.'

She was quite right, and she was wonderfully patient. By the time we were passing the Cocos Islands she had managed to get the following remarkable piece of information into my head. At the bottom of England came the Channel, and crossing that you reached France. Heading straight on down there was more water, the Mediterranean. Across that and there you were, in

Africa! I thought of it as a kind of wet sandwich, a double-decker. England, France and Africa were the bread, the Channel and the Mediterranean the watery filling. I would mutter to myself in a singsong way: 'England, the Channel, France, the Med, and North *Africa*', where I stopped abruptly, unable to proceed any further south.

As a change from geography my mother would read poetry to me, and this I loved. She read beautifully, and I was soon enjoying wandering among 'a host of golden daffodils' and, even more, listening to the adventures of Sir Ralph the Rover. I could look down to the water and imagine the clanging bell and Sir Ralph pacing up and down the deck, tearing his hair in despair. It was almost too graphic, and I shuddered a little and shut my eyes as I thought of the ship striking the rock. Suppose the *Moldavia* were to do that . . . but she sailed peacefully on through the great swelling ocean.

We did a little history too, but as we had no history books my mother told me stories that she thought would interest me. How Victoria became Queen when she was only eighteen and how carefully she had been guarded as a child because of her wicked uncle, the Duke of Cumberland; for the alarming rumours surrounding him had suggested that he might do away with Victoria in order to have the throne for himself. I was also told about poor mad King George III, who had stepped out of his carriage and shaken hands with a branch of an oak tree, mistaking it for the Emperor of Prussia, and that it was during George's reign that English people first went to live in Australia.

With the lessons and games to occupy me, the eleven days it took to cross the Indian Ocean passed quickly, and we soon reached the morning when we saw Australia for the first time and steamed into Fremantle's harbour.

'How do you like Australia?' The question rang in our ears as we stepped off the gangway onto the great continent. It is difficult to feel emotional about wharves, warehouses and cranes, and there had not been any opportunity to form an opinion about Australia as yet. We were met by a mass of reporters, all anxious to glean our very first impressions. Naturally we were tremendously thrilled to have landed at last in the country in which we were to live for the next five years. So we conveyed our very happy and genuine impression that Australia was just fine.

After shaking hands with mayors, mayoresses and a large number of others, all bedecked with chains, ribbons and medals, we were whisked off in a large official car for the eleven-mile drive to Perth, where we were to lunch at Government House. It was a beautiful drive beside the lovely Swan River. There were flowers everywhere, hedges of red and purple bougainvillea, blue plumbago and big bushes of yellow cassia beside the road, all deliciously luxuriant and so, so different from anything I had seen in England.

'Don't forget to curtsy to the Governor, Rosemary,' said my mother. 'Just a little bob will do. Bend your knees and please *smile*.'

I sat ruminating on this and hoping that my knees would know what to do. We were ushered into a huge room with a long row of uniformed and highly decorated gentlemen, interspersed with ladies in their best party wear. It was all very well to have been given instructions how to greet the Governor, but how was I to pick him out among such a fine array? I watched my mother, and waited for her knees to sink a little, but she reached the end of the line without so much as a tremor.

'I'll have to take pot luck,' I said to myself. So I picked out the tallest, best looking and most beribboned gentleman and decided to place my bet on him. Luck was on my side; I had picked the winner. My mother afterwards admitted that in all the excitement she had forgotten her bob.

After lunch we were taken round the garden. There is never a frost in Perth, and roses flower all the year round. Large blue water-lilies with yellow stamens stood six inches out of the water and were massed to form a coloured carpet hovering over the lake. The wildflowers of Western Australia are considered to be some of the finest in the world. One that fascinated me was the kangaroo paw, with its flowers shaped in thickish fingers felted with hairs and slightly rough to the touch. The particular variety we saw that day had bright emerald green and red flowers. The welcome given to us and natural beauty of Perth left a lasting impression, and I have many times longed to revisit that beautiful city and state.

The next part of our journey was to take us through the Great Australian Bight, that Bay of Biscay of the Southern Hemisphere dreaded by all bad sailors. My mother began to lose both her nerve and her sea legs at the mere thought of it. We were beastly to her: 'Of course you'll be sick if you keep on thinking you're going to be. Read a book or something; don't keep on watching the horizon.' Mercifully it stayed very calm.

The days sped by with never a moment to be bored. Usually the Australian coast was within sight. It looked very romantic. Giant albatrosses came close to the ship but not close enough to satisfy David, who wanted to photograph them. 'They really are most unobliging birds,' he said, after ages spent trying to attract them by waving various bits of coloured clothing. 'Just as I think I can get a picture of them, they glide silently away.' And so they did, hour after hour, using the currents of air quite effortlessly and with no apparent movement of their huge wings.

Something of our growing inward excitement at the thought of reaching our new home before long must have spread to the other passengers, for before we reached Adelaide all but four of them were joining in the five o'clock raiding game and finding that they were thoroughly enjoying themselves.

During the last two weeks the nights had been as lovely as the days. As the sun sank away below the horizon and it rapidly became dark, it was as though a deep blue velvet mantle strewn with diamonds had been drawn across the sky. The entire heavens were covered with stars which shone with a brilliance only seen in the clear atmosphere of the sub-tropics. No Pole star, no Plough or Cassiopeia above us now, but up there, among the myriad tiny dazzling lights, shone the Southern Cross. Below, in the water, the ship cut through flashing particles of light, phosphorus, which suddenly shone with an eerie greenish light and then, as suddenly, vanished.

Now we were at Adelaide, which nestles so comfortably into the surrounding arms of the coast. Again, as in Perth, we were met by an army of reporters and photographers. Even the poor captain was fetched from his cabin so that we could all be photographed together.

We began to feel closer to Sydney now, for the Official Secretary to the Governor of New South Wales, Harry Budge, and his wife had travelled all the way to Adelaide to meet us. In those days flying was very limited and the train journey was a very long one, so they had taken considerable trouble in coming as far as they did to greet us. They were kindness itself and a tower of strength. Mrs Budge was a tremendous help to my mother in being able to tell her all about the house in Sydney, the servants and other domestic concerns. Mr Budge looked at us three children—fair haired and blue-eyed— and said, 'My word, you'll be lucky to get them home to England unspoilt!'

Melbourne was our last port of call. There we were able to spend a night with Lord and Lady Somers at Government House. I remember little about this except that, as always, everyone was extremely kind and welcoming, but that the house was rather stark and formidable and from outside had the appearance of a white, sugar-encrusted wedding cake.

My mother was taken for a most remarkable drive up into the hills by Lady Somers. I quote from her diary:

> We went by what I thought was the most impossible road. It was so rough that at one time we had to get out of the car and fill the crevices in the tracks with tree bark and material of that kind before we could drive on. We were enormously amused at being caught by a reporter when a long way out of Melbourne and photographed together on this mountain road. We felt he deserved a Scouts Tracker's badge. The glorious vegetation, the tree ferns and the views impressed me enormously. Lady Somers is young and good-looking and appears so completely at home in her position as governor's wife that she fills me with admiration.

Lady Somers, wife of the Governor of Victoria, and my mother in Melbourne. Lady Somers gave my mother very helpful advice, especially about making speeches, which my mother was dreading.

While we were in Melbourne, great discussions were going on about the way in which we were to be taken off the *Moldavia* when we reached Sydney. Brigadier-General Austin Anderson, my father's private secretary, and his wife (who was to achieve renown as the poet and short-story writer Ethel Anderson) met us here, partly to complete the arrangements for the landing. The *Moldavia* was due to dock at six o'clock in the morning. As this was not a suitable hour for an official reception for the new Governor, the captain proposed holding up the ship for a few hours so as to arrive at a more convenient time. 'Certainly not,' said my father characteristically. 'Why on earth should all the other passengers suffer just because of us.' In the end it was agreed that we should be disembarked early, in the centre of the harbour, into the cruiser HMAS *Australia* and landed officially from her a few hours later, while the *Moldavia* proceeded to berth. I presume that signals were then sent off to Sydney to this effect.

Three days later, very early in the morning of 29 May, there was a bang on my door and in burst Bill. 'Come on,' he said. 'We're all going up on the bridge.' We had arrived.

3 *The Swearing-in of the New Governor*

THE dawn was breaking and the sky behind us was turning to a pink pearl as we stood looking at the long line of coast straight ahead of us. The land towards the right-hand side was high with cliffs; rough waves were breaking at their base. To the left it was lower and there were houses thickly sprinkled over the headland.

'There are the heads, sir.' The captain was speaking to my father and mother, who were gazing at the coastline. 'Botany Bay lies down to the south.' He pointed left. 'That has a more obvious entrance. It's easy to see why Captain Cook missed this one, isn't it?'

The pilot came on board at this moment, and the captain walked over to the companionway to welcome him aboard ship. Everyone was introduced, and the grown-ups chatted for a while until the pilot took command. The sun's first rays were just striking the shore.

'There's North Head to your right, with the weather station, and South Head over there with the lighthouse,'said Captain Allen, pointing half left. He was anxious to see that we understood the lie of the land.

By this time we were steaming slowly through the great gap. 'You need to know your navigation here,' remarked my father. 'I shouldn't care to steer her through that without a few lessons first.'

The captain bent down and spoke to me. 'You won't see your new home yet, my dear. The harbour has long points of land stretching out into it, and we've got to get round Bradley's Head before you can see the full length.'

Just round Bradley's Head, I discovered, was Sydney's Taronga Zoo. It was a fine site for a zoo, on high ground covered with trees down to the water's edge, where the waves lapped gently over the sandstone rocks.

We rounded the headland, and there before us lay the rest of the harbour, breathtakingly beautiful, the water glinting like silver in the morning sun.

We were all talking at once. 'What's that bay, Captain? It's huge. There's a *tiny* one over there. Look at that headland! Oh, what a place! Look at those *trees* and the gardens and *boats*!' Our words tumbled over each other in our excitement, and the other officers smiled at our enthusiasm. There was so much to look at, so much to take in, so many things to learn, that I felt utterly bewildered and stared unbelievingly at the panorama opening up before my eyes. I had never imagined anything quite like this.

By now we could see right up the harbour so that Government House and the Botanic Gardens next to it were visible but still too small to be seen in any detail. The ship anchored, and reluctantly we went below to have break-

Our first view of Government House, from the harbour. In front are the Botanic Gardens, where my father and I walked our dog, Micky, most evenings.

fast. At that moment food seemed trivial, and we could hardly be bothered with it, but I imagine we ate something.

After breakfast we went off to make ourselves ready for the great moment of landing, Father and Charles to put on their decorations and Mother to change her coat and put on her hat. The next thing I remember is being once again on the bridge of the ship, which was steaming slowly ahead towards the cruiser HMAS *Australia* waiting to welcome us. *Moldavia* was dressed overall and must have been a fine sight as with grace and simple dignity she slowly proceeded up the harbour. There were dozens of small craft out that morning, gleaming in the sunlight and casting their little shadows on the rippling water.

'Do you see those great metal arms jutting out from each shore beyond the cruiser?' said one of the officers, pointing to the beginnings of the new bridge that was to span the harbour. 'They will soon form the arch which will support the road and rail underneath it.'

'They look like giant Meccano,' said David, who was a Meccano enthusiast.

The greenery and gardens appealed to my mother. 'Isn't it *beautiful?*' she said. 'All those houses with their natural rock gardens and trees and plants growing down to the water's edge.' She was longing to see the gardens more closely and to explore the edge of the harbour.

Now we passed close to a small fortified island, Fort Denison, commonly known as Pinchgut, we were told, as it had been used as a prison for the first convicts sent out from England. 'They couldn't escape,' explained Captain Allen, 'because of the sharks. Harbour's full of 'em. Don't you imagine you can run down to the water's edge and jump in for a swim,' he said to me. 'Get your leg bitten off in no time!'

By this time we were nearly level with Garden Island, headquarters of the Royal Australian Navy. Here there were more warships and naval craft all dressed overall and glistening in the sun. One of us asked about the next headland, which formed the eastern side of the bay called Farm Cove, in

the vicinity of which Government House and its grounds were situated.

'That's Mrs Macquarie's chair,' we were told. 'Mrs Macquarie was the wife of one of the early governors. She used to sit on those large sandstone rocks waiting to see the packet-boat arrive from England. It took six months to get here in those days, so you can imagine how she felt when she first saw the ship coming into the harbour.' We certainly could; for six weeks we had been waiting for the day when we would arrive in Sydney and at last see our new home. Now we were actually there and in a fever to learn about everything.

We soon found out that the fine park behind the rocky chair in which Mrs Macquarie had sat all those years ago was the Domain. From it you could walk on round to the Botanic Gardens which bordered Farm Cove and then on to the gardens of Government House.

The house was now clearly visible, a long majestic sandstone building beautifully proportioned. A colonnade of arches held up a top verandah and provided a shady terrace for the downstairs rooms. Above the main roof was a tower, and from it was flying the Union Jack.

'There is your home,' said Captain Allen, and wished us every happiness in it. We suddenly realised that within a very short while we were going to have to say goodbye to this charming man and the ship that had been our home for a month and a half. I well remember my parents thanking the captain and officers for all their kindness to us during those weeks, and for a moment a little cloud of sadness shaded the brilliant sunshine.

Below decks a curious scene was being enacted. As one of the stewards put it, 'We're having a fine game with all this Game luggage!' In the part of the ship that we had occupied, luggage was piled to the ceiling. The narrow corridors and alleyways were practically impassable by the time it had all been collected together. It is almost unbelievable that so much could have been taken by eight people, for the list of larger items included twenty trunks, thirteen suitcases, twenty-one wooden boxes, five hat boxes, six attaché cases, four canvas bags and three tin cases of uniform, besides which were packages of umbrellas, golf clubs, tennis racquets, skis, deckchairs, a sewing machine and a large flag! The sum total was *one hundred and eleven packages!* We had certainly come to stay!

A pinnace from HMAS *Australia* was on its way to us. The brass on its deck shone like small suns as it cut its way through the sparkling water. With the gold braid glinting on his uniform and the white feathers of his cocked hat shining in the sun, the captain came aboard to welcome my parents and take them and Charles to his ship. We children followed in another launch with Isabel and Lina.

The Commander of the Australian Squadron, Vice-Admiral E.R.G. Evans (the great Evans of the *Broke*), was at the top of the companionway to greet us, his officers drawn up beside him and the band marching up and down the deck playing cheerful naval music. It was, of course, a dream! What else

Above: *The Premier of New South Wales, T.R. Bavin, welcomes the new Governor at Man-o'-War Steps, Farm Cove. Behind my parents are Mrs Bavin and the Official Secretary, Harry Budge; Charles Gifford can just be seen beyond them.*

Opposite page: *My father, wearing full dress RAF uniform, with decorations, and the delightful twinkle that endeared him to so many people.*

Spectators and a military guard wait in the Government House drive for the arrival of the new Governor. The Astor flats in Macquarie Street (on the right) and the British Medical Association building beyond were, at that time, two of the tallest buildings in Sydney. On the far left is the Conservatorium of Music.

could it be, this gleaming display of dazzling gold and white, flags of all colours waving and dancing in the breeze, a background of trumpets and drums to enhance the splendour, all in a setting of sapphire blue sea and sunshine? Soon we would wake to find ourselves back in the normal life of a comfortable house in rural Somerset. Tea and sandwiches in the Admiral's stateroom, where both Mrs Evans and the captain's wife were waiting for us, helped to dispel the feeling of unreality which had come upon us. So did a wonderful tour, for us children, over the entire cruiser, from the depths of the engine-rooms to the height of the bridge. Up and down companionways and in and out of alleyways we trotted, creeping into gun turrets and gazing with awe at the magazine. Surely no dream could ever include such fantastic entertainment.

At 10.40 we were summoned back to the launch, all together this time, to be landed on the jetty at Man-o'-War Steps. As we slipped away from the shadow of the great cruiser, she fired the first of a seventeen-gun salute. The deep boom echoing over the water shook us almost literally back into the world of reality. No dream could produce gunfire as real as this. With each resounding report my heart gave an answering thump.

Now we were at the quayside, and the scene we beheld cannot be better described than by my mother:

> *The crowds on the quay, the escort waiting, the flags in the sunshine! As Philip stepped ashore the Premier of New South Wales came to meet him. We all shook hands and felt that it was a great moment. We knew directly we met Mr Bavin that he was a man with whom we could be great friends. His charming face looked so kindly at us and his welcome was so warm and sincere. He introduced us to his wife and and all the other official people on the quay who were waiting for us, amongst whom were (the now famous) Mr Lang (Leader of the Opposition), the Commissioner of Police and the heads of the Navy, Army and Air Force.*
>
> *Mrs Bavin gave me the loveliest bouquet of flowers, then we walked along*

the red carpet to the dais chatting to everyone and feeling their friendship towards us. There we stood, in a semicircle. Philip had a welcoming address read to him and then read his reply to it. We then came down from the dais and I waited by the car while Philip inspected the cavalry escort. They looked magnificent with great emu plumes in their turned-up hats, and made us feel that we really were in Australia.

There were crowds everywhere and we felt ourselves being photographed at every moment. Finally Philip and I got into the car, with Charles in front, and drove off amidst cheers, clapping and waving. The escort trotted after us and the children followed in a car behind them. Philip had to salute, and I had to bow and smile as we drove all through the principal streets of the city. There were crowds of people nearly all the way who shouted 'That's right, Sir Philip', 'Welcome to Australia', 'God save the King', and waved flags and gave us such a wonderfully warm feeling of greeting. Finally we turned into the big gates of Government House and were there.

'Sir Philip! Sir Philip! Don't you realise that this house belongs to me and that I should be living here? Please, Sir.' The words of 'the Mad Lady in

Government House viewed from the driveway gate. The Union Jack flying from the tower indicates that the Governor is in residence.

The downstairs verandah and colonnade of Government House facing the garden. This was often used for summer parties so that guests could wander out onto the lawns. The large ficus tree at left used to be lit by fairy lights for parties and dances.

Purple' as we later christened her, trailed off protestingly as she was borne away by the police. She was from a mental home and had managed to hide herself behind a pillar beside the front door. She was the first person to greet the new Governor!

The Lieutenant-Governor, Sir William Cullen, rushed up, and after a word of apology took my mother by the arm and escorted her into the house. 'We do hope you will all be happy,' he said. Happy! Happy! The word seemed to echo and re-echo from wall to wall as we walked into the front hall, through a narrower passage, and on into the main hall, until a feeling of joy was dancing in all our hearts. The rooms appeared full of people, a great moving mass of smiling faces.

Suddenly there was a girl of my own age beside me. We smiled at each other as she said, 'My name is Rosemary, too. I'm Rosemary Budge.' She was the daughter of the Official Secretary who had come to meet us at Adelaide. We instantly became firm friends.

'If you will come with me, I will take you to your seats,' said a kind young honorary aide-de-camp. He collected us young ones together, and back we went to the outer hall, where there was a small staircase leading up to the minstrels' gallery above the ballroom.

We looked down upon a moving scene of brilliant colour. Robes of ermine and scarlet with full-bottomed wigs, uniforms of khaki and blue and the sober black of morning coats were complemented by the ladies in their richest attire. The Town Clerk was an outstanding figure in his long black robes with velvet facings, lace ruffles and a wig. 'Why do they wear *wigs*?' I whispered to Rosemary. 'Are they all bald?'

Hanging on the walls of this magnificent room and adding to the splendour below us were life-size portraits of kings and queens in their most regal apparel. They seemed to be giving their silent approval of the ceremony. From where we sat we could see the dais and my father, in his pale blue full dress air force uniform and glittering medals, standing beside a golden throne. Next to him, in front of the throne, was the Lieutenant-Governor. The Chief Justice and the Premier were on either side. With them were Charles, also in air force uniform , and Rosemary's father. Never before had I seen anything like this, and as I gazed down in wonder I could hardly believe my eyes.

A solemn hush fell on the room. The great swearing-in ceremony was about to begin. The Lieutenant-Governor rose to his feet and in a most dignified voice said, 'The ceremony upon which we are now entering is the swearing in of the new Governor of New South Wales. At the request of the Governor designate, I will first ask the Official Secretary to read the commission from His Majesty the King under the Royal Sign Manual and Signet appointing Sir Philip Woolcott Game to be Governor of New South Wales and its Dependencies.'

The two Rosemarys planting Rosemary bushes at the time of the opening of the Sydney Harbour Bridge. The bushes were obliterated when the new highway was built many years later.

The throne in the ballroom of Government House on which my father sat for part of the swearing-in ceremony. He was reluctant to sit on it at all; he thought it altogether too pompous.

It was absorbing. I sat quite still, watching and listening to the dramatic words while the Official Secretary read the King's commission. Now it was the turn of the Lieutenant-Governor once more.

'In a moment,' he said, 'I will ask the Chief Justice of the Supreme Court of New South Wales to administer the oath of allegiance and judicial oath to the Governor designate. When the oaths have been administered, His Excellency the Governor will sign the proclamation of his assumption of office and immediately thereupon the salute will be fired. Will you please stand.'

More guns, I thought. But there was no time to be apprehensive, for the Chief Justice in his splendid robes was giving the open Bible to my father, who, taking it in his right hand, read the two oaths set out for him on a printed form.

'I, Philip Woolcott Game, do swear that I will be faithful and bear true allegiance to His Majesty King George V, his heirs and successors according to Law. So help me God.'

And then:

'I, Philip Woolcott Game, do swear that I will well and truly serve His Majesty King George V in the office of Governor of New South Wales and its Dependencies in the Commonwealth of Australia, and I will do right to all manner of people after the laws and usages of this State without fear or favour, affection or ill-will. So help me God.'

To see my own father standing there, the Bible in his hand, and to hear him saying those awe-inspiring words—'I will be faithful', 'I will do right', 'So help me God'—stirred in me some deep emotion which I did not then fully understand. Later I came to realise all the pride and poignancy which had touched me that day. My father himself may well have recalled those words two years later—in particular 'I will do right...without fear or favour, affection or ill-will'—so pertinent were they to become.

Meanwhile, the official documents were being signed, and then for the last time the Lieutenant-Governor rose from the gold throne in the centre of the dais and offered it to the new Governor with the words 'I tender to Your Excellency my respectful and my humble duty.' Immediately he finished the sentence the first great boom of the cannon-fire salute shook the room. All that remained to be done now was for the Official Secretary to read the proclamation. The ceremony was over.

The Premier, T. R. Bavin, then extended a warm welcome to both my parents, to which my father replied. As he wrote his speech himself, and it was said to be the best speech made by a Governor for many years, I quote it in full. He delivered it without reading it, and spoke as follows:

'His Majesty instructed me to tell you how he has always followed your fortunes with the deepest interest and sympathy since he first came among you as a midshipman in 1881, how his interest was enhanced by his visit as Duke of York in 1901, and how strong it has remained ever since.

'We have experienced nothing but kindness since we first knew we were coming to Sydney— kindness from Australians in London, kindness from Australians on our boat, and now kindness on all sides here—and I am sure of one thing, and that is that if we do not meet with the same kindness throughout my term of office we shall have no one to blame but ourselves.

Thomas Rainsford Bavin, Premier of New South Wales from 18 October 1927 to 3 November 1930, pictured in the grounds of Government House.

'I have been a soldier and have seen enough of war to be a convinced believer in peace. But if any good results can come from war, and especially from a world-wide war such as the last, I think they lie in the better knowledge of each other and the deeper sympathy between individuals, classes and countries which the coming together of the peoples of the Empire in its defence necessarily and inevitably brought about.

'There is no surer way of making friends than doing a job of work together. Friendship and understanding are a moral and not a material force, but, after all, mankind is finally governed by moral forces, and it seems to me that the spirit of comradeship which grew up during the war years is a priceless possession, the real, true bond of Empire, and to be cherished, extended and handed on to future generations by one and all of us, with all the strength that in us lies.

'I am delighted that the industrial dispute in your coalfields has found a

Opposite page: *The Great Hall and staircase of Government House. At the foot of the stairs is the table on which lay the visitors' book, for those who stayed in the house to sign before they left. A picture of Queen Victoria as a girl hangs over the archway.*

The view from my bedroom window looking across Farm Cove to Bradley's Head. I used to watch the liners coming round this headland and proceeding majestically up the harbour to berth. Charles Gifford gave me a splendid book so that I could identify the ships by their flags and funnels.

solution within the last few days, and I look upon this as a happy augury for the future prosperity of New South Wales and for me, personally, as a good omen for my time among you.'

'Shall I show you your room?' Rosemary was anxious to take me round the house. It was enormous. It had been designed by Edward Blore—the architect of Lambeth Palace—and it seemed to me like a huge Scottish castle, with a lovely home-like atmosphere. We ran up the wide staircase. Half-way up, the stairs divided to right and left, and on the wall at this junction of the two flights was a large portrait of a lady in evening dress. We would have dashed on had it not been for her name neatly printed on the bottom of the frame. It caught our eye and made us giggle: 'The Lady Santry'. We sped on up to the right and into a very long and rather dark passage.

Rosemary opened a door, and a flood of light and sunshine poured out towards us. She led me into a beautiful room with a french window opening on to a balcony. There before my eyes was the harbour, stretched out towards the sea. Lying, it seemed, only a few hundred feet from the edge of the garden was the cruiser from which we had just landed. We stood and looked and talked. Rosemary went through the names of the bays and headlands.

'You'll soon get to know them,' she said, 'and you can lie in bed and watch all the big liners coming up the harbour in the early morning.'

She was right. I soon became a boat-spotter. The larger the boat, the more funnels it had. A four-funnel Orient liner was my greatest delight. I could never resist rushing in to tell my parents when one of these arrived. Usually this was at about 6 a.m., and they seemed singularly uninterested! 'All right, darling, I'll come and look at her a little later on,' mother would say sleepily. It was useless to explain that 'a little later on' my beautiful boat would have turned into her dock and disappeared. The P & O boats were not so large or dramatic, but as they docked much further up the harbour than the Orient liners they sailed even nearer to my window before disappearing under what was slowly becoming the famous Sydney Harbour Bridge.

While Rosemary and I were chatting happily upstairs, my parents were still heavily involved downstairs. After the official ceremony had ended, they were asked to inspect guards of honour which were formed up in the drive. Scouts, Guides and Red Cross (including the Junior Red Cross, aged eight and upwards) were all there. My mother wrote:

> I did enjoy that, but I took so long looking at all their badges that Sir William Cullen came hurrying out saying that he was very sorry, but that we must come in and see all the people inside. We were then introduced to all the Law Lords and the officials. They were all so kind and welcoming and it

Looking east down the harbour from the upstairs verandah of Government House. The cruiser HMAS Australia *used to lie at anchor in Farm Cove, and its bells and bugles were a constant reminder to us of its presence.*

took some time, but finally they all left at about one o'clock. We then just had time to see our rooms before giving the Lieutenant-Governor lunch.

After lunch I had no time to change my shoes, which were dirty from inspecting the Guards of Honour, before we all had to be photographed again and again; in a family and then separately. At 2.15 p.m. we were on the dais again to stand there until 4.15 to receive Addresses of Welcome. We couldn't fidget or even stand on one leg! Philip read his answers to the Addresses and we then shook hands with the people by whom they had been presented. It was then that I felt the Australian grip. You have no idea what it is like, and nor had I, though I had been warned and was wearing no rings! This continued until late afternoon when we collapsed into chairs and had tea. The day had begun at 5.30 a.m. but there was still one more task to be done. Philip and Bill and I went down to the Cenotaph and laid a wreath. This was supposed to be quite unofficial, but a crowd collected at once. We are astonished at how quickly we are recognised by these Australians, and their welcome seems so genuine. We had a quiet dinner that night and to bed at last.

My parents' bedroom, which looks onto the garden. Note the mosquito net at the head of the bed, which was drawn at night to cover the entire bed. The door by the bed leads into my bedroom. These rooms were used by the Duke of Gloucester in 1935 and by Queen Elizabeth in 1973. Now another suite of rooms has been altered and refurbished for royal visits.

As I went to bed that night, I looked out over the harbour from my window. There were twinkling lights reflected in the water, and the watch-bells of the cruiser were ringing out the hours. It was still hard to believe that it was all true, and yet I knew that the memory of the day that had just passed would remain with me for the rest of my life.

4 Our New Home, and Amy Johnson

'COME ON, out of it, it's time to get up.' As the strange voice penetrated Bill's dreams, his mind reverted instantly to the events of the day before, and he answered sleepily, 'Wha' d'you want, photograph?' But the young footman, George, supposed to be well trained, was calling him for breakfast. It was a curious experience for us all—coming down to breakfast for the first time in that large, regal, but very homely house. We were waited on by Turner, the very dignified butler, and George. My father, who was horrified by such formality, soon put a stop to it. 'No waiting at breakfast,' he said firmly. 'We'll help ourselves from the side table.' And that was that.

George never appeared again after that day. It took me some time to find out what happened to him. I kept receiving evasive answers to my questions. At last I discovered the truth from my brothers. George had come in the worse for drink, made a terrible commotion, and fallen down one flight of the back stairs. He had been dismissed.

The first thing I did that morning was to explore the house, which my mother described in a letter to my grandmother:

> Philip and I and Rosemary have a lovely suite to ourselves. A great big bedroom for Philip and me and a lovely little one for Rosemary opening out of it. Both look out on to a verandah and the harbour. There is also a large dressing-room for Philip facing towards the bridge, with a bathroom between us. The view of the harbour is most beautiful. The cruiser Australia is lying in Farm Cove just in front of us so that we can hear her bells and bugles across the water. At night there could be no more glorious outlook with all the lights reflected in the harbour. The boys have bedrooms at the back of the house, with their own bathroom, and the servants' quarters are quite shut off in a separate part of the house. Isabel and Charles have rooms looking out the same way as ours, and further along the same passage is our large sunny sitting-room with the same wonderful view and beyond that all the visitors' rooms.

There was a grand piano in the upstairs sitting-room, and it was here that Isabel gave me piano lessons. She played the piano exquisitely, with rare feeling which came from her heart as well as her hands. Even now, so many years later, I have only to hear the opening bars of Brahms's Waltz in A-flat to be instantly transported back to that long passage and sunlit sitting-room.

It is curious that the memory of the sounds and scents of our childhood stay with us so long. The bells and bugles of HMAS *Australia* (particularly

the reveille played each morning), the screeching of parrots, the hollow, empty sound made by the magpies, so different from the birds I was used to, and the scent of the fluffy yellow wattle and brown flowers of boronia, are all things for which I still have a tender longing.

My mother's description of the house continues:

> *Downstairs, the drawing-room, dining-room and ballroom are very large and official. They are most suitable for entertaining. Philip has a charming study looking out on to a lawn with the most glorious big magnolia tree that I have ever seen. All the secretaries have offices, and also Sergeant Swan who looks after all the security arrangements, and there is a very nice billiard-room.*

I found these rooms very interesting. They seemed to me enormous. I soon discovered that as they were all connected, some of them by the kind of door that is flung open by flunkeys in ceremonial scenes in films, it was possible to start near the front door and run almost completely round the house and back again to the beginning without setting foot in the hall. This was to prove useful later on when I wished to avoid talking to visitors.

Round the walls in these impressive rooms were great portraits of kings,

My mother's upstairs sitting room. A few personal possessions, such as the screen, pictures and rugs, had been brought out from England.

queens, princesses, governors and, as the Litany so succinctly expresses it, 'The Lords of the Council and all the Nobility', a great many of whom must presumably have been imbued with 'grace, wisdom and understanding'. In the ballroom, King George V and Queen Mary looked down graciously, if a trifle severely, from their immense gilt frames. I think I'd have done what they told me, I said to myself; they look rather firm. In the drawing-room, poor, mad King George III and Queen Charlotte, whom I had been told about in my lessons on the *Moldavia*, hung stodgily on either side of the fireplace. Poor Charlotte! I felt sorry for her. Her large mouth was supposed to have made her look a little like a crocodile. My mouth was large too, and I

The dining room, where the portraits of former governors filled the walls. The door beneath Lord Beauchamp's portrait, at the far right, led to the kitchens, and when it was open it had a gap on the hinge side through which I could watch the guests at dinner.

fingered it anxiously and wondered about it. I looked at George III and tried to imagine him shaking hands with an oak tree. He *must* have been a little mad to do a thing like that. His eyes bulged oddly and had a glazed look. I did not reallly care for George and Charlotte.

Further on, on an adjacent wall, hung the elegant Princess of Wales dressed in a black dress with a bustle. On her slender hand was perched a snow-white cockatoo. She's lovely, I thought. Some people have all the luck—to be born beautiful *and* a princess.

The pictures in the dining-room interested me in quite a different way. Old Sir Richard Bourke smiled benignly down at everyone throughout the meal

The drawing room, with its beautiful mirror over the fire-place, a splendid background for the fine chandelier. It was in this room that I found my mother waiting in trepidation for my father and Premier Jack Lang to emerge from the study on the day of Lang's dismissal from office, 13 May 1932.

from his place above the sideboard, but over the door that led to the back part of the house and the kitchens was that quizzical gentleman Lord Beauchamp. Charles had found out all about Lord Beauchamp and how he had distinguished himself in a curious way when he was Governor. In trying to solve the parking problem for a large ball at Government House, he had ordered tickets for the ball to be printed in two different colours, some blue, some pink. The pink ticket holders came in through the front door, the blue tickets through the side door. The blue ticket holders were not pleased, and they referred to their tickets as 'Beauchamp's powders' and to the ball as the 'Seidlitz Ball'—an allusion to the blue and pink wrappers enclosing the two ingredients of Beecham's or Seidlitz powder, which were mixed separately in water and then combined to effervesce. All in all, Lord Beauchamp evidently was not one of the most tactful governors.

Staring at the kindly Bourke and the curious Beauchamp from the opposite wall was Governor Bligh. There he sat with his dark eyes peering into the room. He was a little unnerving at breakfast. Strange and fanciful stories surrounded him, stories of mutiny, cruelty and long voyages. It was enough to stop even a young hearty eater like me from finishing my toast and marmalade.

A few months later the D'Oyly Carte Opera Company came to Sydney. Every Saturday night Rosemary and I were taken to a different Gilbert and Sullivan opera at Her Majesty's Theatre. We enjoyed them all, but after we had been to *Ruddigore* the dining-room portraits took on a sinister air and with only a little imagination I could see the figures stepping quietly out of their frames and walking with measured step in a large circle round the dining-room table.

During the interval on the first night, Rosemary and I were taken backstage to meet Ivan Menzies and his leading lady, Elsie Morrison. It was thrilling to be allowed through the door marked 'NO ADMITTANCE', and when those kind actors and actresses extended a warm invitation to us to visit them whenever we felt inclined, naturally we accepted. Sometimes Ivan Menzies was a jester complete with coned hat and a stick with bells, sometimes a modern major-general or the captain of the *Pinafore*. We were entranced with the ladies too, so charming in their various costumes, and we could hardly bear it when the season eventually came to an end.

We had been in Sydney less than a week when an unusual event took place. Amy Johnson, the first woman to make a solo flight to Australia from England, had recently arrived in Brisbane. The Governor of Queensland was soon on the telephone. 'Can you have Amy to stay?' he begged my parents. 'She is on the verge of a nervous breakdown and must be kept very quiet.'

We agreed at once, of course [my mother recorded in her diary], *and I had beautiful rooms got ready for her. A sitting-room, bedroom and bathroom of her own. The police are to protect the house and keep reporters away. We are told that they 'expect the worst'. Until you have experienced it, it is hard to believe what reporters and crowds here can do! Poor Amy seems to have been very frightened by them. The children of course are thrilled at her coming and we are all intensely interested to meet her.*

My mother relaxing in her sitting room. The whole family would congregate here whenever there was time for us to be together, which was not very often, as my parents' days and evenings were often filled with official engagements.

A later entry in her diary records the arrival:

> Amy has just flown over amid shrieks from all the sirens and hooters on the
> harbour. It was a thrilling sight to see her plane, conducted by about a dozen
> smaller ones, fly right over the house. We couldn't resist going out on to the
> lawn and waving to her. A crowd has collected outside the house already, but
> they are kept well away by the length of the drive and the railings. There
> really is a wild state of excitement about her out here.

That same evening, while we were all eagerly awaiting Amy's arrival
at the house and trying to curb our impatience, there was a knock at the
door of the upstairs sitting-room, which was then flung open by the butler.
'Dr ———,' he announced.

The doctor shook hands formally and then explained his sudden arrival.
'I've been asked to come and see Miss Johnson. Apparently she is not too
well, and her programme may have to be curtailed.' He said that poor Amy
had had a gruelling flight with a forced landing in Rangoon, where her little
Moth plane *Jason* had toppled into a ditch and she had had to wait for it to be
repaired. After this she had met terrible storms over the shark-infested Java
Sea which had forced her to fly so low that her plane had almost touched the
waves. 'On top of all that,' he went on, 'she had never expected such enormous publicity and was completely overwhelmed by her reception in both
Darwin and Brisbane, so I have come to see just what sort of shape she is in.'

Opposite page: *Amy John-
son holding two of my 'treasures'. My mother did all she
could to let the famous aviatrix
rest while she stayed with us,
but it was not easy, as so many
people wanted to see her and
there were many functions held
in her honour.*

The bathroom used by my parents. We loved the stained-
glass window, and I am delighted that it is still there. The
shower and high cistern seemed
quite normal in the 1930s.

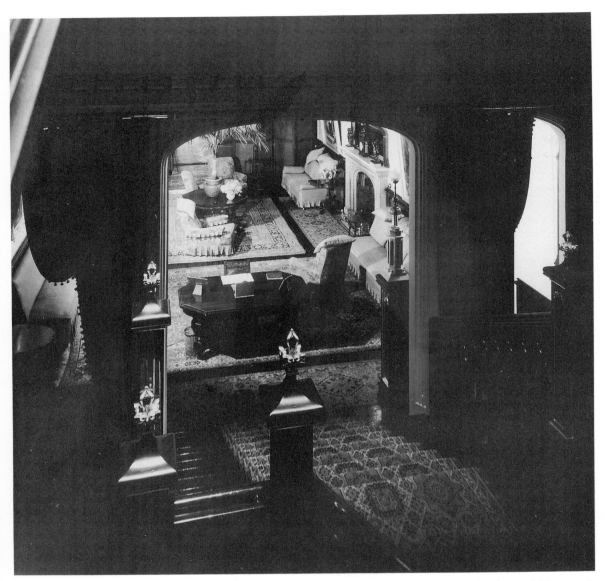

Looking down into the hall from halfway up the main staircase, before it divides to left and right.

'If she's feeling as bad as that,' said my mother, 'I think it would be much wiser if my husband and I met her alone and took her quietly up to her room. So you three children had better disappear and be out of sight when she comes.'

We scurried off to one of the bathrooms, which, strangely enough, had a window through which you could look down into the outer hall and see the front door. Here we knelt on the window sill over the bath and waited. By now it was dark, and we felt like tourists in a hide hoping to see a lion appear from the bushes. We did not have long to wait before the headlights of a car pierced the darkness and we could hear the wild cheering of the crowds. A little, slight, hatless figure holding on to two women and protected on all sides by big policemen emerged and was hurried into the hall. All we could see from the bathroom was the top of her head, but we were quite breathless with excitement.

'I was struck by the sweetness of her smile,' my mother wrote, 'and by her fragile and very gentle look, and I took a liking to her at once. I hurried her upstairs to her pretty sitting-room, full of *masses* of flowers, and put her on the sofa. I told her that her doctor wanted to see her and that, if she wished to, she was to have every meal in her room. She seemed so pleased and grateful.'

The doctor ordered Amy complete rest for a few days but at her special request allowed her to go to the Air Force Ball later that same night.

My parents were dining with the Governor-General and Lady Stonehaven that evening. They were taken across the water to Admiralty House, the Governor-General's official Sydney residence, by barge—really the official launch called the *Premier*, which was always at the Governor's disposal for any trips by water. Because of Amy's arrival they had a rush to get ready, but they looked most romantic as they set off, my father in his full-dress air force uniform any my mother in her gold dress and pearl tiara. 'Thank goodness for that tiara,' she wrote, 'for it was very windy on the harbour and my hair would have been in a *terrible* mess and when we arrived we were taken *straight* in to Their Excellencies without one moment to tidy and conducted by them to the drawing-room where we followed them round shaking hands.' Her diary continues:

> After dinner the ladies came back into the drawing-room and I was standing and talking to them when Lady Stonehaven said to me quite severely, 'Will you please sit down; don't you know that none of these ladies can sit till you do?' I meekly retired to a chair, resolved to remember the rule in future.
>
> The Governor-General dismissed us at ten o'clock as he knew that we had to go to the Air Force Ball. We went by barge and were received at the door of the ballroom with, again, no chance to tidy or powder. There were about 800 people at the ball and many of them told us that they hoped we would be happy. We shall be very hard to please if we are not. The climate, even though it is winter, seems to us quite perfect, as except for our first Sunday we have had nothing but glorious sun and the warmth of an English summer. In the evenings it is cooler and we have a fire and need a coat when we go out. The garden is full of flowers, carnations, roses, arum lilies, interesting shrubs and magnificent trees.

During the ball my father made a short speech. He ended it by saying, 'If Amy Johnson had arrived on the same day as we did, we should have had to carry our own bags up to the house.' This remark went down very well and produced clapping and cheering. My mother was told that her husband had become more popular in a week than any governor before him, that the air force were particularly delighted by his appointment and that he had been nicknamed 'the Flying Governor'.

We did not see very much of Amy during her visit, for in spite of the doctor's instructions she was rushed off her feet. After her first twenty-four hours with us, her sitting-room floor was covered with flowers. There was almost no room to walk. Floral tributes of every kind had poured into the house. She had her own little band of secretarial staff to deal with all this as well as the presents that were given to her. These included two fur coats, a diamond wristwatch, several bracelets and a pearl necklace. Charles amused us by telling us that she had come to him one day and asked, 'Could you please lend me a sponge? No one has thought of giving me that.'

She stayed with us for about four days, and during that time she was only able to dine with my parents once, when, as my mother wrote, 'To our great delight she talked most simply and interestingly about her flight. I asked her if she was never really frightened and she said: "Oh, yes, *rather*, simply terrified" in the most natural way. She told us that she had seen nothing at all on her way here and had had no adventures, which made us laugh. She is such a pretty, feminine girl that it is hard to realise what she has done.'

We were taken to see *Jason* at Mascot aerodrome, now Sydney's Kingsford Smith Airport. The thing I remember most clearly is that the plane was so *tiny*. It was difficult to imagine that it could possibly have flown all that way.

Amy Johnson left us finally at eight o'clock on the morning of 14 June 1930 to continue her flying visits to the capital cities before returning to England. David, without telling anyone, managed to get out to the aerodrome, taking his camera. Together with the press photographers, he pursued the little plane until it took off and faded away into the haze.

My father chatting with a fellow airman, Air Commodore Sir Charles Kingsford Smith, who received his knighthood among the King's Birthday honours in June 1932. My father wrote a foreword to Kingsford Smith's book The Old Bus, *the story of his plane the* Southern Cross.

5 Settling In

SOMETIMES I wonder how my parents got through that first week, for apart from Amy Johnson's flying visit they had to cope with so many things that were new and strange to them, including making speeches. This did not worry my father particularly, but my poor mother was very nervous at first and said that the moment she had to stand up in front of a crowd of people her knees trembled and every thought went out of her head. My father spent the mornings in his study talking with his staff and reading his way into the task he had undertaken. The press were very active that week, and the whole family was subjected to constant interviews and photographing. 'Even Rosemary was interviewed,' my mother wrote, 'by a lady reporter, but no one knows what she said for she made Philip let her see the lady alone in the drawing-room. She is rather indignant because her legs are described by the ungrateful woman as "fat".'

Apart from the official duties, our education had to be settled. My parents hurried off to arrange for Bill to go to the University of Sydney and to see schools for David and me. Besides this, there was the not inconsiderable business of settling into the house and running a large staff.

A few days after our arrival, the butler, cook and head housemaid took my mother on a conducted tour of the servants' quarters, the kitchens, store-rooms, pantries and all those odd little rooms that belong to an establishment that has to look after and feed twenty to twenty-five people most days, sometimes many more. I went with them and acquainted myself with all the back premises, which I found useful and interesting.

After this first tour of inspection, my mother having satisfied herself that the accommodation for her staff was comfortable, pleasant and sufficient, while not luxurious, I do not think that she ever visited the staff rooms again except when she occasionally went down to the kitchens. She had a daily interview with the cook in a tiny sitting-room set aside especially for this purpose. The cook, Mrs Riach, would produce a menu for my mother to look at and then together they would discuss the meals for the day and make preliminary arrangements for any large events that were planned for the near future.

It is worth mentioning here that at that time there were no refrigerators. The nearest equivalent was a huge ice cupboard, filled daily with blocks of ice measuring about two cubic feet. With this primitive method of refrigeration, the cook had to manage dinners for twenty, thirty or even forty people. In the summer months it must have taxed all her ingenuity.

My mother told me that she learned a great deal from her cook. 'What about a soufflé or bavarois for lunch today, Mrs Riach?' she might say, 'Excuse me, milady.' Mrs Riach would make her point gently but firmly. 'It is not at all *correct* to have those creamy sweets at lunch time. They are suitable for dinner, but not in the middle of the day. The right thing then is something such as buttered apples, a flan or a tart.' Or she would concede, 'A fresh fruit salad would be quite in order in hot weather.' Mother would agree. She felt she was in the presence of an expert. Certainly Mrs Riach turned out some splendid meals.

There were two kitchen-maids to help, as well as women who came in daily. Even so, the work must have been hard with a domestic staff of twelve to be fed as well as the office staff ourselves and our visitors.

I would often wander down the long passage from the dining-room to the kitchen, past the large pantry and store-rooms, to see what the cooks were concocting. At the kitchen end of this long passage was a telephone that was used by the kitchen staff for ordering goods from the shops. It did not take me very long to discover that this telephone had a different number from any of the ones in the secretaries' offices. In fact, it was not an extension but a separate outside line. I ruminated quietly on this for a few days until a little plan formed in my mind.

I'll give Charles a bit of a surprise, I said to myself. Liven up all that awful old office work. He must get so bored looking up card indexes all day and wondering whether Mrs S. would like to sit next to Mr H. or whether she ought to be content with Mr G., and whether it would be 'suitable' to ask certain people to dinner. Charles's idea of suitability in this way did not always agree with my father's. I had gathered this from snippets of conversation between them when they thought that I could not hear or was not listening. They were a little naïve sometimes, and far more than they ever imagined passed into my young ears.

After a period of time spent on time-and-motion research, I began to know the habits of the kitchen staff and their activites. Directly lunch had been served, Mrs Riach would retire to her sitting-room, put her feet up, read the paper and snooze away for an hour or two. 'You'll see to the clearing up, Mildred, won't you?' she would say as she took herself off. 'Make sure all the food is covered; we don't want flies in the kitchen.' And having decided that all was in order, she would relinquish her command until about four o'clock. The two kitchen-maids would then deal with the large trolley of dirty dishes in the sinks beyond the kitchen, and with the clatter of china and their own chatter they would be completely oblivious of anything else.

One day after lunch I walked nonchalantly down the passage past the pantry, which was unoccupied, lifted the receiver of the telephone and dialled Charles's office number.

'Government House, ADC's secretary speaking, can I help you?' I heard.

'Yes,' I said in a squeaky, high-pitched voice. 'This is Mildred the kitchen-maid speakin'. The fish for supper's all gone bad and Cook's fainted.'

There was a stunned silence at the other end, and then Charles came back on the line.

'Wh-wh-wh-what h-has happened?'

Poor Charles. The worry of it all had made him begin to stutter. I started

One of my mother's early official engagements—a reception at the Sydney Town Hall— where she had one of her first experiences of making a speech, an unnerving experience in front of so many people.

to describe the scene which was so clear in my mind's eye—Mrs Riach lying stretched out on the stone-flagged floor and the table covered with maggoty fish—but after a few words I could not contain myself and collapsed into girlish giggles. Charles and I reached the dining-room together, where he administered a few carefully chosen words on wasting his and everyone else's time.

The butler's pantry was really more fun than the kitchen, for Mr Turner (as the other servants called him) and William the footman had more time to spare than the cook and kitchen-maids. With any luck, in the afternoon one of them would be polishing the silver and I could sit on the table dangling my legs and chat to him. They were both very kind and seemed to like to talk, and I soon learned a lot about the servants' hall.

Charlie (Charles Reid) was the brother of one of the housemaids, Mary. Charlie was terribly important. 'Nearly as important as the Governor himself,' remarked William. 'Don't know how we'd manage without him, for you see, miss, he looks after *us!* Indeed it was just that. Charlie was the servants' servant. It was he who pushed the crock trolley to the kitchen, wheeled the stores into the store-rooms, washed down the long passages, and laid and cleared the staff meals. He was, in fact, indispensable.

Besides all the chores that were Charlie's life, he had another very important job: the raising and lowering of the flag on the tower at sunrise and sunset. In this he took a huge delight, and these were the moments for which he lived each day, when it was up to him to show that the Governor was in residence. Charlie took this task very seriously. He had worked out exactly how long it took him to get from his back premises to the top of the tower in order to catch the first ray of sun appearing above the horizon in the morning and the last ray as the sun disappeared beyond the city skyline in the evening, so that at these precise moments he could haul on the ropes.

One day Charles Gifford accused him of being late. There was a dramatic scene between them. Charlie propped his broom in the corner of a storeroom, drew himself up to his full height of five feet, and confronted Charles with a glare.

'If you think I'm late with that there flag, sir, you'd best be getting someone else to 'aul it up 'n' down.' With this he turned on his heel and marched off.

Charles reported this incident to my father, who was appalled.

'Good gracious, Charles, for goodness' sake go and pacify him. We can't have Charlie leaving; the whole place would collapse.' Charlie had won the day.

Compared with this, Miss Harris the housekeeper and her team of three stalwart Scottish housemaids were very peaceful. 'She's a marvel,' my mother would say. 'I really can rely on Miss Harris, and Joan too.' (She was

The domestic staff at Government House. Mrs Riach, the cook, is sitting next to my father, and Mrs Harris, the housekeeper, is second from the right in the front row next to my brother Bill. Charlie Reid, the servant of the servants, is standing in the back row second from the left, and Freddie the footman is fourth from the left.

Micky, my father's constant companion, whom he found wonderfully relaxing during the 'Lang troubles'. The Premier was reputed to be unnerved by Micky because Father stroked him while they talked.

the head housemaid). 'They seem to be a wonderful team and anticipate all our needs.'

Miss Harris was in charge of all the bedrooms and bathrooms and responsible for seeing that visitors were comfortable, warm or cool according to the weather, that there was soap in their rooms, flowers on their dressing-tables and all the other little appurtenances which go towards making a guest really well looked after. Her staff would unpack for visitors, lay out their clothes, iron their dresses—for there were no crease-free materials in those days—and make sure they had all they needed.

The staff were all very kind to Lina and made her feel welcome at once. She had two rooms to herself along a small and, I thought, lonely passage.

'Poor Lina, Mummy,' I said one day. 'It must be awful being so far away from everyone. Couldn't we knock a hole through the wall of her bedroom, and then she'd be able to call through to the Official Secretary, or visitors.' I had already worked out that this was geographically possible. I mentioned the idea to Lina, too, but neither she nor my mother seemed at all enthusiastic and just smiled at each other when they imagined I was not looking. Oh well, I thought, that's grown-ups all over!

Inevitably, with the nature of their work and life, my father and mother had to be out a great deal. 'Opening and shutting things', as father called it, in the afternoon, dinners and balls in the evening, and official business and speech writing in the morning.

Looking back I realise that they made a great effort to be with us as much as possible, like ordinary parents. Soon after we arrived, my father bought a dog, Micky, a beautiful Irish setter, immediately adored by all the family. Almost every evening after the public gates had been closed, we would wander into the Botanic Gardens with Micky. It was deliciously cool, and the air was still and fragrant with the scent of the tropical flowers. As the year went on and spring arrived, the gardens became more and more luxurious. Coral trees, flame trees, wisteria, jacaranda, were all a riot of colour, making one pause and gaze in wonder at the splendour of a tropical tree in full bloom. The gardens had been very well planted with a fine selection of shrubs under the exotic trees. Everything grew with a luxuriance unknown in colder

climates. Rhododendrons, azaleas, and camellias flung themselves upwards, every branch alive with blossom. As the evening drew on, the white
flowers stood out against the darkening background until they gleamed in the
deep blue velvet of the night. One of the best of these was the datura, with its
long pure white trumpet-shaped flowers which reminded me of the lilies that
angels in stained glass windows sometimes carry.

After the long day, often crowded with official engagements, those walks in
the gardens did more to refresh my parents than almost anything else. The

Mother and daughter in an idyllic spot.

dog bounding over the grass, the water lapping the rocks at the harbour's edge, and the still beauty of the tropical night seemed to bring a wonderful sense of peace to the family.

Very soon after we arrived in Sydney, the Governor-General came to pay his first official call on my father. It was nearly a disaster for my mother. 'I happened to be in the drawing-room,' she wrote, 'when I realised that he was about to be shown in there. As I was not to be present, I hurried out of the french window on to the verandah. I was horrified to find that the Governor-

A quiet corner of the garden, full of agapanthus blooms.

General's bodyguard was drawn up along the front of the house so that I couldn't possibly get *in* again through the front door. I had to run round the house looking for a back door and brave the footmen who looked a little shocked at my being obviously "in hiding".' She went on to describe how a few days later they were taken up to see the city from the air.

> *Yesterday we all went out for our first flight over Sydney. It was a nasty showery day and in my heart of hearts I hoped 'they' would say that the weather was not good enough to take us up. But there was no respite, and feeling a horrid coward I held tightly on to Philip as we bumped and rattled and roared over the aerodrome.*
>
> *We went in a monoplane that took us all, with two pilots and two people to look after us. We were up for half an hour at 3,000 feet and saw Sydney*

marvellously. I could never have believed how big the city is, without seeing it from the air. It seemed to stretch out indefinitely around us. I am very glad to have gone, but don't much mind if I never fly again!

Sunday came and we made our first of many visits to St Andrew's Cathedral to matins. On that particular Sunday the service was commemorating the Battle of Jutland, and a naval guard of honour was drawn up outside. Once again we were treated to a certain amount of formality, met at the door by the Dean and conducted to our seats. Oh, what a long walk it seemed until we eventually reached the front pew on the left—the right-hand front pew being reserved for the Governor-General, should he happen to be in Sydney. I should have felt much happier had I not had to wear a hat and long sleeves, even in hot weather, but my mother, usually modern in her outlook, considered that in church heads and arms should be covered.

I settled down to listen to the great organ and beautiful singing, and from that day onwards I began to acquire a taste for church music and oratorio which has never left me. I came to look forward to Sundays and to hearing the choir sing and was always disappointed when we had to visit other churches where the music, naturally, was not so fine. In the cathedral choir there was a male alto at whom I stared unrelentingly while he was singing. His high falsetto voice stood out from the rest in descant and part singing. I found him fascinating! It was interesting, too, to hear one's father being prayed for as 'the Governor of this *s*tate', the sibilants beautifully enunciated by the minor canon. Oh yes indeed, there was plenty to watch and to listen to, and I found it vastly more entertaining than the little church at Cricket Malherbie. If only I could have removed my hat and rolled up my sleeves I would have been entirely happy.

The western aspect of Government House, to the left of the front door. In the foreground is one of several magnificent azaleas that were in the garden.

Later that week my parents gave their first official party. It was for all the state ministers, and it happened to be on David's birthday. 'The trouble is, I don't really want to come,' he said. 'I shan't know what to say to anyone.' With a little diplomacy from Charles he was placed between Isabel and one of the young honorary ADCs, and he agreed afterwards that he had really quite enjoyed himself.

Dinner parties were not for me, of course; I was given supper on a tray and packed off to bed. But the night was warm and the pleasant sounds and scents from downstairs attracted me enormously. I slipped out of bed and down the back stairs to a door in the dining-room which led out to the back parts of the house and which I had already noticed had a large crack on the hinged side. Through this crack I watched the thirty guests eating and drinking and chatting away to their neighbours. Very soon William, his bald head glistening from the heat, came out with the remains of the first course. He beamed at me.

'There's a bit of lobster mousse left, miss,' he said. 'You wait there and I'll bring you a spoon.'

He really was a splendid man! He seemed to understand so quickly that little girls were not averse to titbits from other people's dinner parties, and half-an-hour later I went upstairs to bed nicely replete in body, and happy in spirit. William had become a real friend.

Next day my father told me of *his* adventures that evening. Just before the dinner he had wanted to see a list of the guests to be sure of their names and to try and remember them. It was the custom at official parties for the Governor and his wife and any visitors staying in the house to process into the drawing-room *after* their guests had arrived, who were then formally presented by Charles. By the time my father thought about the list, people were already arriving in the hall. He decided to try to reach Charles's office by the back stairs. Very soon he was hopelessly lost and wandering down passages and stairs that he had never seen before. Suddenly he found himself in the kitchen. The cook, confronted without warning by the Governor in full dress uniform complete with medals, only just managed to stifle a scream. She thought she was about to be instantly dismissed, and it was only later in the evening that it occurred to her that it would have been an odd time to dispense with the cook—just before a large dinner party—and that in any case such a procedure would hardly have been carried out by the Governor himself. Father's quiet voice and charming smile reassured her. 'I'm lost, Mrs Riach. Could you please help me to get back to where I belong?'

My mother recorded her own impressions of the occasion:

> *At the dinner party we had of course to learn all the people's names and to do our best to know them at once when we met. This, incidentally, is one of the tasks which I have found hardest in this new life—to remember the names of the hundreds of faces with which we are surrounded and which seem to pass us in endless procession. Philip is so much better at it, and is achieving enormous success.*
>
> *After we had shaken hands with everyone, Philip took Mrs Bavin in to dinner and I followed with Mr Buttenshaw (the Minister for Lands). I could never forget his name for he announced it at once and very clearly:*
>
> > *'Buttenshaw is my name,*
> > *My name is Buttenshaw*
> > *Buttenshaw is my name.'*
>
> *After dinner I sat in state on a sofa while Isabel brought up the ladies in turns for a two minutes' conversation. This she did very well. When Philip came in with the ministers we stood up, and then he chatted to the ladies while I talked to the men. I really liked them enormously—both men and women—and was immensely struck by their kindness of heart and absence of artificiality.*
>
> *One of the ministers won my heart at once as the said, 'Don't think I'm saying this to be polite, but the first moment I saw your husband I knew he was going to be one of the most popular Governors we have ever had. He has two great assets: an honest face and a modest mind. He will be one of our great Governors.'*

My parents walking in a part of the garden largely designed and laid out by Professor E. G. Waterhouse, a world authority on camellias, and my mother.

6 School, Country Trips
and Outings

*David at Sydney University,
which he attended after com-
pleting his secondary schooling
at Cranbrook.*

THE Governor-General came to the house quite often after his first official visit. At the earliest opportunity he gave my mother a piece of advice. 'You will need to be very careful,' he said, 'or your children will become terribly spoiled. Every Sunday you must remind them that it must not matter to them in the very slightest whose children they are!' He need not have worried, for it had never entered our heads to bother about anything of that sort. All we wanted was to be allowed to enjoy the state of paradise in which we had found ourselves. My mother answered him politely and then took no more notice of what he had said. Instead she made us learn three verses of scripture by heart each Sunday. They had to be of a reasonable length; we could not get away with any verse less than three lines long.

Within a few weeks of our arrival we were packed off to school. At least David and I were. Bill went to the university to study geology. David went as a day boy to Cranbrook, in Bellevue Hill, which he much enjoyed. I went to 'a dear little school', Doone, in Double Bay. Miss Cheriton, the headmistress, affectionately known as 'Cherry', was a charming person. She was attractive and sweet and kind, but she was weak.

If I was spoiled at home, I was certainly not spoiled at school, for my life was plagued by a bully who 'got it in for me' almost the day I arrived. She soon discovered that I was physically far from brave. Directly we arrived at nine o'clock she would arrange a fight for the eleven o'clock break, and I would quake through the first three lessons waiting for the awful moment when the bell would ring. By the end of the first year I had had a swollen finger and a badly injured shoulder but had said nothing for fear of reprisals. One day, at her invitation, we were on a swing together. The swing went higher and higher, far higher than I cared for, but I dared not say anything. The next thing I remember was a hard blow on the head and then being dragged backwards and forwards on the ground. I was carried into the school and put to bed. Things became better after that, except that I had to learn to live with frequent headaches for the next thirty years.

The teaching was very mixed. The good part was very good; the bad part was not so much bad as non-existent. We were taught English and French very well, maths and Latin adequately (except that I could never do either subject); biology was excellent, but there were no laboratories, so that chemistry and physics were not taught at all, and for this I suffered sadly later on. History consisted almost entirely of Australian history; practically no British history was taught, so that when I reached an English public school I knew all about Cook's voyages but had not the remotest idea of the fate of Charles I.

I do not blame my parents at all for their choice of school for me. They were charmed by Cherry, the nice house and garden, and they thought that at a small, intimate school I would be looked after. I do think either of them ever realised they had made such a sad mistake.

Apart from the junior school, Cherry ran a finishing school. Here she taught the society girls of Sydney to dress, dance and conduct themselves generally in a manner befitting young ladies. This she did extremely well. Somehow she managed to attract to her finishing school a large proportion of Sydney's 'beauties' and at one time 'the three Margarets'—Margaret Vyner, Margaret Honey, and Margaret Fairfax—who had been launched into society by Cherry, were renowned for their grace, charm and comeliness. The delicacy, refinement and good taste of 'Cherry's girls' was spoken of with reverence by those in high social circles. I have no doubt that in this sphere Cherry fulfilled a need in those days, but the effect on the junior school of having a bevy of beauties on the floor above was unsettling and did much to distract us from our work and make us long to be grown-up like them.

Perhaps it was the exciting life at home, perhaps it was something within me, or perhaps it was the effect of those upstairs' beauties, but something had a bad effect for a time, and I became rude and naughty at school. The mistresses complained to Cherry, who, when pressed, wrote a tactful little note to my mother asking her if she would be so kind as to suggest to me that I should try to be a little more polite to her staff. She told me what she had written and gave me the note to take home. Poor Cherry! She wasted a great deal of time composing that letter, for it was so easy to pop into Charles's

Bill on the day he received his degree at Sydney University.

The Goodison family and myself (lying at left), all from Doone school. We are looking at the goldfish in the fountain pond in Government House garden.

office on my way from the front door to tea in the hall, say hullo to him and unobtrusively drop the note into his already well-filled waste-paper basket. Cherry could hardly be expected to ring up Government House and ask why the Governor's wife had not troubled to answer her letter.

New South Wales, while not big compared with Queensland or Western Australia, is still at least three times as large as the British Isles, and during the five years that he was Governor, my father tried to visit all the major towns and the more remote parts of the state. Sometimes he went by car; more often he travelled by train in a special saloon. My mother nearly always went with him, and she described the first of these journeys, to Grafton, in a letter to her mother:

> *Here we are in our own railway carriage, anchored in a siding at Grafton Railway Station. We are about 450 miles north of Sydney, 40 miles inland. We were met at Sydney station by the station master and conducted to our carriage. It seems so strange to be treated like this, instead of buying a ticket in the ordinary way and trying to get a corner seat!*
>
> *The carriage is most luxurious, with drawing-room, dining-room, tiny bedrooms each for Philip and me, connected by a bathroom with a real bath. There is a small kitchen with berths for two servants, and a compartment for*

Isabel. Charles sleeps on a sofa in the drawing-room. All the rooms are panelled in nice brown wood and there are delightful copper coloured curtains which tone well with the wood. We are in the lap of luxury, the only draw-back being that there is no hot water for the bath when the train stops.

The line is very rough and one gets shaken, but somehow we manage to sleep and it is intensely interesting to peep out early in morning to see the sun rising on real, wild Australia. I had thought that the masses of gum-trees would be much more monotonous than they are, and greyer in colour. Some of them have wonderful trunks 150 feet high, a lovely pearly grey, standing out against the mass of dark green undergrowth. We passed beautiful wooded hills, almost mountainous, glorious glimpses of heavenly blue sea and white sandy beaches, which made us long to stop and get out. It is a very pretty part of the State with some rivers to cross, rather unusual in this country. Once we came to the sad sight of miles and miles of dead trees, sometimes stretching as far as the eye could see, with not a scrap of grass anywhere to relieve the dreary scene. The trees have been ring-barked so as to kill them in order to clear the ground for planting and allow the grass to grow for cattle.

When we arrived, we were met by the Mayor and his wife and various other people, driven on to the racecourse and up to the stand, just like Royalty at Ascot! After being taken to the box and standing for 'God Save the King' things were not nearly so formal and it was very easy and pleasant. Everyone was so friendly.

Prize-giving at Doone school in Double Bay. These are the girls from the 'finishing' school, except for Rosemary Budge, on my mother's right, and Miss Cheriton (Cherry), the headmistress, in the hat. Her bevy of beauties were not allowed make-up, so a group could usually be seen at the bus stop outside the school very busy with mirrors and lipstick.

My mother was not fond of racing, but she had a great love of horses and had enjoyed riding and hunting as a girl, so she much enjoyed seeing the racehorses. 'The big race was very exciting,' her letter continues, 'and was won by a perfect darling of a black horse. He was led into the paddock and I was asked to put a wide blue ribbon round his neck. This was rather difficult to do as he danced about. However I managed to hook it on and he looked so

proud as he went off with it. Then I had to give a cup to the owner and a whip to the jockey which was all rather fun.'

She went on to describe the famous jacarandas, which were soon to become the theme of an annual festival in Grafton: 'There is a marvellous avenue of jacaranda trees here. We are told that it is a sight that you can never forget, when the trees are covered with a mass of glorious blue flowers and the ground underneath them carpeted with fallen blossom.'

The next day my parents were taken out into the country near Grafton for a picnic. 'They had a billy boiling for us and made us real "billy" tea,' she wrote. 'The sun was heavenly and the country so pretty, particularly near the river, and we were very sorry to leave. We found our carriage filled with flowers when we came to say goodbye.'

Sometimes my brothers and I were able to go with our parents on their country trips, but at this particular time we were at school and so had to be left behind. We were well looked after, of course, with that large staff to minister to us, and it was only in the evenings that we occasionally tended to become a little bored, with only ourselves and Micky for company. Micky was a large, cosy dog, good-tempered and huggable. My father and he were devoted to one another and hated being parted, but Micky, like us, sometimes had to be left behind.

One evening, David and I were sitting with Micky in front of the fire; we were discussing him while he slept peacefully on the hearthrug.

'He's jolly nice, isn't he?' said David.

'*Jolly* nice,' I agreed.

At that moment Micky opened his large mouth in a tremendous yawn.

'Gosh! Aren't his teeth huge?' I remarked.

'They look an awful colour,' said David. 'They're dreadfully yellow. But then, of course, when you come to think of it, he never cleans them.'

At once I had a bright idea: 'Why don't we clean them *for* him?' David looked at me incredulously. 'What on earth with?' I thought for a minute. 'What about Vim? Mummy always says that tooth *powder* is really better than toothpaste.'

'Vim would taste *horrid*. Poor old Micky.'

'Well, then, let's go and see if we can find some tooth powder.'

Micky had dropped off to sleep again, but we soon managed to wake him up.

'Come on,' we said, 'walkies.' And he trotted off with us down the passage to my parents' bedroom. There on the marble washstand was a tin of Calox tooth powder and a nice clean toothbrush.

'You go and get a mug of water from the bathroom,' David told me, 'and I'll get Micky to sit still if I can.'

A few minutes later one of us was holding up the large flap of lip while the other scrubbed away at the poor dog's huge, yellow eye tooth. We consoled him with our chatter: '*That's* a good dog. Soon you'll be a booful boy with lovely white teeth.'

Micky sat patiently, looking at us out of his limpid eyes with a sad expression. His teeth seemed just as yellow. After a time we gave up, emptied the mug of water and went back to the sitting-room.

Later that night my mother and father returned from their visit to Grafton.

They were tired and went to bed almost immediately. As we went into their room to say goodnight, we heard my mother's voice: 'My toothbrush looks very odd. It's all flat and squashed. I can't think how it can have got like that. I think I'd better use the one I took with me.' Unknown to us, she heard David whisper to me, 'That must be the one we used for Mick's teeth.'

My father, who believed that to be a king would be one of the worst fates that could befall anyone, decided to liven up his formal letter to King George V by telling him what we had done. Many weeks later a message came back from Buckingham Palace to say that His Majesty had much enjoyed the story about the dog's teeth and looked forward to more letters from the Governor of New South Wales.

However, my father's letters from then on became less light-hearted, as he was beginning to discover that he was going to have to face far graver problems than he had ever envisaged. Many years later he told me that he had never wanted to be a politician and that he had always disliked politics. 'Too much bickering,' he said. 'Always at each other's throats.' From this I feel that the next two years, when the political horizon was dark and clouded, may have taxed him almost to the limit of his endurance.

We had only been in the country a few months before the Great Depression sweeping across the world began to make itself felt in Australia. Words such as *unemployment*, *poverty*, and *the dole* were on everybody's lips. From their conversations, I sensed my parents' anxiety, for the grim realities of a depression did not escape them, and their great concern was for the future of New South Wales and the Australian people.

King George V; he enjoyed my father's story of our cleaning Micky's teeth.

Meanwhile, life at Government House so far as I was concerned went happily on. My father, who loved the sea, bought a fourteen-foot sailing boat and a tiny motor-boat. Before I was allowed out in either of them, my parents insisted that I learnt to swim. Charles was a splended instructor and took me off to a friend's swimming pool, where, after a certain amount of stress and strain on my part and a great deal of patience on his, I mastered the art of keeping afloat in the water. Only one thing spoiled those lovely afternoons on the harbour—the thought of sharks waiting to gobble me up if the boat capsized! I do not remember that it ever did.

One day we went off—a family party—to see the zoo. What we were interested in seeing were the marsupials—the kangaroos, wallabies, wombats and possums, but most of all the koalas. It is difficult to convey our delight at seeing these funny, cuddly, friendly little animals chewing away at the eucalypt leaves in a contented, dreamy, fashion, letting the world go by, or wedged precariously in a forked branch far too small for them, their eyes tightly shut, snoozing away in the warm sunshine. Then there was the platypus. It was difficult to see, for its tank was half-submerged beneath the surface and only dimly lit. We spent a very happy afternoon watching these strange animals.

On the way home across the water we had a magnificent view of the bridge. Its great arch being built out from the north and south shores of the harbour was soon to be joined in the centre and the whole thing was due to be finished the following year.

My mother wrote of a visit to see the bridge under construction. Knowing her lack of head for heights, I am amazed at her courage and her appreciation of that visit.

Our motor boat on Sydney Harbour. The great arch of the Bridge was nearly joined, and we were all waiting for the day when this would happen.

Even to one who hates machinery as I do, the enormous workshops, the immense machines with the great engines pounding, planing and grinding, were an extraordinary and interesting sight. We were taken up 400 ft. in a lift to where we could stand on a perilous platform all among the girders right up in the big arch. All Sydney was spread out below us and we could see the Blue Mountains far away in the distance.

I should have enjoyed it more if I had had a good head, but as there was only one thin rail between us and a violent death—probably to be eaten by sharks in the harbour—I felt very shaky.

At 8 a.m. on 21 August of that year, 1930, a tremendous cacophony of sound rent the air. Every ship in the harbour hooted, screeched and blared with all its force in a great paean of praise. The two huge arms of the bridge had been joined at midnight, being the coolest time for the final operation. The immense arch was complete.

There is no doubt that with the coming of my parents and their young family to Sydney, a new life of gaiety transformed Government House. The first ball was given in honour of a Dutch squadron visiting Sydney. My mother was a keen gardener and as the weather was warm and french windows led out of the ballroom to the garden, she arranged that the verandah and great ficus tree just beyond should be lit by pale green fairy lights. Flame-coloured clivias were in full bloom under the tree, and the effect of the lights on these and the green leaves above them, the fountain playing beyond, and the shimmering water of the harbour in the distance was breathtaking. Guests who were used to Government House gasped with admiration at the alterations that had taken place and in particular the flowers. The *Daily Guardian* described the scene in an article the next day: 'The old pot plants in the vestibule had given place to a bank of pink roses leading to the ballroom. The fireplace was a bower of deep pink peach blossom, and the supper tables were smothered in pale pink carnations. Every nook and cranny in the ballroom overflowed with a wealth of deep red roses—all from the Vice-regal garden.'

Being situated next door to the Botanic Gardens, we were able, from time to time, to employ men from there to work in the Government House garden. My mother, helped by Professor E. G. Waterhouse—famous for his design of the superb gardens of Sydney University and a world authority on camellias—set out to produce an outstanding display of trees, shrubs and climbers. Together they combined the old beauty of Italy, the informality of England, and the tropical splendour of a wealth of flowers which delight in a warm climate. The result after quite a short time was a garden which was a joy to all who walked in it. Many a morning in the spring and summer, as early as six o'clock, I would wander out with my mother to pick roses before the hot sun had reached them. I so well remember her joy at the size of the roses, great blooms easily six inches across. Sometimes a hot wind would get up later and all the flowers would be blown away, but it only needed a day or two before the plants were once more laden with their fragrant blooms.

At the ball the dresses added to the beauty of the floodlit garden. 'Backless frocks', said the *Guardian*, 'were numerous, but capes outnumbered them. Yellow was the most popular shade only rivalled by all tones of blue—truly it was a wonderful party.'

The Governor-General had a young family too: a son and two daughters. The girls, Ava and Ariel, were about my age, and we became friends. I was bidden to tea at Admiralty House. It was only a matter of a few minutes in the public ferry from close to the bottom of our garden to some steps near theirs, and I enjoyed the short trip across the harbour. Ava and Ariel were both at the bottom of the steps to meet me, and, as children will, we danced up them laughing and joking and making a good deal of noise. As we reached the house, the two girls seemed more subdued.

'You'd better come and meet Mummy,' said Ariel, the eldest, and led the way through a maze of dark passages and staircases. She knocked on a door, and a distant voice told us to come in.

The room was very large. In the far corner Lady Stonehaven sat writing at her desk. She glanced up, and her formal voice made me shiver.

'Come over and curtsy to me, my dear,' she said. Her manner frightened me, and my knees knocked as I walked over the endless carpet towards her. Her two daughters had stayed by the door, obviously anxious to get the proceedings over as quickly as possible. I do not remember my return journey over that carpet, but I know that when we had at last closed the door firmly behind us we rushed away with all speed to the relaxed atmosphere somewhere at the top of the house.

'I don't want to go there *again*,' I told my mother. 'Ugh! It was formal!'

There were plenty of other children's parties that were quite informal, however, the nicest of all being on board the naval vessels in the harbour. Rosemary and I usually went together and had tremendous fun. The sailors really seemed to enjoy their ships being overrun with children, and they gave us a glorious time. Great parties of us were packed into a well-netted platform and swung by a huge derrick right up high over the side of the ship and down to within a few inches of the water, up again, and then safely down on to the deck, where another group were waiting eagerly for their turn. Canvas chutes were fixed from one deck to another, and a constant stream of children climbed up the companionway to slide their way down to the bottom again. Even the barrels of the great guns were used to ride on—well supervised, of course, by jolly, smiling Jack Tars.

For me—apart from school, where I was never really happy—these were halcyon days. The comings and goings in the house intrigued me. We always seemed to be entertaining visitors, and there was a constant bustle and activity. As yet I knew very little of the political worries that continually beset my poor father.

One of our earliest visitors was Sir Hugh Allen, principal of the Royal College of Music in London. He was kind to me and did his best to develop the music he appeared to find in me. He took me to a concert, and we sat up in the gallery so that he could explain the instruments of the orchestra to me.

My parents gave a large dinner party in his honour. I loved to watch my mother dress for these occasions. She looked so pretty with her soft fair hair and beautiful evening dresses, and I took a great interest in what she wore. That particular evening, when she was putting the finishing touches to her face, there was a knock at the door and David came in.

'Go and see where you're sitting, darling,' she said to him. 'Then you won't have any difficulty when we all reach the dining-room.'

David was still a little lacking in confidence over dinner parties. He went off obediently to look at the place names and returned a few minutes later with a puzzled expression.

'Mummy, it's very odd, but I'm sitting next to Daddy.'

My mother, normally very patient, answered a trifle irritably. 'Don't be silly, David! How *could* you be? Go and have another look!'

The next time he came in his face had a look of astonishment. 'I *am* sitting next to Daddy, and what's more, all the ladies are down one side of the table and all the men down the other.'

'I'm tired,' I said suddenly and disappeared to bed, turning my face to the wall and feigning sleep.

My mother in a part of the garden she designed known as the Spring Walk, or Lady Game's Walk. I recognised some of the plants on my return in 1973.

Downstairs there was pandemonium. Bells rang, secretaries were summoned, ADCs rushed madly back and forth from office to dining-room, table plans in their hands and worried frowns on their faces. 'You can't imagine the commotion,' David said as he described the scene to me next day. 'It was ghastly.' But in a short time everything had been readjusted and, with the dexterity of conjurors, Charles and his aides had replaced the cards in the all-important order of precedence.

'Perhaps Rosemary did it,' suggested Isabel.

'Rosemary!' My mother spoke sharply. 'She wouldn't do a thing like *that!*'

My father remained unperturbed. It was only years later that he told me that he had always felt a little disappointed that my joke had been nipped in the bud.

7 *Political Problems*

THOMAS BAVIN, the Premier of New South Wales, was a constant visitor to the house. My parents liked and admired him very much indeed. This is made very clear in a letter written by my father to my grandmother:

> *Thomas Bavin is an excellent man, a real tower of strength. He is often at the house and I value his thoughts and opinions greatly. He comes here with the Executive Council, to which all the Cabinet belong and together they advise me on state matters to which I have to give my official approval. Unfortunately poor Bavin is a sick man and I wonder, sometimes, how long he will be able to stand the pressures. We are in a tough position here, with wheat and wool prices falling rapidly, and Bavin is trying desperately to promote a policy of more work with less pay. It is not an easy job for him.*
>
> *Sir Otto Niemeyer has been sent out here to advise on the financial situation. His opinion is quite simple; that Australia is living beyond her means, but I doubt if his advice will be acceptable to the Labor Party.*

It was not. Bavin lost the election held on 25 October 1930, and six days later he came to the house to tender his resignation. This was sadly received by my father. J.T. Lang, leader of the Opposition, arrived a few hours afterwards and was invited to form a government.

On 26 November the new parliament was opened. My father wore ceremonial dress, as is the custom, and was escorted from Government House to Parliament House by a troop of mounted police. Strictly speaking, the Governor does not open Parliament, but by invitation of the Premier he reads the opening speech. He is bound to agree to both the speech and to the ministers chosen by the Premier.

While he was changing into the correct uniform, my father's thoughts reverted to that evening a few weeks before when he invited Lang to form a government. Would Lang be able to cope with such a responsible position, he wondered. Had he the experience to resolve those nagging problems that kept occurring: how to reduce the ever-rising unemployment and how to ensure that his 'people', as Lang called them, had adequate housing and food. Had he (Lang) the economic knowledge to carry out his reforms? My father could not help having certain misgivings. The appalling poverty and conditions of Lang's youth had made him resolve to smash the capitalist system, which *he* considered responsible for the present troubles. That may be all right later on, Father reflected, but Lang is ahead of his time, and he may well kill the goose that lays the golden eggs if he goes too far.

These troublesome thoughts were still going through the Governor's mind as he drove to Parliament House. He found himself wondering what the crowd themselves were thinking as they waved and cheered the procession on its way up Macquarie Street that spring afternoon. The majority, no doubt, believed that a new leader with a new broom would sweep the present troubles away, and to them the future looked bright; for after all, Lang was the leader they had elected. But maybe there were some who felt apprehensive.

For the time being, however, life went on much as usual. There was the surfing and boating to enjoy as the summer came on, and many a morning I would set off with Bill and David to Bondi Beach at six o'clock, taking a circuitous route round Sydney to pick up Bill's large number of girlfriends for a dip before breakfast. No doubt there were some 'green-eyed' ladies among them, but the party that arrived on the beach always seemed cheerful enough to me.

About this time my mother and Bill went off to New Zealand to see an aunt and uncle who lived in Christchurch. Father, David and I were left to look after ourselves, which was not very difficult considering the number of servants who were only too willing to pander to our needs. Writing to my mother, I told her how 'Daddy and I put kerosene on the drains'. This curious pastime was in order to try and reduce the number of mosquitoes which bit us incessantly. The Australians did not seem to bother about them, as there was no malaria and the wretched little insects must have long ago tired of Australian blood. But to an Englishman, fresh from England, they were torture. The letter ends: 'Daddy is very well, but rather tired poor old man.'

Poor dear man! No wonder he was tired. Mr Lang paid weekly visits to Government House. Father described his difficult situation in another letter to my grandmother:

Bill and David with Sadie Budge (the Budges' eldest daughter) on Bondi Beach.

My parents in the gardens at Hillview, the Governor's country house at Moss Vale.

Lang keeps pressing me for eighty more members for the Upper House. He wants to push through the legislation to abolish the Upper House altogether. He maintains that this was in the election manifesto and therefore is what the people wish.

I shall play for time! I have the power to dissolve Parliament but I feel it would be unwise to use that power so soon after an election and risk Lang being returned with a greater majority. On the other hand he can well ask for me to be recalled to England if I continue to refuse his requests. This will not solve anything, it will merely mean a new governor coming out here and being faced with the same situation.

When my mother returned from New Zealand, my father took a short holiday in order to clarify his mind. He went camping with Bill and some friends near Mount Solitary in the Blue Mountains. The peace and quiet far from the city and crowds and political troubles did much to restore him.

In December we went to Moss Vale, in the southern highlands, where in those days the Governor had a country house called Hillview, a long, low, timbered house, informal and comfortable, surrounded by wide verandahs. The house stood on a hilltop, and it was pleasant sitting under the large shady trees in the garden and looking down over the Australian countryside. Here we spent Christmas, a hot Christmas, utterly different from the Christmases in Somerset. It was strange without holly or mistletoe, and even the plum pudding lost its attraction in temperatures of 90°F. We rode and swam and picnicked, and enjoyed ourselves, though differently from in England.

We had our own ponies, including my own small grey, Leo. He was very quiet and placid, and as far as I was ever able to enjoy riding, I enjoyed it with Leo and my father. There were plenty of young people about, and the days were filled with riding or swimming picnics in a creek at Gunrock—a wild bushland area with a freshwater pool. Sometimes we went on long expeditions and walked all day down into the valleys—wild valleys filled with ferns and orchids and gum trees. I suppose it must have rained, but those six weeks seemed to me to be filled with sun and warmth. At night we slept on the verandahs, but the kookaburras disturbed us with their laughter early each morning. My brothers fixed up a tin of stones in the particular tree which the kookaburras fancied and, with a long rope from the tree to their beds, rattled the tin to scare the birds. Of course, the rattling stones were just as disturbing as the laughter.

We took some of the junior members of the domestic staff of Government House to Hillview with us, while the more senior staff had their holidays. Myra, one of the kitchen-maids, came with us as cook. She was a congenial soul and let me mess about in the kitchen and taught me to make scones and cakes. Freddie, the under-footman, came too. He felt very important in charge up at Hillview. He had bright red hair and was very erudite; he had been well educated—at all events in English.

I well remember a lunch party one day, quite a large party, for my parents had plenty of friends at Moss Vale whom they liked to entertain less formally than in Sydney. Freddie was waiting on us, and the conversation was about some well-known quotation. There was a discussion about which particular novel it came from. Someone suggested it was Dickens—or could it be Jane Austen?

Father and David riding at Moss Vale, one of their country joys.

Swimming with friends at Gunrock Creek, near Moss Vale—David, top centre; Bill having his leg pulled by his playful sister. The creek was deep in the bush, and the road to it was a rough, stony track.

'Perhaps it is from *Emma*,' said my mother gently.

'Excuse me, milady,' Freddie's voice carried across the table as he handed the vegetables, 'but it's a quotation from *The Wide, Wide World*.'

There was a pause in the conversation while the lunch party digested the information and the fact that Freddie had supplied it. The silence was eventually broken by my father who, with his delightful smile, said, 'Thank you, Freddie, that is *most* useful.'

Meanwhile, the political scene was becoming worse and worse. The Depression was deepening day by day; unemployment was rising rapidly, and the

Another glorious picnic at Gunrock Creek—David and my father standing.

numbers of poor and down-and-out were steadily growing. Back in Sydney after the holiday at Hillview, we found evidence of this at the doorstep of Government House. Even I could realise how bad the situation was becoming. The Domain was full of families who had been turned out of their houses because they were unable to pay their rent and were sleeping rough. Some were lucky enough to have arrived there in time to occupy the caves made by overhanging rocks near the water, including Mrs Macquarie's Chair, and in these they set up home. Others rigged up canvas shelters, some slept on the public seats, and many more simply slept on the grass. Altogether, at that time in Australia, with a population of well under ten million, there were

approximately three hundred thousand men out of work. The problems were fearful.

The first thing my father did on his return to Sydney was to order his salary to be cut by one-third. He also reduced the amount of entertaining at Government House. He was very anxious, though, that none of his staff should become redundant, so he decided that almost all the functions at the house should be for charity and that only essential visitors should be asked to stay.

Among those who were asked to stay were the Baden-Powells. By that year, 1931, the Scout and Guide movements, which Robert and Olave Baden-Powell had founded, had not yet reached their quarter-century, but they had already spread to almost the entire world. 'B-P', the greatest leader of youth that the world had ever seen, had a quite remarkable personality and a wonderful sense of humour. 'There are half a dozen people in this world whom I can never see again,' he told us. 'I've dropped such terrible bricks.' His wife, Olave, was filled with remarkable drive and energy but could be boring. It was difficult to find any subject other than guiding in which she was interested.

'Why aren't you a Scout?' she asked Bill. (David and I were exonerated, both having been enrolled a year or two before.)

'I'm busy,' he answered her simply. 'I'm in the

A family party at Hillview, with Mr Budge standing behind my mother.

middle of working for my degree.'

This to Olave's way of thinking was no proper reason for not being a Scout. I only hope that she heard a year later that he had received first-class honours and the Deas Thomson Scholarship.

Lord and Lady Baden-Powell with my parents in Government House garden. Olave Baden-Powell is standing between my father and her husband; my mother is wearing a gold sash as the Guides' Chief Commissioner in New South Wales; the co-operative Micky does not need my restraining hand.

I found the Baden-Powells' visit fun, particularly the enormous jamboree at which ten thousand Scouts and Guides, gathered together from all over New South Wales, marched past that remarkable couple, who stood for hours acknowledging the salutes from the prodigious stream of youth. My parents would have enjoyed their visit more had they not been weighed down with the political and financial worries of the state.

Every morning that he could manage to spare the time, my father would walk out into the Domain and chat to the people camped there, until they came to watch and wait for the Governor with his lame leg and his dog. For some, it was the only thing they had to look forward to in the whole day. He never seemed in a hurry and was always anxious to listen to their troubles and offer all the advice and help he could. Years later, long after he had left Australia, men were still receiving pensions left by him, to be paid to them till they died. He made many friends among those down-and-outs, and every day a queue formed up at the back door of Government House to be fed. They were never turned away.

One day I was at the dentist in Macquarie Street. Lina had taken me there. While we were waiting, I wandered out onto the balcony where a small boy was leaning over the railing and gazing down into the street below.

'My father drives one of those taxis,' he said. 'What does yours do?'

David, myself and Bill making a scarecrow at Hillview (to keep the kookaburras away?). By now we had become true Aussies with Aussie hats.

One of the dossers in the Sydney Domain lying under the rocks at Mrs Macquarie's Chair. (Photograph by Max Dupain)

I looked at the great house standing in its gardens, the sweeping drive curving up to the fine porch, all of which could easily be seen from the balcony, while I thrashed around in my mind for an answer.

'He doesn't do anything very much,' I said at last. The boy looked at me pityingly and then across to the Domain. Suddenly I realised what he thought—my father was down-and-out!

That evening my father teased me: 'I don't do anything very much, is *that* what you said? Here I am, worried to death by all the unemployment, working myself to the bone for His Majesty's Government, wrestling with my friend Lang, and then you say I don't do anything very much.' He grunted, but there was the usual twinkle in his eye.

A few days later, everyone's thoughts were directed towards a shattering event—the Napier earthquake. There have been hundreds of earthquakes in New Zealand, and many go unnoticed except by the seismologists, for they occur in remote places where there is no habitation. Some, however, like the one in Napier, devastate towns. In that February of 1931 even the New Zealand coastline was altered. Napier and Hastings were both a shambles, and two hundred people were killed. Compared with the vast numbers affected

A pensive unemployed worker contemplates his future beneath a Moreton Bay fig in the Domain. (Photograph by Max Dupain)

Tents of the unemployed gave the Sydney Domain the appearance of a camp site in the bush.

by the huge earthquakes of India, Chile, and such places, this may seem a small affair, but to someone caught in such a terrifying event it was a fearful experience. Such was the feeling of Norah Jellicoe, daughter of the Governor-General of New Zealand, Lord Jellicoe, who was in the area at the time. She had been indoors when the earth suddenly heaved itself up in violent tremors. She tried to get out of the room, but the door had jammed and would not open. The windows would not open either. She was trapped and alone, and as she looked out of the window the tennis court came towards her in great waves. She was simply terrified, and even weeks later, staying with us in Sydney, she could only sleep with the light on and the door open.

The vice-regal life had to go on in spite of all the political difficulties. Sometimes my parents would go to as many as five charity balls in a week, never getting home until after midnight. Next day there were hospitals to be visited, with new wings to be opened; schools to be inspected; fêtes, sports, and official functions of every kind. Most of these functions involved making a speech—sometimes three a day—and all had to be written and delivered. For good measure, there were dinner parties and visitors.

The Stonehavens had left, and their place had been filled on 22 January by

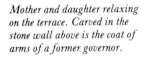

Mother and daughter relaxing on the terrace. Carved in the stone wall above is the coat of arms of a former governor.

The Governor, in number 2 boat, enjoying himself with the shire president on the dodgems at the Cessnock Show. Charles Gifford in number 9 is evidently having a good time too.

Sir Isaac and Lady Isaacs. He was a small man, very Jewish, a very shrewd lawyer and extremely clever. As small men sometimes do, he had married a big woman who looked as though she might dominate him, but he never allowed this. They were the kindest couple, very nice to me, and I remember them with much affection but also, I must admit, with some amusement.

His Excellency liked to use his great brain. There was little he did not know of Ancient Greece, the Roman Empire, practically the whole of the Old Testament, and many other abstruse subjects. He would read up some less well-known parts of Jewish history and then, when he had mastered his subject, he would take his place in the hall and wait for my mother to appear.

A cheerful wave for the Bexley Scouts, with the Salvation Army looking on.

Sir Isaac Isaacs, in full dress uniform of the Governor-General, on the top verandah of Government House. He had an amazing knowledge of many subjects, particularly the Old Testament.

'Do you know about . . . ?' he would begin, and launch into the cultural history of the Jews in 4000 BC or delve deeply into the real meaning behind the story of Jonah. My mother found this trying. She realised his brilliant mind needed these subjects to satisfy it, but she had not time to sit down and listen to long dissertations on the Jews or anyone else during a busy morning.

'I don't know *what* to do,' she complained one day when she saw Sir Isaac lying in wait at the bottom of the stairs for the second time that morning. 'I must go and see the cook.' 'I'll take you down Mr Budge's staircase,' I said. 'You just go along the top passage, down his stairs, through the offices and out into the passage near the dining-room, and there you are.'

Lady Isaacs (sitting) with my mother, probably at Government House, Canberra. The two families often stayed with each other.

My mother looked a trifle shocked and started to persuade me against such an underhand idea.

'Come on,' I told her, 'or you'll *never* get anything done.' And I pulled her along until she finally gave in.

'It worked wonderfully,' she told my father later. 'But I felt rather bad, avoiding the poor old man like that. I'm not sure I could ever do it again.'

My father was too wise to reply.

The visitors I remember best were the bishops. During the year there was a large conference of bishops in Sydney. Thirty of them came with their wives to lunch. Charles, who was to introduce them, went to breakfast with them all to learn their names. This was a formidable task, for not only had he to memorise the name of the town from which each bishop came—and some were Aboriginal names such as Wangaratta—but he also had to remember the names of their wives. He was wonderful. He only made one slip, he confused Mrs Hart with Mrs Head, but then as everyone told him, the heart is not far from the head.

Some of them stayed with us, and I was allowed to have dinner downstairs while they were there. I think my mother thought that it would be good for me to have to talk to them and that they would be understanding. Poor things! They patiently endured my endless childish chatter, and I only remember them as charming and sympatheitc.

There was Bishop Harold Crotty from Bathurst—who years later gave the address at my wedding. There was Frederick Waldegrave Head, the Archbishop of Melbourne, whom even I as a child recognised as outstandingly saintly; and there was a delightful man, Bishop Francis de Witt

The Most Reverend F. W. Head, Archbishop of Melbourne, and Mrs Head with my father in the garden. A very fine Christian, Archbishop Head frequently preached on the Melbourne beaches, where he attracted large audiences. 'If they won't come to me, I shall go to them,' he said.

Batty from Newcastle, who seemed to know exactly how to entertain a youngster.

'Fetch me two cups, my dear,' he said to me one day, 'and I will show you how to pass a sixpence from one to the other.' I sped off to beg the cups from William, who was left gaping at such a strange request from a bishop. Having inverted both cups and placed the sixpence under one of them, the bishop waved his hands, airily exclaiming 'Abracadabra' in a truly sepulchral voice.

'Now,' he said, 'the sixpence has moved from one cup to the other. That is easy! The *difficult* thing is to get it back again.' By this time I was wide-eyed watching this large dog-collared man's hands passing backwards and forwards, his whole face concentrated on the job in hand.

'There you are!' he exclaimed, lifting up the original cup and finding the sixpence. He enjoyed the joke as much as I did.

He was accompanied by his wife and his two sisters. The sisters were very large ladies with round, rosy faces to match their stature. My father called them 'the little Batty girls'. They smiled large, beaming smiles from the moment they got up until they went to bed. In fact, they may even have smiled while they slept. They were delightful.

I cannot leave the subject of bishops without mentioning the Bishop of Carpentaria, S. H. Davies, for in some ways he was unique. Before he arrived to stay, my mother asked to see Miss Harris, her treasured housekeeper.

'Miss Harris'—my mother paused, searching for words, and began once more—'Miss Harris, I want you to warn Mary [the under housemaid] about the Bishop of Carpentaria.' Miss Harris's face remained impassive. She was far too well trained to display any emotion.

'You see, he is used to sleeping on the lawn—he doesn't like a bed—so he sleeps on the floor wound in a sheet!'

I can hear my mother's voice now as it rose higher and higher with the strain of having to convey such extraordinary information. She need not have worried.

'Very good, milady,' was all Miss Harris said, as she quietly left the room.

Our next visitor was the Russian-born concert pianist Mark Hambourg, a total contrast to the bishops in every way. 'Haf you a peeano?' he asked almost before he was inside the front door. He was rushed to our upstairs sitting-room where he continued to play for hours. *Bang-bang-bang!* went the poor piano as he hammered up and down the keyboard relentlessly. I was so fascinated by the noise he could produce with one pair of hands that I invited a girl or two from school to come and listen to him. We sat on the floor in the passage outside the sitting-room. As schoolgirls will, we chattered and giggled, and of course he heard us. Suddenly the door was flung open and with his tousled head shaking with rage and a voice that matched his piano-playing, he bellowed at us, 'Go avay you naughty leetle gairls, you distairb me.' We fled down the passage.

My parents liked to entertain with musical evenings. At least Mother did, and Father, although unmusical, saw the wisdom of such evenings, when a relatively large number of people could be entertained at a cost compatible with the financial state of affairs of the country at that time. I was in favour of musical evenings, for I was always allowed to stay up for them and enjoyed the light refreshments that were provided half-way through as well as the music. One night, just before such a party, my mother was getting ready as usual in her room.

'Go and see if Mr ——— is all right,' she said. 'I think he's in the ballroom practising. Ask him if he wants anything.' Mr ——— (I forget his name), a tenor, was to sing to us, and I found him running through his music.

'Mummy says are you all right and do you want anything?' I said bluntly. His answer surprised me.

'Could you get me a raw egg, my dear? It oils my throat.'

I tore off to the kitchen and confronted Mrs Riach.

'Please, Mrs Riach, Mr ——— wants a raw egg. He says it oils his throat,' I explained, for she looked very doubtful.

'Don't stand there gaping!' she rounded on the poor kitchenmaid. 'Go and fetch Miss Rosemary an egg at *once*.'

'What *in*?'

There was a moment's pause while Mrs Riach considered how an egg should be served raw to a visitor.

'Why, in a cup, of course,' she answered fiercely to cover her uncertainty. The egg looked a little lonely in the cup, but I supposed it was what was wanted. I took it back to the singer, who slid it into his mouth and swallowed it all to once, while I stood staring at him, fascinated.

That week there was a tremendous storm. The sky became darker and darker as great clouds blew up over the city. We stood and watched at a window. The wind was shrieking round the house and rising to hurricane force. It was a Saturday afternoon, and the harbour had been dotted with yachts, some of which had not been able to get home before the storm began and were now lying with their sails on the water. The wind whipped the harbour into a frenzy until it appeared to rise up in a vast mass and mingle with the clouds in one enormous grey swirling conglomeration. The trees in the garden, particularly the tall slender firs, were swaying backwards and forwards like mad things. They almost touched the grass, so violent was their agitation. As we stood and watched, there was a bang, and one of the windows blew *outwards* onto the verandah, where it smashed into a thousand pieces. A few moments later the wind dropped, the harbour water returned to its normal self, the dark clouds disappeared, and bright sunshine lit up the garden. The sudden change of scene was so dramatic as to be almost un-believable.

'Those poor people out in the Domain and other camps, what will they do?' cried my mother. 'Any sort of shelter they have managed to put up will have been swept away in that fearful storm.'

My father went to the Domain immediately to see what could be done. He found that some luckier folk were being housed in 'Hammond Hotels'. The Reverend Robert Hammond, rector of St Barnabas's, Broadway, and a canon of St Andrew's Cathedral, had established his first Hammond Hotel in 1908, in an old warehouse in Newtown, to rehabilitate some of Sydney's destitute. He had opened his most recent hostel—the sixth—in November 1930 in Blackfriar's Street, not far from St Barnabas's, to allow single men to take advantage of the government's issue of rations for the unemployed; single men could receive rations only if they had some approved place at which the rations could be cooked. On the evening of the storm the queues

The world-famous pianist Mark Hambourg. He is reputed to have advertised that he could teach the piano in ten lessons.

for food at the back door of Government House became even longer than usual.

Although the tropical storm had passed, the political storm was gathering strength. On 20 March the federal parliament in Canberra had received a cable from London to the effect that the Westminster Bank wanted to be certain that the British bond-holders would be paid their interest by the New South Wales Government. Jack Lang argued that if so much money had to be paid overseas, then he could not pay the men on the dole. He considered that no Australian should starve to death, and on 26 March he told the Prime Minister, James Scullin, that New South Wales would not meet the interest due overseas. Canberra was appalled by such a statement. The press and the public were shocked almost beyond belief by the shameful policy of 'repudiation', and the country was thrown into a state of unprecedented commotion.

At the same time, Lang renewed his request for more members for the Upper House so that Labor would have a majority and be able to pass legislation that would otherwise be rejected. My father, having taken legal advice, again refused this request. Lang then intimated that he would take

steps to have the Governor recalled. On 1 April a cartoon appeared in the *Bulletin* depicting Lang as the owner of a bulldog called 'Game' and talking to King George V. The caption read: 'Hey! Your Majesty, if this dog gives us chaps much more trouble, you'll have to take him back. You get ready and pick out a nice poodle!'

Naturally, being young and only partially aware of the tremendous events through which the country was passing, I enjoyed the excitement and the strange pictures of 'Daddy' in the newspapers. One evening I was busy on the floor cutting out some of these cartoons. My mother was sitting beside me waiting to go to a ball. My fingers slipped and I cut a slit, fully four inches long, near the hem of her gorgeous apricot satin evening dress. I was appalled.

'Oh Mummy! *Look* what I've done. Oh, your beautiful dress!'

Her sweetness showed itself in her complete calm.

'It's all right, darling, we'll *stick* it together and no one will ever know.'

It was trivial compared with the arguments that were raging over the political rights of state governors!

Lang claimed that the Government was elected by the people to govern the state. It was thus the will of the people that it governed. The Governor must therefore take the advice of his ministers. The opposite view was stated clearly by the Australian Workers Union, namely that Lang had *not* kept to his election mandate and that the Governor had every right to refuse his request for the extra members to enable him to push through his bills. The Governor himself decided that he had reached a situation where it would be unwise and improper for him to follow his ministers' advice to swamp the Upper House with extra members *until he had evidence that it represented the real desires of the people*. The situation was summed up by the *Northern Star*, Lismore, on 11 April in an article that read as follows: 'Occupancy of the office of Governor of New South Wales is not a bed of roses, nor a mere round of pleasure. At present the Governor is faced with serious problems. Whatever he does he will be subject to criticism.'

In July the Legislative Assembly insisted on a cable being sent by the Governor to Whitehall expressing their views. While the Government was waiting for a reply, Lang held a rally in the Domain. My mother wanted to go and listen but was strongly discouraged by my father.

'Couldn't I walk into the Domain with dark glasses and a hat pulled well down over my face and listen to what Lang has to say?'

Father was firm. 'No, no, certainly not, you might easily be recognised while you were there, and in any case you'd never get out of the house incognito as it is surrounded by police.'

Turner, the butler, went instead. He came back angry and shaken. 'Oh, sir, I really don't know how to tell you what Mr Lang said. It was *dreadful*. He tried to turn the people against you.'

Even my father was taken aback and hurt when he eventually managed to persuade the loyal Turner to tell him what Lang *had* actually said. Apparently he had addressed a gathering of some eighty thousand people, and the gist of his speech was that the Governor should do as he was told by his ministers. 'It is either this or you accept the position that the Governor can come out here and rule you,' he said, to cries of 'Send him home, Jack; send him back!'

Jack Lang addressing an outdoor meeting. Lang had a harsh and pugnacious voice and manner, but he was a determined and self-confident leader with an enthusiastic following.

The Premier had gone on to say, 'The question is simply this: Will the people govern; will their elected representatives govern for them, or will the Governor? Which way do you—the people—want it?' And back came the thunderous response: 'Your way, we want *your* way.' He said he would fight while ever he was in harness. 'I will give service, and not all the King's horses or all the King's men will deter me.'

Meanwhile, an answer to the cable had come from Whitehall. It was very much in favour of my father's views, which gave him a stronger position. J. H. Thomas, the Secretary of State for the Dominions, had said that the issue was one for the Australian people to decide, and he had left my father to make his own decisions. References were made to 'Governor's Letters of Instructions'. These letters say: 'The Governor shall be guided by the advice of the Executive Council but if, in any case, he shall see sufficient cause to desert from opinion of Council, he may act in the exercise of his Powers and Authorities in opposition to the opinion of the Council, reporting the matter to us without delay with the reasons for his so acting.'

The answer from England was a knock for Lang, but he persisted with his request for additional Upper House members. For some months father continued to stand out against this, but in the following November, after many weeks of thought and deliberation and realising that Lang had been elected by the people with a large majority and had subsequently won every by-election but one, he agreed to give him twenty-five extra members.

Before doing this he sent for Bill and David. My mother was entirely familiar with the situation. 'I'm afraid you may have an unpleasant time for a while,' he told them. 'There will be criticism, and you are unlikely to escape.' They agreed but said they would put up with it and that he must do what he felt was right.

The flood of abuse and criticism that followed my father's decision was like a tidal wave. There was a public outcry. Publicly and privately my parents were attacked by people at all levels of society. The press, of course, took advantage of this, and those men in the public eye who had strong views were quoted daily. 'This is a clear indication that the Government has gone red and has been endorsed in that action by the King's Representative,' declared Sir Arthur Cocks, a former Liberal Treasurer. 'I am astonished at the number of appointments which have been made,' said the Leader of the Opposition in the Upper House. Even Thomas Bavin said that he was at a loss to understand why the appointments had been made.

On 21 November the London *Daily Telegraph* reported that there was no foundation whatever for the suggestion that the Governor's action was the result of either instructions or advice from Imperial authorities and that 'no such instructions or advice were either asked for or given. Sir Philip Game said he acted entirely on his own responsibility, and without making known his intentions to the Dominions Office. He only informed the Secretary of State of his action *after* it had been completed.'

Letters came by every post suggesting that my parents should go home to England, that they were not wanted in Australia, that Father should be called 'Sir Spineless Game' or 'Red Game', even suggesting that he was being bribed by Lang. The vehemence of the letters was not reduced by the sometimes eccentric expression and spelling:

Dear Lady Game,

I am enclosing a few lines for your and Governor's perusal, will you please ask your hubby how much Lang pays him on the quite to keep him in power?

Sugest to your hubby to change his name from Game to Coward—it would be more suitable for his stamp, ask him to pack up his trunks and go back where he comes from, he is not wanted in Australia, if not he will be tarred and feathered before very long.

Yours etc,

People came to Government House and struck their names off the visitors' book. Others wrote to refuse invitations they had already accepted. Some people even cut my poor parents in public and refused to speak.

Father went to the races on Boxing Day. 'I did not want to go,' he wrote to my grandmother, 'but I didn't want people to think I was hiding from the storm. Racing people are real old tories . . . so I put my head in the lion's mouth. No one bit it off, but a coolness was often noticeable.'

I do not think he minded the abuse very much. His conscience was quite clear, as he makes plain in another letter: 'I remain quite unrepentant, as I feel convinced that what I did was both right and wise, but I wish things could have been different for Gwen's sake.'

My mother was very distressed, particularly when a few personal friends made it clear that they no longer wanted her friendship; but she was cheered by many who stood by her and remained loyal, including the staff and others who, even if they disapproved of what had been done, did not allow their disapproval to become personal.

My mother among her flowers. She took an enormous interest in the Government House garden, and a good many shrubs that she planted still grow there.

8 The Opening of the Sydney Harbour Bridge

WHO should open Sydney Harbour Bridge? This was a problem that caused discomfort among those responsible for the ceremony. It was as irritating as a sore finger to an already sick body, for the worry of the Depression and the political situation were enough without this added vexation. But the crowds that poured into the city and thronged the streets and the edge of the harbour on that brilliant day in March 1932 knew nothing of the difficulties and frustrations that had beset those who had planned the dazzling pageant. Never would they forget the scenes and colours they were to see that day, the splendour and stateliness of the processions beneath that great arch—superb in its symmetry and grace of form. To them it was a day of rejoicing, a day of wonder, and for a time they forgot their troubles as they watched and waited in the golden sunshine.

The preparations had begun many months before, months fraught with difficulties large and small, real and imaginary, but all rotating round that central question: Who was to declare the bridge open? In Canberra the staff of the Governor-General considered that, since their master was the King's senior representative in Australia, he should be given the honour. 'No, no,' said the Premier. 'This is a *state* affair, not a federal matter.' 'Very well,' acceded Canberra, 'then let the state Governor do it.' But the Governor felt differently: Lang, as Premier, ought to carry out this historic task. Lang wholeheartedly agreed!

On this basis the preparations went forward, and elaborate plans for the processions, the guards of honour, the escorts, the bands, and all the panoply of a great state function were laid before my father. He threw up his hands in horror! The whole ceremony was to last three to four hours; there were to be eight, possibly nine, speeches, and gun salutes for His Majesty, the Governor-General, all the visiting governors, and himself. Very complicated movements of troops and officials were planned to take place in a somewhat confined space. There were to be almost no arrangements for dealing with casualties and totally inadequate toilet facilities.

'It's impossible,' he told my mother at tea one day. 'I must get Lang to cut it down by half. *Nine* speeches and at least eighty guns.'

'Eighty *guns*,' I said. 'Oh no! You can't have that, Daddy. Poor old Micky would be *terrified!*'

Some weeks later, after many meetings and seemingly endless talks and discussions, the tension began to ease and reasonable plans were formed.

Then a royal spanner was thrown into works. King George V declared

that he wished the Governor to open the bridge. This was indeed a blow, for it meant so many last-minute alterations and a return of all the problems, not least those of human relationships. After considerable thought, Father sent a cable to the King explaining the difficulties and asking, very humbly, if the arrangements might be allowed to remain, and in due course a cable came back from Buckingham Palace stating that the King agreed to this. (But he was evidently displeased, for at a royal garden party in 1934 he told my father, kindly but firmly, that he had wished him to open the Sydney Harbour Bridge.)

During the Lang troubles a right-wing faction had emerged under the

The Governor and the Premier ride in style together in the Governor's Crossley at the opening of the Sydney Harbour Bridge on 19 March 1932.

leadership of a former military officer, Eric Campbell. It was known as the New Guard. Its aims seemed reasonable and honourable—absolute loyalty to the Monarchy and Britain, faithful and honest government and full liberty for the individual—but the movement was a nuisance, and its activities were causing my father some concern. Its plan was to present a petition from the people to the King to dismiss the Lang government. Ten men were then to be appointed to govern instead. The choice of these ten men would obviously have posed endless problems and might well have ended in a dictatorship. The members of the New Guard were morally at war with Lang; they were determined that he should go and that he should *not* be allowed to open the Bridge.

But on this great day—Saturday, 19 March 1932—all seemed to be forgiven and forgotten. The people basked in the glorious sun and the joyful atmosphere. It had been an exciting week at home. The house was bursting at the seams with visitors. The Governor-General, Sir Isaac Isaacs, the Governor of South Australia, Sir Alexander Hore-Ruthven, and the Lieutenant-Governor of Victoria, Sir William Hill Irvine, and their respective wives had all come to stay. With them they had each brought their ADCs and several other attendants. We were a huge party, and even that large house could hardly contain us. The ballroom had to be turned into a dormitory for my brothers and the other young men. Charles slept in a tent in the garden.

I enjoyed the hustle and bustle, the comings and goings and even the little bits of gossip that inevitably crept into the conversations between the staff of each governor. 'Did you know,' whispered one aide to another, 'that the Governor-General of New Zealand was not invited because Canberra didn't want him stealing the show from *them*!' No, there was never a dull moment with so much to listen to and so much to watch. The young aides were fun and always made time to talk to me. Some, like Captain Bracegirdle and Captain Shannon, who were particularly kind, I shall never forget.

There had been a flurry in the house the day before. Charles had come in in a great state of agitation to my father, pointing out that there was only one bathroom for the use of all the senior visitors.

'It's no good fussing, Charles,' said father. 'They'll just have to take turns! There's really nothing we can do, except import a couple of hip baths'—this was added with a naughty look in his eye—'and I can't see Daisy Isaacs enjoying *that* very much.'

The thought of Lady Isaacs climbing into a hip bath reduced Charles to a fit of his famous laughter, but he was still very concerned. 'I'll have to have a word with the other aides,' he muttered. 'Must have an order of precedence. Won't do for the Governor-General to be waiting about while the Lieutenant-Governor splashes around quite unconcerned.'

It was nearly as complicated as the perplexities of the opening ceremony, and I do not know how it was resolved. I do remember, though, a constant flow of ladies along the passage by my bedroom to the lavatory at the far end. The door was discreetly hidden by a pair of thick dark brown curtains, and many a vice-regal head could be seen peering delicately between them in order to avoid the acute embarrassment of being seen to emerge from such an unrefined quarter. When the coast was clear they would scuttle to their bedrooms.

Early on the morning of the opening, my brothers and I and Rosemary Budge were standing to one side of the dais and watching the processions arrive. Mr Lang was already there in a grey lounge suit and Homburg hat. This, incidentally, also displeased King George, who was a stickler for details of dress and considered that the Premier, if he *must* be allowed to open the Bridge, should have had the grace to wear a morning coat and top hat on such an auspicious occasion.

Stretched across the roadway was the blue ribbon which was to be cut by Mr Lang. VIPs were arriving every minute to the accompaniment of cheers from the crowd. Dr J. J. C. Bradfield, the engineer in chief (unmistakable with his large forehead), and his wife; R. T. Kitson, vice-chairman of Dorman Long & Co., the contractors; and cabinet ministers were among the most notable. Then the cheering broke out again even louder than before as my parents arrived with an escort of mounted police, my father and Charles in their full dress air force uniform and my mother dressed in brown. They were followed immediately by the Governor-General and Lady Isaacs accompanied by light-horsemen carrying red-and-white pennants. Lady Isaacs wore a lapis-blue georgette dress bordered with grey fur and a black hat with blue feathers matching her dress.

Their arrival provoked a petulant remark from Mr Lang to my mother.

New Guard member Francis De Groot holds his sword high as a policeman rushes to restrain him. De Groot cut the ribbon before the Premier could perform the ceremony of officially opening the bridge.

'I'm afraid of the Governor-General coming in on this,' he said. 'It's our show, not his. It's a state affair.' My mother soothed him to the best of her ability, and he settled down.

The ladies' dresses appealed to Rosemary and me. Mrs Bradfield was in navy-blue crêpe de Chine, the Lady Mayoress in royal blue. Mrs Lang was wisely demure in navy georgette (which suited her large frame) and a matching navy hat. We studied them closely, staring at each in turn, until a fanfare of trumpets called our attention away from them to my father. He was about to unveil a tablet officially naming the bridge as the Sydney Harbour Bridge and the roadway across the bridge as the Bradfield Highway.

He then read the official message from His Majesty King George V:

'I have learned with great pleasure that the Sydney Harbour Bridge has now been completed, and I desire to congratulate my people of New South Wales and all who have been concerned with the planning and construction of the bridge on the successful conclusion of the enterprise.

'Today, which sees the formal opening of this magnificent triumph of engineering skill, will be memorable in the annals of New South Wales. It will be remembered with legitimate pride and satisfaction by all who have played their part in the conception, design and execution of this great work—the largest arch bridge in the world.

'It is my earnest hope that the bridge may be a means of increasing the prosperity and of contributing to the comfort and welfare, not only of the citizens of Sydney, but the whole of the people of New South Wales.'

My father then said that he had officially replied to the King on behalf of the people as follows: 'The people of New South Wales and all those who have helped in the completion of Sydney Harbour Bridge desire to express to His Majesty their unbounded loyalty and affection and to tender to him their heartfelt thanks for his gracious message on the occasion of the opening ceremony.'

The sun was still shining out of a blue, cloudless sky. It was very warm. My mother put up her sunshade to protect her face. As she was standing next to Mr Lang, he, too, benefited from the shade. The press were quick to make much of this, and she suffered a certain amount of censure and ridicule in the papers next day—for having protected the Labor Premier's head from the sun!

Lang then delivered his opening speech. He had only just finished when the crowd just beside us was startled by a great commotion. A member of the New Guard, Francis De Groot, dressed in military uniform and flourishing a sword, rode forward on a horse and slashed through the blue ribbon stretched across the highway, shouting as he did so, 'On behalf of decent and loyal citizens of New South Wales I now declare this bridge open.'

It was a dramatic moment!

The crowd gasped in amazement at the horse and rider appearing in their midst apparently from nowhere. Captain De Groot had managed to mingle with the Governor-General's escort. It was astonishing that he was not noticed, for not only was he incorrectly dressed with a cap instead of the usual hat, but his horse, not being a trained military mount, had slipped on the road during the procession to the bridge and caused its rider to lose his place among the escort. Ironically, De Groot was actually helped back into the procession by a policeman who kindly held up the traffic for him! He had only been on the bridge a few seconds, with just time to sever the ribbon, before he was dragged from his saddle and hustled away by the police. The horse, being unused to crowds, was restive, and it took a little time before it, too, could be led away by a policeman. It was amazing that in all that commotion there were no accidents.

Dr Bradfield seemed to have had a premonition that something of this sort might occur. He had wisely arranged that the electrically fired rocket, the signal that the ribbon had been cut, was not to be connected until the very last moment. Captain De Groot's sword did no more than slash the ribbon in half, and it was only a matter of minutes before it could be tied together again ready for Mr Lang to cut with his special scissors. They were a very beautiful pair of scissors, made of Australian gold and mounted with six flame-coloured opals. The handles had hand-wrought representations of flannel flowers, waratahs and gum leaves entwining themselves round a picture of

My father stands calmly watching as Premier J. T. Lang cuts the ribbon which had been retied after De Groot had severed it with his sword. Charles Gifford (far left) looks a little more anxious: Is all going to be well this time?

the bridge, and on the blades was inscribed: 'Presented to the Hon. J.T. Lang, M.L.A., Premier and Treasurer of New South Wales, by Dorman Long and Co. Ltd., Contractors. Opening of Sydney Harbour Bridge March 19th, 1932'.

'As the blue cord fell apart, nine aircraft swooped out of the western sky in groups of three,' reported the *Sydney Morning Herald*. 'The two outside formations soared to avoid the concrete pylons at either end of the bridge, while the three central planes crossed over the great arch with a precision that spoke of the triumph of aerial navigation and a skill that evoked the wonder and admiration of onlookers.' Boats of every size and description passed under the bridge that day, making a great cacophony in the network of girders by sounding their sirens in cock-a-doodle-doos. RMS *Maloja* was led in procession by the proud little pilot vessel *Captain Cook*. The great Orient liner RMS *Orford* followed, and then a host of others. In between, darting in and out of the great liners, were tiny craft of all descriptions, like bees buzzing round honey. More staid, but allowing themselves a little frivolity in the shape of bunting, were the brisk little tugs which fussed round the liners like nannies with their charges. The harbour was a *mass* of boats, their brilliant flags proudly fluttering in the breeze. Every nation was busily showing its admiration for Australia's feat of engineering.

The day was only the beginning. The celebrations were to continue far into the night and indeed on through Sunday and Monday. At a great service of thanksgiving on the Sunday, large crowds were addressed by the Anglican Primate of Australia, Archbishop J. C. Wright. The service took place on the bridge itself.

Still apparently unwearied and rejoicing, more crowds collected on Monday to watch a pageant, another procession and the unveiling of a tablet by my father on the northern end of the bridge. The words on the tablet were 'This tablet was unveiled by His Excellency Sir Philip Game, G.B.E., K.C.B., D.S.O., Governor of the State of New South Wales, on 21st March, 1932, to commemorate the linking of the Northern Suburbs with the City of Sydney, and the Pacific Highway with the Bradfield Highway.' For this ceremony he was presented with a magnificent gold key by the Mayor of North Sydney, who said that 'a new era had dawned for the northern suburbs'. My father replied that although the key unlocked no material barrier, he hoped that it would open, symbolically, the door of friendliness and understanding. The key commemorates his first official entry into the northern suburbs by way of the bridge; hitherto he had always crossed the harbour by car ferry.

I doubt if Charles need have worried himself unduly over bathing arrangements for the VIPs at Government House, for they were hardly ever there long enough for more than a quick wash. On Saturday, after the official opening, they were all whisked off to lunch aboard the *Maloja*. For tea they were guests of the Orient Steam Navigation Company on board the *Orford*. By the time they returned to the house, having been out since nine o'clock in the morning, all they had time to do was to rush hastily upstairs, throw off their shoes and change into evening dress for the great Venetian carnival on the harbour.

Never will I forget that evening! The harbour glittered as a diamond. Thousands and thousands of lights sparkling from the tiny craft and big ships were reflected in the dark water. It was as though the heavens had descended upon the harbour. Great searchlights pierced the darkness above, roaming the skies like the ribbons of a giant maypole. They enclosed the multitude of ships, some of which moved ceaselessly back and forth; others lay still, but all formed a carnival of light. It was like fairyland. In Farm Cove a special display of illuminated boats plied their way silently round and round HMAS *Canberra*. One represented a huge whale with a red eye, another a giant bird in flight; others were simply covered with lights from bow to stern.

We were out on the water in the *Premier*. Rosemary Budge had come with us, and she and I with our healthy young appetites tucked happily into the sandwich supper on board. We had never had such an evening.

At eight o'clock the fireworks display began. From different parts of the harbour great rockets shot into the sky to fall like molten gold into the water. Sometimes the stars released from the rockets hung in the sky before they fell, sometimes they darted about, hither and thither, in frenzied search of a goal. There would be a burst from Fort Denison and another from the foot of the bridge meeting in a great arch to fall slowly down—the stars changing their brilliant colours as they fell: blue to green, green to red, red to gold. It was as though the whole sky that night was lit by great curtains of colour.

Then suddenly the fireworks ceased. Every searchlight was trained on the bridge. Their light gave the great arch a look of silver against the darkness, and spanning the harbour from north to south it was majestic in its beauty. It was the Queen of the Night.

We came alongside Man-o'-War Steps to walk quietly, as we thought, up

Crowds stream across the Bridge after the formal opening ceremony. At the fiftieth anniversary of the opening, in 1982, the Bridge was once again closed to motor traffic and the public were allowed to walk across on the roadway.

the little road to the house, but we were met by a great seething mass of people. It was almost impossible to get through. Lady Isaacs, who, considering it a gala occasion, had dressed herself in all her finery, got lost in the crowd. Jewels dripped from her ears, clung to her throat and cascaded over her ample bosom. My father was agitated. 'She might so easily get robbed,' he said, and he was very relieved when she appeared a few minutes later, bedraggled but intact, escorted by policemen.

The tremendous crowd pressed in upon us from every side, and the police had to go before us to clear a way. 'Poor things, the police have got 'em,' shouted someone as we passed, pushing our way single file through the mill-

The Mayor of North Sydney, Alderman Primrose, presents the Governor with the key to the northern suburbs on 21 March 1932. Dr Bradfield is seated on the right of the front row, holding up the leaflet.

ing masses of people. Eventually we reached the side entrance to the grounds of Government House. The gate was just being unlocked by Charles when the lodge-keeper rushed out. 'Oh no you don't!' he said, and slammed it in our faces. It took him some time to recover from his confusion when he discovered that, by banging the gate, he had shut out the Governor.

It might be supposed that this was the end of a perfect day, that the visitors all said goodnight to one another and retired to bed. I was the only one to do this; everyone else went off to join eighteen hundred people at the Bridge Ball held at David Jones's ballroom in aid of the Tresillian hospitals, to dance on and on into the night.

9 *Dismissal of the Premier*

DURING the early autumn of 1932, my father, and sometimes my mother too, spent over a month journeying to country towns, sometimes by car, more often by train. Down to Tumut, up to Newcastle, out to Condobolin! The country folk appeared to forget the political upheavals, judging from the tremendous welcome they gave my parents, and it was a relief to feel the loyalty and support coming to them from the crowds they met on those country tours. They had received unpleasant letters from people all over the state about the granting of the extra Legislative Council seats, but presumably those who felt deeply angry were in the minority. Even so, it was hard work. On one particular tour my poor father made twenty-six speeches, his day beginning at 9 a.m. and ending at midnight. No one who has not had to do such work could realise how exhausting it can be. I often wonder how they stood the strain of the continual travel as well as the heavy political burdens.

Whenever he was at home in Sydney, my father and Micky and I would walk in the Botanic Gardens at dusk. He seemed refreshed by Micky's enthusiasm for a walk and by my eternal questions and chatter. Sometimes there was time for a sail, and my father would teach me and explain the mysteries of jibing, going about and sailing before the wind. When my brothers were free they would come too, and *how* we enjoyed those afternoons on the harbour as we crossed and recrossed that lovely stretch of water.

A week after the opening of the Harbour Bridge, the Sydney Royal Show opened. It was a special show that Easter, with record numbers of entries and exhibitions and a grand parade of cattle that formed up in the shape of the Harbour Bridge. Rosemary and I adored the Show. Although we were interested in the agricultural exhibits and the ring events, what we really liked were the sideshows. Everything we could wish for was there, all the fun of the fair and even exhibits that were not fun but which we steeled ourselves to go and see, such as the cow with five legs, a rather revolting freak of nature. Fairy floss is one of the things I remember best, great masses of pink, sugary froth into which we buried our faces until we were literally up to our eyes in sticky, sweet nothingness, for it immediately melted away in our mouths.

After Easter my parents paid a visit to Bathurst. There, in the usual manner of visits of that kind, they opened a hall, visited a hospital and school, and tried to meet as many of the people as possible. During one of these official functions, Father stood up to make his speech and, try as he would, he could not remember whether he was visiting Bathurst or Orange.

A friendly rivalry exists between the two towns. For a moment he stood there nonplussed, then his quick wits came to his rescue.

'Citizens of Orange,' he began.

A roar from the crowd made it abundantly clear that he had chosen the wrong town.

'I thought that would get a rise out of you,' he said.

Early in May my father went to Narromine, a town lying to the north of Sydney and to the west of the mountains of the Great Dividing Range. He went by himself while my mother stayed at home with us. Could they have foreseen the future, she would undoubtedly have accompanied him, but how could either of them have guessed that his visit would cause such an uproar.

Narromine is not, as far as I know, very different from many other towns in New South Wales. A place where people farm, teach, tend the sick, minister to the bereaved, and go about their business in the hundred and one ways that people do in every town. It would never have come into this story had my father not gone to the agricultural show, where he was welcomed by the Mayor.

In his welcoming speech, the Mayor referred to the unsettled state of the country and hoped that the Governor would be able to find a solution to the difficulties confronting the people. My father replied: 'I agree that affairs are in a chaotic condition, but as the country has had self-government for seventy-five years and the people have accepted the responsibility of self-government, it is the duty of the people and not of the State Governor to find a way out of the trouble. I will, however, help as much as I can to bring about a state of peace.'

This statement opened floodgates of abuse. Many Australian newspapers, national and local, in editorials, articles and letters, took him to task. 'The Governor has broken a long and quite skilfully dignified silence by opening his mouth and putting his foot in it,' wrote one. A letter appeared in the *Cumberland Argus* in which the writer said:

> *Dear Sir Philip,*
>
> *Every day people are asking 'Why doesn't the Governor dismiss Lang?'. . . . The only solution lies in an election and we look to you to provide the opportunity for holding one. . . . You must agree, Sir Philip, that Mr Lang has got us in a hopeless tangle. . . . Why allow us to drift on the rocks. . . . The Premier has announced on several occasions that he will not resign, come what may; so it is up to you to bundle him out of office. This step must be taken sooner or later; so why delay?*
>
> *Yours in despair. . . .*

Some were sarcastic in their attack and included an air of disbelief that such a statement as that made at Narromine could have fallen from the lips of the Governor. I quote from the *Bathurst Times* in an article headed 'Did the Governor say it?'

> *There are people who had believed that Sir Philip Game included in his conception of the responsibilities of the high office that he fills a recognition that the people whom he was appointed to govern are entitled to protection from the political bullies and law-breakers whom our system of democracy*

permits to be thrown to the surface from time to time. They had thought that the duty of a representative of the King went deeper than opening shows and attending first nights at the theatre. . . . Have they been mistaken? Public confidence has entirely gone and no man knows what is going to happen next. A prospect of the complete disorganisation of the whole machinery of government makes a gloomy and even desperate outlook, which the State Governor is reported to have said we can settle amongst ourselves!

Sometimes the attacks were even more personal. One well-known man speaking at Molong remarked that 'nothing could be expected from Sir Philip Game as he was thoroughly spineless.' But the worst of all, in my parents' view, was a cartoon in the *Bulletin*. It was a picture of my father representing Pontius Pilate washing his hands. Underneath was written: 'AS IN THE DAYS OF OLD. "It is the duty of the people, not of the Governor, to find a way out of the present trouble."—*Sir Philip Game at Narromine*. "Pilate took water and washed his hands before the multitude, saying 'I am innocent. . . . see YE to it'."—*Matthew xxvii. 24.'*

It is only fair to say, however, that some of the press saw the situation in a different light and were able to write more impartially and from a wider point of view. On 5 May the Melbourne *Argus* included an article that sought to do this. The writer said, 'Most people are not versed in constitutional usage, and they are not always patient under constitutional restraints. . . . Those who enjoy responsible government must take responsibility for all the consequences of their acts, including their votes.' The *Age* in an article on 6 May added its censure to those who persistently criticised and pleaded for and even *demanded* Lang's dismissal from office:

The situation in New South Wales becomes worse, and there is widespread agreement as to who, politically, is exclusively at fault. There are, however, many conflicting councils as to what might be the most swift and equitable way out. The suggestions made are as mixed as are almost certainly those making them, but it is quite possible to sympathise with those citizens of New South Wales who feel that in circumstances so humiliating they should not be compelled to stand impotent. Apart from such sympathy, however, there can be nothing but censure for the still persisting attempts being made to involve Sir Philip Game, the State Governor. It is grossly unfair to him and it is quite gratuitously importing constitutional issues into an already sufficiently acute controversy. . . . Presumably one of his indisputable rights, both as Governor and individual, is to act when and as he thinks fit. Apart from legal considerations the ethic of the situation is that the Governor should abstain from the very appearance of partisanship, leaving New South Wales's people to find a way out of their troubles. These people may most justifiably wish to get rid of their present Premier, but there should be an abandonment of the palpable attempts to use the Governor as a dislodging lever.

My father returned to Sydney to find that my poor mother had, quite unwittingly, caused a stir of her own. She had attended a performance of the five best plays in a one-act-play competition organised by the Australian Play Society at the Aeolian Hall in Sydney. At the interval Mother told Isabel, who had accompanied her, that she did not care for 'the distasteful

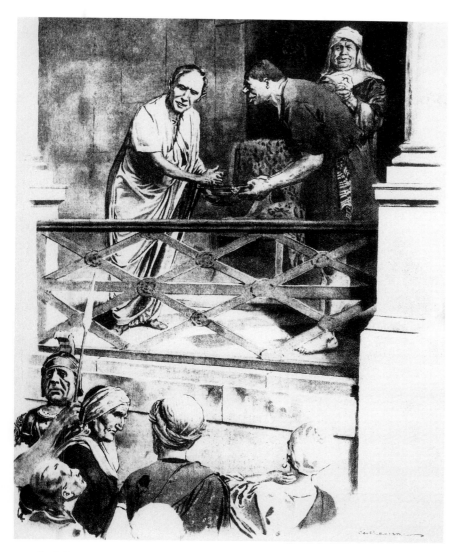

The cartoon that appeared in the Bulletin on 11 May 1932 which distressed my parents. It compared my father's statement at Narromine, regarding the responsibility of the people of New South Wales for their own affairs, with Pontius Pilate's washing his hands of the fate of Jesus. (Mitchell Library, State Library of New South Wales)

tone' of the plays, and together they decided to leave. There would probably have been no trouble had not a press reporter from the *Sydney Morning Herald* happened to walk past the theatre as they came out. He saw the crown on the car and made further inquiries. Next morning the newspapers were full of the incident, and for the next few days there were reports of comments from church leaders and others, mainly in support of Mother's protest. The Dean of Newcastle, in a sermon, said that the whole community owed a debt of gratitude to Lady Game for her courageous action. I asked my brothers about it, but all they would say was that the plays were 'very unsuitable'. Years later I discovered that both plays had a theme of free love and one had an occasional mention of birth control; but the last straw, as far as my mother was concerned, was when the two men discussed their girlfriends' underwear.

The previous December, federal elections had been held. The Scullin

Labor government had fallen from power, and in January Joseph Lyons, leader of the recently established United Australia Party, had formed a new government. This had been a blow to Lang. The new federal government was not keen to lend him money, especially when they considered his past refusal to meet interest repayments. The state finances were in the doldrums. Lang contended that there was plenty of work—all he needed was money with which to pay the workers.

My father waited and made his own judgments. It is obvious from a letter he wrote to his mother-in-law that he was not going to let public opinion sway these judgments:

> *Personally I am not assailed with any doubts as to the right and wise course for me to take. The course of events may eventually force me to take drastic action, but I haven't the slightest intention of doing so unless and until I think the time has come. So all I am doing now is to sit back and watch the combatants. The press barrage is very intense in its efforts to galvanise a supine and feeble Governor into action and it is backed up by the individual and collective efforts of a great many well-meaning people whose intelligence is blinded by fear, outraged feelings and principles, and other considerations good and bad. But hard words break no bones and if I can only keep in subjection the natural masculine joy of a good old scrap, I have some slight hope of pulling through and for the moment find the situation far more interesting and stimulating than embarrassing.*

He was, however, upset by the attacks both personal and constitutional upon Lang by *The Times* of London. The letter continues: 'By the way, all you get in England is the case as it appears to the die-hard anti-Labor element; an entirely one-sided view.'

One Sunday during all the turmoil, my father took Bill aside.

'Would you do something for me?'

'Of course.'

'I want you to take me to Double Bay to see someone. I want you to drop me at his front door and then drive away as quickly as possible, returning for me after an hour. I should be grateful if *you'd* do this, as a chauffeur might be noticed, and I should like to use *your* car.'

It has taken many years to discover who it was my father visited on that memorable Sunday afternoon. From information I have been able to glean from those who remember the 'Lang days', it seems likely that my father had earlier consulted Colin Campbell Stephen, whom he had had occasion to visit before and who in turn referred my father to a cousin, Alfred Consett Stephen, senior partner in Stephen Jaques and Stephen, a long-established legal firm in Sydney. A. C. Stephen lived at Prudhoe, a quiet house on New South Head Road, Double Bay. The fact that Bill drove my father to Prudhoe on Sunday indicates great secrecy; someone would undoubtedly have noticed if Stephen had come to Government House.

We can assume that my father consulted Stephen with regard to his position, constitutionally, over conflicts that might occur between Lang and himself. Stephen later told his family that he had said to the Governor, 'You cannot do anything now. Wait until Lang acts and becomes a rebel to the Crown, and then you can and *must* act.'

Lang had hoped that he might abolish the Upper House and then introduce a capital levy, but this he was unable to do. As a last desperate measure to obtain money, he tried to tax mortgages, but the bill, although passed, was never implemented.

Meanwhile, in order to get round the New South Wales Government's refusal to pay the interest on overseas debts, the Commonwealth Government had paid the bond-holders and passed the Financial Enforcement Act to recoup itself by appropriating the state's funds. Lang challenged this legislation in the High Court and also withdrew state funds from the banks in cash and held it in the New South Wales Treasury. When the High Court upheld the legislation, Lang directed the New South Wales Government departments to pay revenue directly into the Treasury in cash. In response, the Commonwealth issued a proclamation requiring state officials to pay specific revenues into the Commonwealth Bank by 11 May.

On 10 May Mr Lang had a confidential circular issued to government departments telling them to follow his earlier instructions not to pay money to the Commonwealth. It is possible that my father might never have seen this circular had it not been shown to the Official Secretary, Harry Budge, who, realising its vital importance, took it straight to the Governor. My father, considering that an intolerable situation had arisen and that an infringement of law could not be permitted, wrote Mr Lang the following letter on 12 May:

> Dear Mr Lang,
>
> *I understand a circular was issued by your department to the various Government Departments in connection with the disposal of moneys which have been attached by the Commonwealth under the Financial Enforcement Act.*
>
> *If this is so, I should be glad if you will furnish me with a copy.*
>
> Philip Game

Premier J. T. Lang and my father in serious conversation. (Mitchell Library, State Library of New South Wales)

An answer came from Lang that day enclosing the circular, which had been issued by order of his cabinet.

My father answered immediately:

Dear Mr Lang,

I have received a copy of the circular for which I asked you.

It appears to me that the terms of this circular direct public servants to commit a direct breach of the law. . . .

I feel it my bounden duty to remind you at once that you derive your authority from His Majesty, through me, and that I cannot possibly allow the Crown to be placed in the position of breaking the law of the land. . . .

He then went on to ask the Premier either for proof that the instructions in the circular were within the law or, alternatively, that he would withdraw it immediately.

Lang, after a preamble, ended his next letter abruptly: 'The only reply you can be given is that the circular cannot possibly be withdrawn.'

The next letter seems to me to be remarkably restrained and courteous. It was written on the morning of 13 May.

Dear Mr Lang,

I have just received your letter of today's date. I gather from it that you do not dispute my view that the circular in question is a breach of the Federal law.

You will, I am sure, realise that I cannot allow the matter to rest where it is. Before considering what further action I may feel bound to take, I should prefer to discuss the whole position with you. I shall be available at any time today convenient to you.

Philip Game,
Governor.

The house seemed deserted when I came in from school that afternoon. Then I met William in the hall.

'Hullo, William, where is everyone?'

William's pleasant round face was creased in a frown.

'The Governor's got that Mr Lang with him. Been worrying him off and on all day. Never seen such comings and goings with letters and messages. He's a real headache, that man—never leaves your poor father alone.'

'Oh, *he* won't mind,' I said. 'After all, it gives him something to do, and anyway it makes a change from opening fêtes and wings of hospitals and things, and writing all those *awful* speeches. But why has everyone been coming and going, William? How exciting!'

'Political trouble, I shouldn't be surprised. Always stirring up trouble, *that* one is,' he muttered, and then added hastily, realising that he might have overstepped the mark, 'Her Ladyship is in the drawing-room, miss.'

My mother was kneeling up at the window looking out at the garden and harbour. The bulbuls were pecking the lawn, their flame-coloured patches making brilliant spots of colour against the green. Willy wagtails ran about searching for food and wagging their tails from side to side.

'Isn't it funny the way their tails go sideways?' I remarked. 'Everything

out here seems upside-down. Have you seen the moon, Mummy? The man's face is on its side—he looks more like a rabbit, really.'

But my mother was in no mood to think about Willy wagtails or the man in the moon.

'Daddy's got Mr Lang with him. They're having fearfully important talks. It's just possible that Mr Lang will be dismissed and that we shall have a new Premier and things will be better. But of course if Daddy's wrong we might have to go back to England.'

'Oh gosh! I do hope we shan't,' I said. 'I've just been chosen to be Alice in *Alice in Wonderland*. Anyway, when are we having tea?'

My mother was saved from having to decide how to deal with me by the sound of the study door opening. The two men emerged: Mr Lang, large, square-jawed, heavily built, his Homburg hat in his hand; my father small, spare and lean, beside him. They walked slowly through the hall, talking as they went quietly, amiably, on to the outer hall to say goodbye. They shook hands, and the man with the bigger frame passed out of the great door watched by the spare lean figure whose strength lay in his gentleness.

The Premier had asked the Governor to put into writing the substance of the discussion they had had that afternoon. This my father proceeded to do immediately, with my mother and Mr Budge, both in a state of tremendous excitement, standing either side of his desk and giving advice.

The letter that emerged reads as follows:

Alex Gurney's Bulletin *portrait of Lang called 'After the Sacking'. Lang was a caricaturist's dream; his eyebrows, teeth, moustache and height were often emphasised.*

> *Dear Mr Lang,*
>
> *At our interview this afternoon you requested me to communicate my views by letter.*
>
> *The position as I see it is that Ministers are committing a breach of the law. While you did not admit this, you did not deny it. Your case, as I understand it, is that Ministers are determined on their action in order to carry on the essential services of the State.*
>
> *Into the aspect of justification it is not, as I conceive it, my province to enquire. My position is that if my Ministers are unable to carry on essential services without breaking the law, my plain duty is to endeavour to obtain Ministers who feel able to do so.*
>
> *As I have already pointed out to you in my letter of the 12th instant, it is impossible for me to put the Crown in the position of being a party to an illegal action.*
>
> *If Ministers are not prepared to abide by the law, then I must state without hesitation that it is their duty under the law and practice of the Constitution to tender their resignations.*
>
> *I await an early reply, as I am sure you will agree that the present position cannot be allowed to extend over the week-end.*
>
> *Philip Game,*
> *Governor.*

The answer was immediate:

> *Dear Sir Philip,*
>
> *If your letter of today's date means that you are requesting the resignation of Ministers, you are hereby informed that your request is refused.*
>
> *Yours faithfully,*
> *John T. Lang.*

My father was not easily daunted. He wrote his final letter to the Premier at once:

> *Dear Mr Lang,*
>
> *Your letter informing me that Ministers are not prepared to tender their resignations has just reached me. In view of this and of your refusal to withdraw the circular, I feel it my bounden duty to inform you that I cannot retain my present Ministers in office, and that I am seeking other advisers. I must ask you to regard this as final.*
>
> *Philip Game,*
> *Governor.*

The dismissal had taken place officially. Even Micky seemed happy, his tail flaying backwards and forwards between the teacups laid out in the drawing-room. An excited buzz of conversation filled the room—curious, disjointed, jerky. The atmosphere was one of adjustment. What has been? What now? What next? My father, pale and strained, got up, sat down, got up again. He was shocked. Certainly he was not 'with us' that day at tea. His poor head was trying to rid itself of the fears, the worries and the perpetual troubles that had beset him for so many months—tough political assignments that he had not wanted or liked; problems that he, ultimately, had had to solve alone. He needed rest and time to recover from them, and no one understood this better than Micky, who sat by his master's knee and licked his hand.

The house was in a turmoil. I did no prep that night. The comings and goings, particularly of the press, who wanted interviews with everyone and asked for endless details of the day that had passed, were thrilling. What did school work matter with so much history being made at home!

At 6 p.m. Bertram Stevens, the leader of the Opposition, arrived at the house. He stayed an hour. Interviewed as he left he said, 'His Excellency has sworn me in as Premier and has commissioned me to form a government.'

Later that evening I asked my father a question. 'What will you do, Daddy,' I said, 'with all the people who crossed their names off the visitors' book?'

He thought for a moment before answering.

'I think I shall put them on probation for a little while.'

A few nights later my mother and father went to an opera at Her Majesty's Theatre. To their utter astonishment, as they reached their seats in the dress circle, the whole theatre rose to their feet clapping and cheering them for some minutes. When at last the applause died down, my mother was searching in her bag for a handkerchief; the tears were streaming down her cheeks.

After Lang's dismissal, my father received many letters of congratulation. One of these was from a lawyer, R.G. Menzies, later Sir Robert Menzies, Australia's longest-serving Prime Minister. In the letter, Menzies explained that he had been reluctant to write earlier:

> Although the opinion of a lawyer might have been of interest and possibly of assistance to you, it seemed to me that the opinion of an active politician might prove only an embarrassment and as I confess to being both a lawyer and a politician, I came to the conclusion that it would be an impertinence on my part to offer any opinion at that stage. We have now, however, reached a point in time at which the controversy which arose over your much criticised failure to dismiss the Premier, and your subsequent much applauded decision to remove him for a breach of law, may be regarded in a disinterested way as a striking episode in our constitutional history. Under these circumstances and after this interval of time, you will perhaps permit me to express views which, in common with many other members of the Victorian Bar, I have, throughout, entertained.
>
> Briefly, the newspaper demand that you should dismiss a Premier on the ground that there was some reason for believing that he no longer enjoyed the confidence of the electors always seemed to me to be based upon an absolute

Jack Lang's successor, Bertram Stevens, standing in the grounds of Government House after he had been commissioned to form a new government.

misconception of the constitutional position of a modern Governor. Under the Australian system of universal suffrage and triennial Parliaments, with a legally recognised and responsible Cabinet, it must, in my opinion, follow that so long as a Premier commands a majority in the Lower House and so long as he is guilty of no illegal conduct which would evoke the exercise of the Royal Prerogative, he must be regarded as the competent and continuing adviser of the representative of the Crown. For a newspaper to urge a dissolution because in its opinion the Government has lost the confidence of the electorate is a mere impertinence. The constitutional authority of a Premier rests almost entirely upon his success at a general election and upon his continued authority in the popularly elected House. . . . It would, in my respectful opinion (and in this I am expressing the majority view among reputable lawyers in this State), have been nothing short of a calamity, if, during the very great constitutional crisis, New South Wales had possessed a Governor who had subordinated the constitutional authority of a Governor to the purely opportunist demands of those who found the constitutional restrictions irksome.

This kind letter must have greatly comforted my father. Even I know that he always felt distressed at having had to perform such a disagreeable duty.

Labor was defeated overwhelmingly at the subsequent election in June. Some might argue that the election result was a verdict by the people on the rights and wrongs of my father's action in dismissing the Premier.

10 Travels and Visitors

AFTER the excitement and dramatic events of the first half of 1932—the political tussle between the state and federal governments, the opening of the Sydney Harbour Bridge, the dismissal of the Premier and the subsequent election—life for the Governor resumed its normal routine: presiding at official meetings, visiting schools and opening hospitals, attending charity balls and other functions, as well as making country tours and entertaining visitors. On one of their tours, to the southern border of New South Wales, my parents took David and me with them. We were to visit the fertile land of the Riverina, watered by the great Murray and Murrumbidgee rivers. But first we were to go to Menindee, out west on the Darling.

We went by train from Sydney in our special saloon, leaving at eight o'clock one morning and arriving at Menindee at 6 a.m. the following day. During the first morning our journey took us over the Blue Mountains and the great grazing country of their western slopes. By the afternoon we were on the plains beyond. The immensity of those plains makes them fascinating, as they stretch on and on towards the great central heart of the continent. I had never imagined such country, and stared out of the window at the flat bare land as the train chugged its way west mile after mile.

In those days Menindee was a dreary little town set in the midst of sparse, sandy waste. It looked arid and barren as we stepped out of the train the next morning. I could not imagine how people could endure that dry, flat, monotonous country. True, the Darling river ran beside the town, but it was sluggish and dull as it meandered through the saltbush-covered earth. We were

An improvised kitchen erected by one of the unemployed families who were living in Menindee at the time of our visit.

Some of the makeshift dwellings and their occupants as Menindee in September 1932. The thirteen-year-old girl in the centre of the lower picture at left, kept at home on the advice of the bush nurse, was the only absentee from school.

there in spring, and the sun shed a delicious warmth, but in a few more months it would blaze down pitilessly and the temperature at noon might well reach 115 to 120 degrees Fahrenheit.

To the stalwart Australians, used to the heat and full of a grand, pioneering spirit, it was home. They were undaunted by the climate and the loneliness. The anxiety they suffered at that time was something quite different. It was the misery of unemployment.

After a most friendly and welcoming civic reception, my father received a formal deputation from the unemployed, telling him of the deplorable conditions in which they were living. He promised that he would visit their camp that same afternoon.

He was appalled by what he saw. People were living in a state that might well have been considered unfit for cattle. Rough huts, or humpies as they were called, had been erected out of any available material. Some people were lucky enough to have found wood; many made do with sacking tied to posts. Without proper fencing it was practically impossible to grow vegetables, for any that sprouted were quickly demolished by rabbits or goats. In these wretched conditions parents were trying to feed and bring up their children. Even sanitation was limited, and there had already been an outbreak of enteric fever. Clearly the situation was intolerable. My father promised that directly he returned to Sydney he would discuss the problem with the Premier and that they would do their utmost to help.

During the two weeks that we were away, my mother and father, who had always taken a tremendous interest in the work of the Bush Nursing Association, took every opportunity to visit the nurses wherever there was a centre. The following extract from a nurse's diary shows the type of women they met:

2 a.m. Cold stormy night. Knock on door, voice says, 'Sister please come at once to Mrs M.' Up quickly, seizing maternity bag, I walked a mile through wet, black soil. On arrival found bed practically useless so I got a door taken off a shed and put across to raise it. Baby born at 4.30 a.m.— left mother and child at 6.30 a.m. both comfortable.

Just got back when a lorry arrived and driver said, 'Sister will you come and see Bill? He's been breathing bad all night,' After a six-mile drive in the lorry I found a child of two suffering from bronchitis. Poulticed him and fixed up tent bed with brooms and sticks on cot and left further treatment and directions.

8.30 a.m. Snatched breakfast, then off two miles to child with gastric attack, then on five miles to elderly man with gallstones. Fixed him up comfortably until he could be got to a doctor.

11.00 a.m. Back to consulting room to treat seven patients who were waiting for me.

1.30 p.m. Hurried dinner and off nine miles by car to see small boy with pneumonia. Took him to hospital and returned by 5 p.m.

5.30 p.m. Confined mother for twins in a camp 20 miles away. A child had walked 11 miles to the nearest neighbour to ask her to phone me.

8.30 p.m. Fixed up mother and baby of early morning case.

10.30 p.m. Saw bronchial child, who was better.

12 midnight. Just got to bed when a call came from man badly burned. Stayed with patient and did all I could, but he died at 5 a.m.

11 a.m. Went to bed, but up again at 1.30; had dinner and then started on visits and dressings again.

A bush nurse with my parents. They were deeply impressed by the nurses' selfless devotion to the people of the interior.

It is not surprising that my mother considered these nurses as the angels of the bush, prepared as they were to endure hardships, loneliness and even danger to be doctor, nurse and comforter to the people of the outback. Sometimes the nurses came from England, and sometimes they received a considerable shock when they reached some tiny township outback, where they were to spend two years or more in conditions unimaginable at home. There was the case of a young woman—only in her mid-twenties—arriving from Britain. She was taken to her bungalow in which one room was to be her surgery. The house was comfortable and clean but very basic; it was up to her to make it a home. She unpacked, turned on the taps, had a bath, washed her hair, washed her clothes; then the water stopped flowing. After struggling with the taps for a while, she ran into the main street to find a plumber. The first person she asked for help gave her a wry smile. 'A plumber won't help yer, miss,' he said. 'You've used up all yer rainwater, and sometimes it don't rain here for five years.'

No doubt some of their patients, too, thought of those women as angels: the mother whose baby was delivered by a nurse who risked her life fording a swollen river on horseback; or the man who had tried to take his life by cutting his throat and then, wishing he had not, had sent for the nurse to stitch it up! There are countless stories of this kind, and my mother listened avidly to such tales. They pierced deeply into her thoughtful, sensitive nature.

Leaving Menindee, we drove thirty miles south to spend the weekend as guests of the Rankins at Netley station. The house stood close by the Darling, which, at this point, though still slow and peaceful, was far more beautiful. Fine eucalypt trees grew along its banks, their branches sweeping down to the water and in many places forming shady arches overhead. David and I spent the weekend swimming in the river and canoeing up and down that lovely stretch of water. We revelled in the joy of being able to use the river at any time and would have liked to stay there many more days.

Canoeing on the river Darling while staying at Netley with the Rankins.

All through that trip we were accompanied by the Right Reverend R. C. Halse, Bishop of the Riverina. By some he was nicknamed 'Never-in-'er', for he frequently travelled all over the state. We called him 'the Mintie Bishop', as he always carried a box of Minties with him. He was a charming man who seemed to enjoy showing us his enormous diocese. We had now reached the extremity of the Riverina as it was delineated in those days, having driven to Wentworth, the town at the junction of the Darling and the Murray, and then followed the Murray upstream through the fertile fruit-growing land.

The weather was perfect and the oranges that we picked as we walked through the citrus groves were warm from the sun. They were the most delicious oranges I have ever tasted, so full of juice that much of it splashed on to the ground as we ate. As well as the orange groves, there were lemon and grapefruit trees, and the air was full of a tangy fragrance.

At Mildura we saw the huge packing stations for the dried fruit. Great boxes of raisins were being packed for export. It was all scrupulously clean and very tempting to my young fingers. We spent several nights in the district. Unfortunately our accommodation in a commercial hotel was not up to the hygienic standards of what we had seen during the day, and I woke in the night to watch rats crawling up the sides of my window, silhouetted against the moon. When I felt brave enough I crept out from under the mosquito net and bolted into my mother's bed, while my father obligingly spent the rest of the night in mine. A few days later we reached Hay, where we boarded the train and started the long journey back to Sydney.

The next few weeks were tremendously busy. My mother's aunt Alice and uncle Malcolm and their adopted grown-up daughter Patricia were coming to stay. 'We must give them a happy time,' said mother, who was very anxious for them to enjoy their visit, for they were not young and she felt that they had made a tremendous effort by coming all the way from England. Also, it was through them that she had originally met my father.

'The Mintie Bishop'—the Right Reverend R. C. Halse, Bishop of the Riverina. Menindee was in his diocese.

It was spring, the weather was warm, and the surfing season was beginning. For some reason Patricia had managed to arrive in Australia without a 'bathing dress'. She hurried off to the shops to buy one and came back looking very pleased.

'I've bought a beauty,' she told us. 'It's white and it should look jolly nice when my skin tans.'

Next day we went surfing before breakfast. We were tucking in to a hearty meal when Aunt Alice came sailing into the dining-room.

'Oh Patricia, my darling, *how* did you get on? It must have been so lovely at Bondi. Was your new bathing dress all right?' she gushed and smiled as the words tumbled out. Luckily she did not notice Bill, David and me filling our mouths with food in an effort not to laugh. Patricia was subdued.

'It was all right,' was all she said.

Aunt Alice, a discerning person, was not going to be put off.

'What do you mean, dear? Didn't you enjoy yourself?'

'Oh well,' said Patricia, 'if you must know, when I got into the water my bathing dress became completely transparent.'

Aunt Alice's little shriek lives with me still.

'Oh, *Patricia!* Oh, darling! What did you do? Oh, oh . . .' Her voice trailed off in utter consternation. Patricia calmed her down.

'It's all right, Mother. I crawled on my tummy to my towel and wrapped it round me.'

The crowds that came to Government House for the two-day fête in aid of the Bush Nursing Association. Both house and garden were used; security in those days was nothing like the problem it is now.

*More crowds in the drive and
outside the front door during
the fête for the bush nurses.*

Apart from the affair of the bathing dress, my great-uncle and aunt's visit
went off very happily. One of the highlights of their stay with us was an
enormous two-day fête in aid of the Bush Nursing Association. During the
Depression at least ten centres had had to be closed down. My parents were
so distressed by this that they offered to lend the house and garden for a gala
fête to raise money.

It was the first time that a Government House had been used in this way,
and it proved to be a perfect setting. The garden was a blaze of colour, which
provided an attractive background for the marquees, stalls and sideshows.
One section, called 'Australia Street', was arranged exactly like a shopping
precinct. Every type of shop was there and everything for sale had been
given, some of it from the far corners of the state. There was even a special
post office in the grounds to entice the philatelists. I wish I could say that I
was able to enjoy the fête; unfortunately I was ill in bed and could only see
the thronging masses of people from my window.

Nearly fifteen thousand people came to the fête during those two days. For
many, of course, it was an attraction to be allowed inside the house as well as
the garden. There was an art exhibition in the drawing-room, and in the
ballroom there were half-hour plays, concerts and dancing displays. At night
the trees were lit with coloured lights as a setting for rhythmic dancing and
ballet on the lawns. There were very few expenses, for the committee and the
twelve hundred helpers all gave their services free; the result was that £5,550
was able to be sent to the Bush Nursing Association.

I soon recovered from my illness and was able to go on the bush picnics my
mother arranged for her aunt and uncle. Sometimes we went out for the day
in the *Premier* to Middle Harbour, where in those days there were no houses
and the bush came down to the water's edge. One glorious day we were taken

A pretty scene at the fête. The two young woman sitting on the edge of the lily pond are twins Jean and Gwen Ramsay.

to the National Park, south of Sydney, by Alec Chisholm, the well-known naturalist and a great friend of my father. Alec had spied out the land beforehand and was able to take us straight to places where he knew we would see lyrebirds, bowerbirds and other equally exciting wildlife. The lyrebirds appeared, stalking majestically along under the bushes, their magnificent tail feathers held like a train behind them, but even Alec could not persuade them to hold them up to form the famous lyre. The black satin bowerbird was much more obliging and danced around his bower while we watched enthralled. The bower was made of twigs formed into two cone-shaped structures, and the space in between was filled with anything blue the bird had been able to find; there were bits of blue china, a blue marble, and even a laundry blue-bag! It was difficult to tear ourselves away from the enchanting scene.

This was not my father's first visit to the National Park (now the Royal National Park). On 15 February he had opened Governor Game's Lookout on the plateau overlooking Era Beach in the southern section of the park. He loved the wild country, and the view of the coast with the Pacific rollers breaking on the golden sand had rested his mind for a few hours from the fatigue and worry of those trying months.

On Sundays Aunt Alice and Uncle Malcolm came with us to St Andrew's Cathedral. As they sat next to my parents, I moved a little further down the pew until I was exactly opposite the pulpit. One Sunday, while they were with us, the sermon was preached by a new canon. He must have been an extremely good preacher, for I was listening to what he said and watching him intently. He was the sort who moves about while speaking, making gesticulations to press home his point. One of these gesticulations was so violent and so sweeping that it knocked the Bible right off its rest. Without flickering an eyelid, the canon leant right out of the pulpit and caught it neatly in his left hand—'low down in the slips', as my father put it. The congregation gave a great gasp, their oohs and ahs sighing through the cathedral like a breath of wind. The canon went calmly on as though he were quite used to catching the Bibles he knocked flying from pulpits.

There is no doubt that, in one way or another, Aunt Alice and Uncle Malcolm were well entertained during the weeks they spent in Sydney.

Clara Butt, who was our next visitor, I remember well. She was a massive woman, at least six feet tall, with shoulders as big as an average man of that height. She had to have a powerful frame, for her voice, possibly the most noble contralto voice there has ever been, could only have been produced from such a solid frame. She had a sympathetic face and a personality to match it. She and her husband, Kennerly Rumford, came to stay with us several times, and during one of those visits she told us children to call her Aunt Clara. I imagine that she was on Christian name terms with my parents, but this I do not remember.

Everyone enjoyed her concerts in the Town Hall. Her songs were patriotic, romantic and, in the nicest way, sentimental. They were songs she must have heard in her youth, songs such as 'Madam, will you walk; Madam, will you talk' and 'I will give you the keys of Heaven'. She sang the latter song with her husband, reducing the enormous volume of sound of which she was

A picnic during a country tour in winter. The back seats had been taken out of the cars to use as seats on the ground.

The naturalist Alec Chisholm shares a joke with my father at a Scouts' hut.

capable, to blend with his pleasant but, in comparison, quite ordinary, voice. She filled the Town Hall—there was never a spare seat—and her voice carried to every corner. She could have filled any hall in the world.

Her concerts usually ended with 'Rule Britannia', to remind us that we were all part of the great British Empire, and left us feeling exhilarated, inspired and loyal. She could certainly stir the emotions and carried her audience throughout the evening from heart-rending Victorian sentimentalism to soul-stirring patriotism. I adored listening to her but usually came home feeling nervously exhausted.

Almost all our visitors were extremely nice, but occasionally an awkward one crept in. The man who followed Clara Butt was one of these. I cannot

Dame Clara Butt, one of the world's finest contraltos. Her voice matched her size; a splendid person in every way.

remember his name, and no one really seemed to know why he was coming to stay, or for how long! After a fortnight even my mother's patience was beginning to give out.

'I really *do* wish he'd go,' she said. Next day Isabel developed scarlet fever. Ah, thought my mother, now he will leave. She approached him gently.

'Mr ———, my secretary has got scarlet fever. I expect you'd rather leave, as of course you wouldn't want to catch it. We shall quite understand . . .' Her voice trailed off as he interrupted her.

'I'm not in the *least* afraid, thank you.'

He stayed another week and then announced that he must catch the eight o'clock train the following day.

'I'll order the car for you,' said Mother, 'and arrange for you to have an early breakfast.'

'Thank you, I've done all that,' he answered.

For once my mother was not amused.

The sweetest and most gentle couple that ever came to stay were the new Archbishop of Sydney, Howard Mowll, who replaced Archbishop Wright in 1933, and his wife, Dorothy. It was difficult to believe that they had been missionaries in China and had been attacked by brigands. Dr Mowll had seen his wife's wedding dress being borne away on top of a long pole by evil-looking men. This was the only story they would tell about their adventures in China, preferring to keep silent about what had obviously been horrific experiences.

Before the Mowlls arrived, my mother went to look at their rooms. She did not usually do this, for Miss Harris was utterly reliable, but on that particular afternoon something prompted her to make sure that everything was in order. She was well satisfied; the rooms looked charming, with flowers on the dressing-table, towels neatly folded, and the curtains slightly drawn to keep the strong sun from pouring in. She was just turning to leave when she saw two books by the Archbishop's bed. How thoughtful of Miss Harris, she said to herself. Then she read the titles: *For Sinners Only* and *Death Comes to the Archbishop*.

Howard Mowll, who became Archbishop of Sydney in 1933, and his wife, Dorothy. The Mowlls and my parents became lifelong friends.

11 A Trip to Lord Howe Island

IN THE summer of 1932/33 the cricket test series between England and Australia that came to be known as the 'bodyline series' was played in Australia. It was fun watching the cricket in Sydney, in spite of the heckling crowd who had for the time being suppressed their political grievances and substituted for them violent opinions over the Ashes. They gave vent to their feelings by rolling oranges onto the pitch, among other things. But when we went back to school after the Christmas holidays, to be English was to be considered not merely a blackleg but an outcast, and for me it was pure misery. How *could* Jardine, the captain of the MCC team, himself an Englishman and therefore supposedly a fine sportsman, allow Larwood to pitch the ball to maim a succession of congenial Australian batsmen? I did not know! I loved both countries and did not mind who won, but I minded the questions and the heated arguments into which I was unwillingly drawn. The words of the old songs of those passionate days of cricketing still produce a disagreeable feeling within me:

> *Hammond and Sutcliffe and Jardine*
> *Convinced me that I was a sardine.*
> *No one believes I'm a mermaid,*
> *But really and truly I am.*

Had I known then that some forty years later Messrs Lilley and Thomson would engender the same high feelings with their bouncers, I might have withstood the barrage of abuse a great deal better.

My parents suffered too, as my mother recorded in her diary:

> *There seemed to me more ill-feeling over this particular form of cricket with its 'body-line bowling' than even over politics. I always felt that Jardine could have done more than he did to soften the bitterness and to greet the Australian hosts with a smile instead of rather aggressive looks. We had both teams to lunch at Government House during the Cricket Week and did our utmost to produce a happy feeling, by combining cricket jargon with the French language on the menu—'Soupe Siècle de Sutcliffe', etc., but I'm afraid the effect did not last beyond the moment, and watching the Test Matches was always rather agonising, so that it was with extreme thankfulness that we saw them all depart.*

With the ending of the cricket season, my own little private life was much happier. I was having lessons in musical history and appreciation, which I

'Hammond and Sutcliffe and Jardine . . .'. Douglas Jardine, captain of the MCC team that toured Australia in the summer of 1923–33—the notorious Bodyline series—is in the centre of the photograph between Walter Hammond and Bert Sutcliffe.

enjoyed, and thanks to Lina and her untiring efforts I won an open prize in French conversation. Obviously the right constellations were crossing the sky that year—for me, at least. For the numbers of unemployed in the state, it was another matter. Their situation distressed my father, and he was tremendously pleased to receive a letter from the silver-lead mining centre of Broken Hill, written by the unemployed themselves, asking him to visit them. The letter suggested that very little had been done by the Government to relieve their suffering, and ended as follows:

> *Your Excellency may rest assured that our purpose, though mainly guided, admittedly, by a consideration for our wives and children who are suffering dire want, is not to belittle your Office, but to solicit your aid in a worthy cause.*
>
> *Yours in destitution,*

My father replied carefully that he would be delighted to accept the invitation and would welcome the opportunity of seeing for himself the conditions under which his fellow citizens lived at Broken Hill, *provided* that politics were barred. He made it perfectly clear that he was not prepared to interfere with the politics of government, past, present or future—that was not his role—but that he had, indeed, great sympathy for the people of Broken Hill in their suffering.

My mother and father travelled the seven hundred miles west over the plains by train. Food was taken with them, and they arranged to live and to have many of their meals in the train, so that they would not be a burden to the people who were out of work. 'It was the most interesting "Outback" visit that we made,' my mother wrote. 'We were surprised and thankful to be so warmly greeted in that poor derelict town, where we found many of the people living in shacks built of old kerosene tins and sacking. It was arranged for me as far as possible to visit the women and Philip the men, in the camps for the unemployed.'

The conditions were appalling. The people had very little food and nothing to do, and it was very distressing to my parents to see so many children growing up learning to do nothing whatever, simply because there *was* nothing to do. It was almost impossible to grow food, for the soil was very bad and water had to be bought out of the dole rate, which was ridiculously inadequate. The vegetable allowance per person was threepence a week. Shoes were a problem, for if they were worn out by work or even walking, they were impossible to replace. One of the camps my father went to see was known as Chateau de Tar Drums. There he met a man preparing lunch in his 'sitting-room'. It was an unroofed area surrounded by corrugated iron, and at the side was a kennel which was the poor man's bedroom. His bed was made from bagging. Even so, the people seemed amazingly cheerful and had managed somehow to keep their pathetic dwellings remarkably clean.

Of course not everyone was out of work, and between their visits to the unemployed my parents had some bright intervals. A huge ball was given at the Palais de Danse to raise funds for the unemployed and the Far West's Children's Health Scheme; as nearly nine hundred people attended, it was

Unemployed men prepare to go out cutting wood for Broken Hill.

almost impossible to dance, but the charities benefited enormously. There was also ladies' afternoon for my mother, organized by all the Broken Hill churches. While she was enjoying herself and looking at the wonderful wild-flowers that had been collected, my father was busy at the Town Hall with the Citizens' Committee, discussing the unemployed.

In any town in such a condition, feelings can run high and emotions become out of control. There was an incident in the Town Hall that afternoon that caused a stir. In a public speech, one of the aldermen faced round towards my father and shouted at him, 'You are shoved on us. Ninety per cent of the people do not want these governors, but they are shoved on to us, and what are we to do?'

Father took no notice and referred to it later in Sydney as 'only a little hot air', but it provoked some strong protests from all over the state, one of the most interesting being from a man named Charles Thomas. He was a Domain 'dosser' of many years' standing and acted as spokesman to the *Sun* for Sydney's down-and-outs. 'Many a time he'd come down here,' said Thomas, referring to the Governor and his visits to the Domain. 'God knows,

Unloading wood for the unemployed at Broken Hill.

Camps of the unemployed at Broken Hill. In the foreground is a tar drum of the kind used, with bagging and corrugated iron, to construct the Chateau de Tar Drums.

Rear-Admiral R. C. Dalglish, officer-in-chief of the Royal Australian Navy, stands between my parents on board HMAS Canberra at Lord Howe Island.

he's one of the best we've ever had. I've been here off and on since 1920 and had several governors, but he's the only one who ever spoke to you. Yes! That man stands out on his own. There's not one man who ever slept in the 'Dom' who will say a word against him.'

By the time they left Broken Hill, my parents felt that they had talked to almost all the inhabitants of that pathetic city. They came away determined to see that more help should be sent out from Sydney. My father had long talks with the Premier and evidently made it clear that he felt that Broken Hill had been sadly neglected by the Government during the Depression. This had an effect, and more help was forthcoming. A few years later one of the few good things brought about by the coming of World War II was that the mines reopened and Broken Hill became a prosperous, thriving place once more.

A few weeks after my parents returned from Broken Hill, an invitation was extended to our whole family by the Commonwealth Government to visit Lord Howe Island, that tiny scrap of land out in the Tasman Sea about 435 miles north-east of Sydney. It was suggested that we should travel in HMAS *Canberra*. To be taken to a tropical island in a cruiser was something that had never entered out wildest dreams, and we were in a state of feverish excitement as the date for our journey drew nearer.

The news excited the *Labor Daily* too, but in rather a different way. On Saturday 12 August, under an enormous headline proclaiming 'Governor

The guns of HMAS Can-
berra which caused so much
noise and vibration during our
voyage.

takes a jaunt', was an article which said in part: 'The Commonwealth Government, with an utter disregard for the economy which it has forced on its
employees, has made H.M.A.S. Canberra available to transport the Governor of New South Wales, Sir Philip Game, and Lady Game on a tourist trip
from Brisbane to Lord Howe Island and back to Sydney next week, at an
estimated cost of £2,000.' On inquiry at Government House, however, the
Labor Daily was informed that the Governor was visiting Lord Howe Island
because it was part of New South Wales and was, therefore, within his juris-
diction. HMAS *Canberra*, it was stated, would not remain at the island and
the Governor and his party would return to Sydney in the island steamer
Morinda. After this short, sharp statement, no more was heard from the *Labor
Daily*.

We boarded *Canberra* in Brisbane, where she had just been overhauled and
freshly painted. My parents were piped on board, and the Admiral was at the
top of the gangway to greet us. He bent down and kissed me, and I remember
feeling very self-conscious. We were given the captain's quarters, large well-
furnished cabins right in the stern of the ship. From the moment she went to
bed the first night my mother never got up again until the morning we reached
Lord Howe Island. It was a very rough voyage; the *Canberra* pitched, rolled
and yawed the whole way, her stern going round and round in a continuous
circular movement. With my mother ill and ship's complement consisting of
65 officers and 735 men, I felt embarrassingly feminine. I longed to be a boy
and fit into the scene better. It was so easy for my brothers; they were taken

down to the engine-room, shown the guns and chatted to by the sailors, and I found myself spending a lot of time playing patience on the floor of the captain's cabin. A table would have been useless, but the cards stuck nicely to the carpet, however much the ship rolled.

The journey took two and a half days. On the second afternoon David came in to talk to me.

'Have you seen Mummy?' he said.

'No, why?'

'She's pea green!'

I rushed off with all speed to see this extraordinary phenomenon. He was absolutely right; she looked terrible.

'Are you all right?' I whispered anxiously as I stood by her bed, fidgeting nervously from one leg to the other.

'I will be when the ship stops,' she said bravely, and motioned me to leave her alone in her misery.

Back in the day cabin, David and I were playing cards together; there was a knock on the door and a sailor came in, his cheerful smile lighting up at the sight of us on the floor.

''Scuse me, sir,' he said to David. 'Could I take the pictures down, please? There's going to be a firing practice, and sometimes the vibration knocks 'em off the walls.'

We helped him stack them neatly in a corner, and David disappeared up on deck to see what was going on. I sat with my back to a wall, my fingers in ears, waiting for the first bang. I did not have long to wait. *Boom! Boom!* went the guns, while the ship shivered and shook, reeling under the tremendous shock.

A little while later I ventured up onto the deck. The noise seemed less in the fresh air, and with my brothers for company I forgot to be nervous and quite enjoyed watching the puff of smoke, the recoil of the guns, and then a little burst several miles out to sea.

Below left: Crowds wait for us to come ashore from the small boat that conveyed us from the Canberra, *which stands out to sea looking very romantic. We had to be carried from the boat and set down on the beach.*

Below: The horse-drawn sledge in which my mother and I were taken from the beach over the sandy road to Lord Howe Island's 'Government House'.

Landing at Ned's Beach.

A Souvenir

AUGUST 16TH 1933.

H.M.S Canberra at anchor.

His Excellency the Governor
AND
Lady Game's
VISIT TO
Lord Howe Island.

Singing The National Anthem.

Returned Soldiers' Welcome.

Mt Lidgebird and McGowen.

Government House.

Road to Ned's Beach.

E.E. Giles
Photographer
Lord Howe Island

The next morning we stared at what must be one of the wonders of the world, a huge towering pyramid of rock. Great wild waves surged against the base of the steeple-like crag but were dwarfed by the eighteen hundred feet of basalt pointing to the sky. My mother had surfaced and seemed to have recovered, though the sea was still far from calm. A grey mist lightly veiled Ball's Pyramid, giving it a sinister air. We were all enthralled.

'I *thought* you'd like to see that,' said the Admiral. 'It's only eleven miles beyond the Island, and it seemed a pity not to see it close by.'

Nobody mentioned the *Labor Daily* or the acid headlines that might be printed should it be discovered that we had actually sailed an extra twenty-two miles at the expense of the Government! Instead, my parents thanked the Admiral warmly for his thoughtfulness, and I even forgave him his kiss.

Slowly the ship turned and made its way towards the little island just visible on the horizon. We came close in and waited just outside the coral reef separating us from a lagoon that hugged the shores.

'It is the most beautiful island I've every seen.' My mother never spoke a truer word. There it lay, this little emerald isle seven miles long and in places only half a mile wide, all by itself in the midst of the ocean, hundreds of miles from any other inhabited land. The skyline was jagged with peaks, mostly sharp-pointed hills, but to the south there were two mountains, their great walls rising sheer out of the water. The island was covered with dense forest giving way to fine, grassy slopes, which in turn led down to the palm-covered shores and white sandy beaches.

Very soon we were transferred to a small boat which took us in through the reef, across the turquoise water of the lagoon to the beach, where we were

A card of photographs prepared as a souvenir of our visit to Lord Howe Island in August 1933.

Opposite page: Palm fronds bend to the prevailing wind in the solitude of the island, with Mount Lidgbird in the background.

carried ashore by sailors and set down on the sand to be greeted by the entire island population of 170 people, the children forming a guard of honour. What a wonderful welcome we had from those people, and what a glorious three days they gave us on their island! It was indeed *their* island, for although they welcomed visitors, no one could buy land who had not been born there or married an islander. The most that any outsider could hope to be was a 'temporary permanent'!

After the beach reception, my father and brothers walked to 'Government House', while my mother and I were taken by sulky, a little carriage on runners which, drawn by a pony, slipped along the sandy paths like a toboggan. It was a delightful way to travel. Government House on Lord Howe Island must be the only one of its kind in the world—a charming little bungalow standing among palm trees—two tiny cannons guarding the entrance to the small drive. The cannons did not look as though they had ever fired a shot in anger, and we could not imagine that it would ever be necessary in this idyllic spot. The house was pleasantly and comfortably furnished. The one thing that stood out as being utterly remarkable and unlike anything we had ever seen before was the bathroom. The bath stood on carved iron legs, and at its head was a hooded monster. We were told that this was the chip heater and that when we wanted baths all we had to do was to light a fire inside it and in a few minutes it would produce boiling water. It did. We all had a crack at lighting the fire, piling in crumpled newspaper, sticks and then logs. In no time at all the Monster was blazing away merrily, emitting crackles and sparks like a bonfire on Guy Fawkes night. Father was the first to try out the hot water system. He had only been in the bathroom a few minutes before we heard his shrieks.

'How do I get any cold water? Help! It's boiling! I'm being scalded!'

We yelled back all kinds of instructions.

'Turn on the cold tap.'

'Shut the ventilator.'

'Push in the damper.'

Aquaplaning behind a speed-boat on the turquoise water of the lagoon.

David up a palm tree. Note the sacking round his feet to help him grip the trunk.

Everyone was full of good ideas. No one listened to the poor occupant, vainly trying to tell us that there *wasn't* a cold tap, and that he could not find the damper or any kind of ventilator. Eventually my mother managed to push her way into the bathroom and extract my father, looking rather like a boiled lobster. We came to the conclusion that the lagoon would provide a happier place in which to wash.

The islanders looked after us magnificently during those three days. We managed two climbs, one long and steep, up the side of a mountain to the Goathouse, a cave from where we could see almost the entire island lying below us. Out on the reef, we were shown the gorgeous coloured coral below the water through a glass-bottomed boat, and in the evenings we danced at the lodges (guest houses) where we also had all our meals. Of course my parents sometimes had more formal entertainment, a visit to the school and hospital, and a reception in the palm-seed shed. Apart from the tourist trade, the island derived its income from the sale of seeds of the endemic 'Kentia palm', which was a popular decorative plant all over the world. The seeds were in constant demand, since it is not easy to produce fertilised seed except from palms grown on the island itself—a curiously interesting botanical fact.

While my mother and father were busy, Bill, David and I were wonderfully entertained. We were taken on picnics, shown how to climb palm trees and swing on the aerial roots of the banyan trees and, best of all, given lessons in aquaplaning on the lagoon. Round and round we went, standing on a board pulled behind a speedboat until sheer exhaustion forced us to stop. We could not imagine anything more entrancing than that island. We could have stayed there for ever.

On the morning that we were due to leave, the skies were dark with storm clouds. Outside the reef, tossing up and down on the waves, was the tiny three-thousand-ton steamer *Morinda* in which we were to travel home. The islanders had gathered on the beach to say goodbye, and as we stood and sang 'Auld Lang Syne' together I could hardly bear to be torn away from that island paradise.

The *Morinda* was an unsavoury little boat. My cabin was near the engine-room and galley, and the combined smell of oil and greasy cooking took away my appetite. I hardly saw my mother at all until we arrived in the blessed haven of Sydney Harbour and climbed *up* the gangway to the quay.

A few days later the Admiral came to tea.

'Since you enjoyed the trip so much, why don't you ask your husband to take you to Norfolk Island?' he asked my mother. 'After all, that belongs to New South Wales too.'

'It doesn't,' I said bluntly. 'It's federal.'

My mother's voice was chilled as she told me to fetch her a handkerchief, and the steely look in her eye made it plain that I need not hurry back!

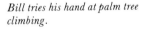
Bill tries his hand at palm tree climbing.

12 *People of the Inland*

HARDLY a day went by without someone coming to Government House for a meal, a meeting or an interview. It was never dull. All sorts of people passed in and out of its doors, from the little milliner Irene Brown, who, in common with many others, had fallen on hard times and been helped by my mother to rebuild her business, to eminent politicians. One of the most interesting of the many visitors was that amazing Presbyterian missionary John Flynn, who was instrumental in founding the Australian Inland Mission and the Flying Doctor Service and whose stories of the Outback were as enthralling as anyone could wish for.

Not many years before we had come to Australia, Flynn had been travelling through the great heart of the continent on his camel, jogging along by day and sleeping rough by his little campfire at night with only the native bush creatures for company. On and on he had ridden, through his vast parish, visiting some of the fifty thousand Australians living in that isolated country, scattered over hundreds and hundreds of miles. They were there because the cities needed them, needed the wool and meat from sheep and cattle and the minerals from under the earth.

As he rode, he thought of the stories he had been told of children whose lives could have been saved if only medical help had been available. He remembered, too, small graves he had been shown by distraught parents, graves under gum trees or beside a rocky, dried-up creek, marked only by a rough wooden cross or a pile of stones. It was wrong, *wrong*, he thought to himself, that these people should have to live in constant dread of illness or accident, and he dreamed of a 'mantle of safety', as he called it, to cover the folk of the Outback. He pictured small hospitals, each with a radius of about three hundred miles, strategically placed throughout those vast inland areas. He thought of the Kimberleys, up in the extreme north-west, an area of some 120,000 square miles, served by only two doctors. Or the Northern Territory, a region the size of Western Europe, where there was only one doctor to cover that vast tract of land. No wonder some of the men of the Outback never married; they felt they could not ask a woman to share the fear and the loneliness, and those who did faced a constant worry for their wives and families.

Two great problems confronted Flynn: the immense distances involved and the lack of communications. Alice Springs, for instance, that small outpost right in the centre of Australia; anyone ill in Alice had to travel by horse or buggy, or even on foot, for anything up to twenty days to reach the rail-

The Reverend John Flynn, out in the bush, attends to his car while a meal is being prepared. The celebrated inland missionary was one of the many interesting people who stayed at Government House.

head at Oodnadatta, and then another six hundred miles south by train to the nearest hospital in Adelaide. Small wonder that many of the sick never reached hospital at all. At the time when Flynn was riding his camel across the wide open spaces of the interior, there was only the telegraph wire crossing Australia. It stretched the eighteen hundred miles north and south from Darwin to Port Augusta, with a small telegraph station every hundred miles where an operator kept in touch with the outside world. People came hundreds of miles to 'talk' to a doctor over this wire by way of the operator in Morse code, giving their symptoms and listening to his advice. But they could be given no medicine or surgery. It was a desperate situation.

Flying was in its infancy, but Flynn was undauntable, and he dreamed of a flying-doctor service from his small hospitals which would reach the people of the Outback, and a machine they could use to contact the Flying Doctor.

In 1920 a new aerial service had been started in Queensland, known as the Queensland and Northern Territory Aerial Services Ltd, so familiar now as Qantas. Flynn approached them and told them what he needed, and after some years and considerable difficulty they managed to produce a plane that would take a patient lying down as well as the pilot, a doctor and a nurse.

One other great difficulty still lay ahead. There had to be some means by which the people of the inland could get in touch with a doctor. It had to be something simple, which anyone could use, even a child if necessary. A great deal of wireless experimentation was going on at that time; even so, it was several more years before a brilliant young man called Alfred Traeger, after innumerable difficulties, invented a small, neat transceiver with a pedal-operated generator. This was a great step forward but still not ideal. It was difficult for people not experienced in Morse, and especially in an emergency, to pedal away at the generator bicycle at the same time as tapping out the message. Certainly no child could have used it. Traeger made the real breakthrough when he produced a special typewriter which converted plain language into Morse code by means of a Morse-sending keyboard.

For Flynn's dream to become a reality he had to have money. A great deal of this he collected himself, travelling round the big Australian cities telling them stories of the inland. Stories such as of D'Arcy, a young man in his prime who was thrown from his horse while mustering cattle. He was found by his friends and taken two hundred miles to a man with 'some medical knowledge', who, under instructions over a telegraph wire from a doctor in Perth, operated on poor D'Arcy with a penknife and a razor blade. Meanwhile, the doctor made a valiant attempt to reach D'Arcy, seventeen hundred miles away. He began his journey by taking the steamer from Perth up the west coast to Derby. From there he went by car nearly three hundred miles to Hall's Creek. It was a nightmare journey, sometimes straight through the bush and over almost impossibly hostile terrain, full of gullies, rocks and tree stumps. When at last he reached his destination he found that the patient had died twenty-four hours earlier.

This and other similar stories touched people's hearts, and triumph came for Flynn when in May 1928 Doctor K. Welch and his pilot set out in the first flying ambulance in the world to save the life of a man who had cut his throat.

Soon after we had met John Flynn, David and I were lucky enough to be taken on a country trip with our parents to the far north of the state. As we boarded the train for Dubbo, we were full of high spirits. Flynn had fired us with enthusiasm to see as much as possible of the real Outback. Up in the Brewarrina district we would be touching only the very fringe of the enormous area over which he had ridden; even so, it was wild, isolated country unlike anything we had seen before. From Dubbo we went on by train to Tarcoon Siding, a small stopping place in the middle of nowhere on the way to Bourke.

We did not go to Bourke itself because my father had been there the previous November and would have gone on to the places we were now about to visit had he not been washed out by torrential rain and floods. It was the first time in twenty years that Tom Ruthven, the local 'chauffeur', who had always driven state governors round that part of the country, had been defeated by the weather. 'I never let one of 'em down,' he had said. But this time, after skidding, bumping and sliding all over the road from Bourke to Brewarrina for twenty miles, they became hopelessly bogged. My father jumped out of the car and, together with Tom, Mr Budge and others, dug furiously in the cloggy clay. After a little while, Father, covered from head to foot in mud, was heard to mutter, 'If only Mother could see me now.'

'She wouldn't recognise you, sir,' said Tom, grinning.

'Is it often like this outback?' asked my father innocently.

'You're not outback *here*, sir. You've gotta be back o' Bourke afore you're outback,' answered Tom.

Eventually a relief car containing the Mayor came out from Bourke. Together they all started back along the slushy road. In a few miles the car, whose engine had been sorely tried, boiled. Father offered Tom his hat to dip in a muddy pond.

'Oh no, sir, I wouldn't use your hat.'

'Go on, I've got another one.'

But Tom Ruthven could not bring himself to do this. He found a small glass, and with all the men forming a chain they eventually filled the radiator. By all accounts it was a riotous party in those strange, muddy surroundings, everyone grinning and laughing and the Mayor, full of *esprit de corps*, whistling 'Shuffle Off to Buffalo'. They arrived back in Bourke at 2.30 a.m., and my father and his party returned to Sydney later that same day.

On *our* trip, however, the weather was kind. We were met at Tarcoon by Brother Ley (Leyland Bird, later canon of Guildford Cathedral, Surrey, UK) and taken to Charlton sheep station, where we stayed the night. Brother Ley was a Bush Brother, one of the intrepid band of Anglican missionaries who had formed themselves into the Brotherhood of the Good Shepherd in central Queensland in the 1890s. They had a strict rule: they had to agree on majority rule of themselves by themselves, to remain unmarried for the five years that they served in the Brotherhood, and to be paid only about ten shillings a week. They worked in pairs and went out into the bush to seek the people, some of whom were not keen to be sought, but others who came to regard a Bush Brother as friend and guide. It needed strength of character to overcome the loneliness and difficulties. Brother Ley had been given the task of planning our tour and looking after us in that strange, distant country. We could not have had a better guide or companion. His cheerful, smiling face and twinkling eyes matched his good humour.

I shall always remember that trip up north. Perhaps it was that each day was different, with some new experience; perhaps it was the kindliness of the people in showing us their wild land; certainly it was largely due to Brother Ley's vivacity. We were driven from place to place, all with astonishing names, Goodooga, Angledool, Gunnedah and Boggabri. Sylvia, Brother Ley's car, usually followed in a cloud of dust, but sometimes she proudly led the way over the plains. Once or twice I travelled in Sylvia.

'How do you find the way?' I asked, gazing out at the sandy earth covered with saltbush, no road and hardly even a track.

'Oh well, you know, there are landmarks. A short way back we passed the old stove, and later on we'll come to the dead cow.'

It never occurred to me to ask why the dead cow remained there. I can only imagine that it must have been a bundle of bones. Every now and then a great herd of kangaroos bounded away at high speed, frightened by the noise of the cars, while emus ran alongside, peering in at the windows, immensely curious to see the human beings inside. Sometimes great flocks of galahs flew over us, their rose and grey plumage very pretty in the sunlight.

The Bogan River at Charlton station, where we stayed during our trip in the north-west of New South Wales.

On one of these drives we suddenly spied a car coming towards us. As it drew near we all exclaimed with delight, 'The Mintie Bishop!' Sure enough, it was the Bishop of the Riverina, miles from his own territory. Only a minute or two passed before he was handing round his famous bag of Minties.

At night we stayed on sheep and cattle stations. One night some of us were most comfortably housed by the bush nurse. This was a nice change, for some of the stations where we stayed were very primitive. One particular station had deep trench latrines at the bottom of the garden. The trenches were nothing like deep enough, and the result was absolutely revolting, a ghastly, reeking stench and thousands of flies!

'Rosemary!' My mother spoke softly. 'The only *possible* place is behind the oleanders.' There was a thick group of these not far from the latrines and they proved useful as well as pretty!

It was very warm, and almost everywhere we slept on verandahs after dancing in the evening at nearly every town we visited. By day we saw shearing sheds, bore-drain delvers at work with teams of horses—sometimes there were as many as eighteen horses in a team—and then, the highlight of the tour, we were taken to see the opal mines at Lightning Ridge.

A team of horses we met on our trip out west stand patiently harnessed up to their empty wagon, which had just had an immense load of wool taken off.

At the Lightning Ridge opal mines. My Mother was fascinated by the rough, wild country and the miners; photography was one of her hobbies.

Opposite page: Clothes don't matter when the conversation is interesting. My father listens intently to a miner's story.

Here we descended sixty feet down a vertical shaft sitting astride a wooden trapeze and being lowered by winch, one at a time. At the bottom a miner led the way as we scrambled, doubled up, along the low, narrow tunnels to be shown the opals in the rock. My father very nearly had a bad accident at the bottom of the shaft. He was still getting himself on to the trapeze when the winch above started to pull him up. As he could not bend his right knee—owing to the skating accident in 1926, which left him with a permanently stiff leg—he was lying nearly flat and would have been pinned across the narrow shaft entrance.

'Stop! Stop! He's not ready. Wait a minute. Don't pull, don't pull.' Our frantic screams and shouts echoed along the tunnels and up the shaft. Mercifully they were heard at the surface and the winch was stopped, but it was a nasty moment, for he could so easily have had his back broken.

Back in the town we were shown how the opals are cut and also saw a display of opals of every kind, from the pearly milk-white to the gleaming black, which sparkle and glitter, sending out little darts of vivid, fiery colour. Another day we crossed the border into Queensland for half an hour, returning to sit on the fence between the two states which stretched for seven hundred miles in a straight line. After a farewell ball at Walgett, we left by train for Sydney at five o'clock in the morning.

When we had been in Sydney nearly four years, my parents began thinking over their plans. After much deliberation and heart-searching, they decided to take David and me back to England, for David to go to Cambridge and for me to go to boarding school. They then planned to return to Australia in time for the Duke of Gloucester's visit in November. Meanwhile, Dr Mowll, who had since became Archbishop of Sydney, and his wife offered to look after Bill. This proved to be a highly satisfactory arrangement.

Archbishop Mowll preaching in St Andrew's Cathedral.

I was growing up and enjoyed the parties and dances in Sydney. It was going to be different in England, and I felt dreadfully sad at the thought of leaving Australia. I would have liked to stay on and on, enjoying the sea and the sun and the outdoor life which had become a part of me. One night, not long before we were due to leave for England, I walked on to the verandah from my bedroom; the moon was full and shone straight down the harbour, making a long silver ribbon on the water. Someone was playing the gramophone, and the strains of Liszt's 'Liebestraum' floated out through the windows. It was romantic, and I had to swallow to rid myself of the lump which *would* keep coming into my throat. But youth is resilient and looks forward. There is always the great adventure round the corner. I began to think of the journey we were soon to take, and at the thought of Fiji, Honolulu and the Rockies I became more cheerful.

Even so, a week or two later, as David and I stood on the deck of SS *Niagara* and waved to a little knot of young folk who had come to see us off, my eyes were filled with tears. When the ship's hooter gave its familiar deep boom as it moved away from the quay, and the pink paper streamer that Rosemary and I held between us parted in two, I made a silent vow: One day I will come back.

13 Afterword

IT WAS not until thirty-nine years later that I was able to fulfil my vow to return to Australia. Meanwhile, my parents had a hectic seven weeks in England before they went back to Sydney for the rest of their term of office at Government House. Their short holiday was filled with family affairs and a few official engagements. My mother tells about one of these in her diaries.

> We were asked to Garden Party at Buckingham Palace. To my consterna-
> tion I found that we had to be introduced to King George V and Queen Mary.
> To my intense discomfort the King kept Philip talking so long about Mr
> Lang and all the happenings in New South Wales that we couldn't pass on
> and Queen Mary was impatient and wanted to get rid of me!
>
> The King had always resented the Bridge being opened by Mr Lang and
> now, in a joking way, 'told Philip off' about the man who had represented
> him wearing a felt hat! One of the ADCs remarked laughingly, 'But Sir,
> you know that Sir Philip is very fond of Mr Lang.' There was a great deal
> of laughter and we felt forgiven but HM was obviously determined to have
> his say in the matter.

The Duke of Gloucester's ship, HMS Sussex, *moored in Farm Cove with a welcoming formation of sailing boats, motor launches and ferries. In those days the naval establishment of Garden Island (where HMAS* Canberra *is moored, top left) was an island; it was later joined to the peninsula of Potts Point (top right).*

Government House had been redecorated for a visit by the Duke of Gloucester while my parents were away. Before they left for England they had taken trouble to choose wallpapers and materials but found on their return a totally different colour scheme not at all to their taste. My mother wrote: 'We were faced with some rather bewildering effects. The worst was a terrible frieze in my bedroom which looked for all the world like starfish and bananas. I apologised to the Duke, to whom we gave this room, and he said he wished he had had his revolver and he would have taken shots at it.'

The Duke brought four friends on his staff, and each of them had a valet; add to this a few detectives and secretaries and one can see that a good many people had to be accommodated. Miss Harris, the beloved housekeeper, lived up to all expectations, and on the glorious sunny morning that the Duke arrived, the house looked welcoming and beautiful despite its rather strange décor.

The Duke of Gloucester salutes the welcoming party as he steps ashore at Farm Cove.

Philip went down to the quay to meet HRH in the formal dress for an arrival of Royalty, top hat, morning coat, with one star as his only decora-

tion. *I was rushing round the house putting the last touches to the flowers and seeing that they were as perfect as possible in HRH's room when the telephone rang and Philip warned me that they would be at the house in ten minutes. The official time for the arrival was half an hour later, but HRH was so nervous and shy that the formalities could not be prolonged and the time had to be cut short. I was hot and dishevelled in a cotton frock and never, ever, have I had to make such a quick change. Cinderella was nothing to it! I got to the door as the car could be seen in the drive, hoping that no agitation would be visible, and only the calm smile of a welcoming hostess used to such minor situations as receiving Royalty in her house! Philip brought him in, and as we walked beside him into the drawing-room he said: 'How curious it is the way one knows directly one comes into a house if one is going to be happy there.' This set me completely at my ease, and from that moment he seemed at home and I lost all my shyness of him.*

Before one of our dinner parties of fifty-four people he said to Philip, 'Tell them to talk to me and not wait for me to begin. I'd rather they said, "Do you like salt?" than nothing.' This was a great success and everyone found him so easy and pleasant to talk to. For the dinner the table was decorated by an expert who had kindly asked to do it. There was a long flower arrangement all down the centre, and in the petals of the flowers tiny electric light bulbs were cleverly hidden. At dessert the other lights were turned out and the flower ones turned on, and they glowed through the petals with a lovely effect.

Fireworks at the Venetian Carnival on the harbour during the Duke's visit.

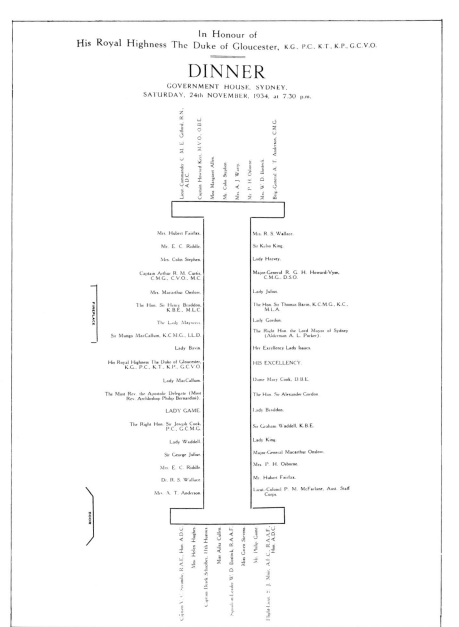

The seating arrangement for a dinner in honour of the Duke of Gloucester held at Government House on Saturday 24 November 1934. (Mitchell Library, State Library of New South Wales)

Philip greeted our guests and waited with them in the drawing room until Charles's voice announced 'His Royal Highness'. After all the introductions had been made, Philip said: 'Will you honour my wife, Sir', and he took me in. As far as I can remember the dinner went well, and Mrs Riach, who was an excellent cook and had a friend to help her, did not fail us, and HRH seemed relaxed.

The pièce de résistance of his visit was the glorious display of fireworks and a Venetian Carnival on the harbour after dinner. We invited a hundred guests to see this display and I can honestly say that it was the most wonder-

In Honour of His Royal Highness
the Duke of Gloucester
K.G., P.C., K.T., K.P., G.C.V.O.

Menu

Grape Fruit

Schnapper à la Morny

Poulet Maryland

Soufflée de Fraises

Bouchées Hollandaises

Dessert

Café

Government House, Sydney.
22nd November 1934.

ful and beautiful sight that could be imagined, and I don't think that anywhere in the world could anything more glorious have been planned for any Royalty. It was a great pleasure to Philip and me when HRH came up to us at the end of the evening and said, 'I must tell you that I have enjoyed this evening more than any other in Australia.' Philip turned to General Anderson, who was with us, and said, 'I take you to witness that', and we all laughed very happily. We afterwards discovered that HRH had a passion for fireworks.

After one of our dinners we had a little dance, and some young ones were

My mother and father flank the Duke of Gloucester in a photograph taken during his visit. Bill and Charles Gifford are in the back row, third and second from the right. In front of Charles is Ethel Anderson, poet and short-story writer and wife of General Austin Anderson (far left), the Governor's private secretary. Next to General Anderson is Harry Budge, the Official Secretary, with Mrs Budge sitting in front of him. The Premier, Bertram Stevens, is on the far right of the front row.

especially asked to meet the Duke. At one time during the evening he was completely lost and later on he said to us, 'Do you know where I was? I was at the bottom of the garden with my partner and we nearly fell into the pond.' So we gathered he had enjoyed that, too.

The Government gave a garden party at Government House for four thousand guests. 'Philip made all the arrangements,' my mother wrote. 'Various people were warned to be at special points to be introduced, and he took the Duke on a royal progress through the gardens. It was a lovely day and the garden looked its best with really beautiful flowers, the large gaily decorated marquees and the ladies in their pretty dresses and hats.' The Duke spoke to her one evening about his home life. He told her that his parents wished him to marry and that he said to them, 'How can I marry when you never have anyone to the house that you would *wish* me to marry.' She asked him if he could not do some entertaining on his own, and he told her that it would be very difficult because his father *hated* entertaining. Evidently life at home was not very easy, so my parents were particularly pleased when, later on, he married the charming Lady Alice Montagu Douglas Scott.

There is no doubt that the Duke's visit had been a great success and that he had enjoyed his time with my parents and felt relaxed and happy, and they had much enjoyed having him not only for the honour and excitement but because they found him so humble and charming in manner. My mother wrote of his departure:

It was a great thrill to see the Royal Standard flying alongside the Union Jack above the tower, and to hear the sentry marching to and fro in front of the house all the time the Duke was there. When the morning came that he was to leave the country and fly to New Zealand, Philip had to go ahead to the aerodrome to be ready to see him off, and I was left to say goodbye in the hall. He came down the stairs with a large photograph of himself in a silver frame and a beautiful silver salver, both of which he gave me. I felt that he had had a happy few days in spite of the very strenuous work and the number of engagements which gave him no rest at all. For ourselves, it was a wonderful ending to our five years in New South Wales.

After this very thrilling time we had to concentrate on goodbyes, which was far harder work than we had expected. Everyone was too kind for words, and there were endless dinners, meetings, balls and farewells of every sort.

The Archbishop and Dorothy his wife came and dined with us quietly, and it was hard to say goodbye to such dear friends as they had become in the short time we had known them. The last service in the Cathedral reduced me to tears, I'm ashamed to say. It had been such a happy place for us, and though at first the arrival there had seemed formal, with an ADC leading, sitting in the front pew, and hearing 'The Governor of this State' prayed for, I had got used to all that, and it had become a real spiritual centre for me. I asked for the choir to sing 'O for the Wings of a Dove', which they did most beautifully, and the Archbishop conducted us to the door to say a last good-bye. This, for me, was the saddest farewell of all.

On the last evening, quite unknown to us, Charles had arranged a little programme of dancing and music among the trees in the garden of Government House. It was beautifully done, and a great surprise. We looked out

The Duke and the Governor riding down the track at Randwick Racecourse.

Father says farewell to the Duke at Mascot before his departure by air for New Zealand.

and saw figures dancing gracefully in a lovely green light, from hidden electric lamps. This kind thought of Charles's touched us deeply, and I realised still more what a loyal and affectionate friend we had in him.

The next morning seems to me a blur of memories, starting with all the servants lined up in the hall as we passed through to shake hands, and hard it was to say goodbye to me dear Mrs Riach, our cook, and Miss Harris, the best and kindest of housekeepers. Girl Guides and Boy Scouts lined the drive, and to my astonishment all the Sydney Hospital nurses came out and stood in their white nurses' uniform in front of the Hospital to wave as we passed. The lump in my throat got bigger. We had to drive through several streets as a farewell and everywhere crowds seemed to be waiting with cheers, and at one point flowers were flung into the car. Then at last we were taken to the quay and found we were allowed to get into the 'Premier' and be taken to our ship. Bill of course was with us, and also Charles. The last and saddest farewell was to Charles, who was remaining in Sydney. . . .

We watched from the deck of our ship to see the beloved harbour for the last time, and waved farewell to a parade of a regiment that was lining the nearest shore after we started to move. Then came the Heads and the long last look; Sydney was gone for ever, and I think a bit of each of our hearts was left behind there for always.

A group of lady friends gathered to farewell my mother (centre) before her return to England display a range of matronly fashions of the day.

In today's terms I suppose my father would have been called a workaholic. Certainly he did not spend nearly as much time as many of his friends in taking a holiday. My mother always said it was really a blessing in disguise that he broke his legs so often (five times!), as that gave him an enforced rest. He arrived back from Australia at the end of April 1935 to be told by Lord Trenchard that he had been recommended by him to follow him as Commissioner of the London Metropolitan Police. My father accepted and was sworn in the following September—with a broken leg and a nurse in attendance.

As the Commissioner has to live within the metropolitan area—a twelve-mile radius from the centre of London—my parents bought a house on Ham Common, near Richmond. The term of office for the Commissioner is usually about five years. Little did any of us realise that the Second World War would come upon us and that he would work on until he was almost seventy, another ten years.

Within two or three weeks of starting his work he asked to see the documents relating to royal funerals. Four months later King George V died, and my father had all the complicated procedures at his fingertips. He had foreseen that there is little time to arrange such things. After the funeral and the subsequent abdication of Edward VIII, he had the enormous responsibility of organising the police for the coronation of George VI. I doubt if anyone felt more relief and happiness than my father did as he rode on his splendid

Father, Mother and Bill, with General Anderson and Charles Gifford, proceed up the gangway of the ship taking my family back to England. The tension is relieved by the faces in the portholes.

Opposite page: *Putting on a brave face, my parents wave goodbye from the* Premier *before leaving the Australia they loved.*

white horse in front of his police force in the huge coronation procession, wearing the dark blue and silver uniform of the Commissioner and the cocked hat with its white feather waving in the breeze. For his organisational work at the coronation he was made Knight Grand Cross of the Royal Victorian Order.

As Police Commissioner during the years immediately before the war, my father had to deal with Fascist and Communist demonstrations and an IRA bombing campaign. There was constant trouble between the Fascists and the Jewish communities in London. Typical of these troubles was a proposed march by Fascists near the Jewish quarters of the East End of London on 3 October 1937. The *Daily Telegraph* reported: 'Jewish representatives have asked the Commissioner of Police, Sir Philip Game, to ban the proposed Fascist march.' The march was not banned, but my father, having examined the intended route, went out himself into the street to confront the Fascist leader, Sir Oswald Mosley, and order him not to proceed along that way. The route was altered and the trouble averted.

When the war came he organised the role of the police in air-raid precautions and relief. He never told us much about his work at that time; I imagine a great deal was secret, but it has been said that he dealt effectively with the problems and the consequent high level of police morale was an important factor in the survival of London during the blitz. When London was being bombed night after night, he went straight to the bombed areas, whatever time it was. His driver, Wiseman, told me something of those nights: 'Your father is terribly brave, Miss Rosemary—just stands there talking to the police, rescuers, firemen and all the bombed-out and shocked folk and never seems frightened. I always want to get under the car, but how can I when Sir Philip keeps on standing talking while the bombs whistle down.' My father eventually retired in 1945.

To get back to 1935, while our parents were away for those last few months in Australia, David went up to Cambridge to read modern languages and I went to Wycombe Abbey School. I found it hard after the glorious freedom of Sydney, but I much enjoyed all the music. During the holidays we lived with our grandmother.

When our parents and Bill returned to England, we all had a joyful reunion. Our happiness was made even greater when Bill married Anne White, whom he met almost as soon as he reached home. He joined the Persian Oil Company as a geologist in the field. Two years later the family rejoiced when they told us they were expecting a child. I shall never be able to forget that day in March when a telephone call came saying that both Anne and the baby girl had died in childbirth. As soon as possible, Bill went off on a geological expedition to Greenland where, I imagine, he worked out his grief among the lonely snow-clad mountains. On 1 June 1939, just before the war came, he married Vera Blackburn, daughter of Sir Charles Bickerton Blackburn, chancellor of the University of Sydney. Bill and Vera had known each other when we lived out there, and she was in England just at the time that he needed her most.

In the early days of the war, David was waiting to go into the Royal Naval Volunteer Reserve, Bill was working as a scientist (a reserved occupation) not far from London, and I was nursing in the Red Cross. My mother also

My mother and father relaxing on holiday.

Opposite page: *The Commissioner of the London Metropolitan Police in full dress uniform.*

nursed for a time but was unable to continue because of arthritis. She subsequently took the book trolley round the hospital wards. In 1942, I gave up my nursing and went into the Women's Royal Naval Service. I was not a good Wren, but in many ways I enjoyed the life—except for a strict dressing down by an irate captain for plotting a submarine in the middle of Norway!

And so it went on, the war, the bombs and what Churchill called 'the toil and sweat'. In October 1943 came that ghastly day bringing a telegram for my parents from the War Office. David had died. He had been stationed at Taranto Naval Base in Italy. A British ship had been blown up the day that he became ill and the hospital was full of casualties. David's bed was put in a corner of the ward and he was told he had flu. Four days later, he died of poliomyelitis.

The dreadful blanket of darkness that descended on the family with this news was only lifted when, a year later, I became engaged to Nigel Harmar. My mother and father began to live again and rejoiced in our happiness. Nigel had been growing cotton in the Sudan. He joined the Sudan Defence Force when the war came and fought in Abyssinia and

Above: *A trio of uniformed wartime service personnel— Father as Police Commissioner, myself as a Red Cross nurse, and David as a lieutenant in the RNVR.*

Right: *Going to Bill's wedding: my mother's sister Dorothy, my mother, my grandmother.*

Eritrea against the Italians. It was only when that part of the war came to an end that he was able to come home to England on leave and we met. The day after we became engaged, he returned to Africa. Thirteen months later he came back; the war had ended, and we were able to be married.

A fortnight before I was married my father went up into the loft one afternoon to get a standard lamp. He would not let anyone help him, fell down the ladder clutching the lamp and lay in a heap at the bottom. He could not stand, and I guessed what had happened. When I rang up the doctor and said that I thought Father had broken his leg, his reply was understandable: 'My God! Not *again*.' This was the fourth time, but luckily, only a small bone in his heel had been broken, and with the skilful use of plaster and an iron stirrup he was just able to walk up the aisle with me, *he* leaning heavily on *my* arm.

After our marriage, Nigel and I went to live in the Sudan. I returned to London the following year for the birth of our first child, Veronica, and after another year in the Sudan we came back to England for good. Nigel took up teaching and, after a few years, and the birth of our son, Robin, he was offered a job at Summerfields Preparatory School in Hastings and we came to live in Battle. In October 1960, our third and last child was born. We called her Juliet, but her brother and sister nicknamed her 'Pommy'. Because my father had been given the Order of the Bath (GCB) after his retirement from the police, Juliet was able to be christened in the Henry VII Chapel—the

Nigel and I at the time of our engagement in 1944.

'Bath' Chapel—in Westminster Abbey. My father was now eighty-four and becoming more frail. Juliet's christening was the last time he left his home, and three months later, on 4 February 1961, he died peacefully in his sleep.

After my father died, my mother, who was seventy-nine, came to live next door to Nigel and me. She built a small house onto ours and lived there for eleven years until she died in April 1972. She was a very knowledgeable and keen gardener and made a very pretty garden round her new house. When she could no longer garden herself, she would sit outside and direct her gardener. It was only because of her arthritis that she gave up driving her car at the age of eighty-five. Baby Juliet was her constant care and delight and greatly helped her to accept her widowhood. She lived to see Veronica marry the Reverend Adam Smith and was able to share in the joy of their first child, Lucy. She saw Robin growing up, and Bill and Vera and their children visited her frequently, all of which gave her enormous pleasure. Sadly we laid her to rest just after her ninetieth birthday.

After our wedding at St Andrew's Church, Ham Common.

What of the others who had been at Government House in the 1930s—Lina Arnold, Charles Gifford, Isabel Crowdy, the Budges?

I have known Lina longer than anyone else in the world, and she has always been a wonderful friend to me. We have met many times over the years, and always at some point the conversation goes back to the 1930s and the fun and happiness we had together. Lina left Government House before I did; I was growing up and could look after myself. Some years after she left she married a fellow Swiss, Arthur Holderegger, and in 1948 they opened the Chalet restaurant near Circular Quay in Sydney. Unfortunately the marriage did not last, and Lina took on the business by herself in 1953. The Chalet became famous for its excellent food and service, and many people were dismayed and sad when Lina retired in 1979.

Charles Gifford stayed in Sydney when my parents left and became the organising secretary of the Royal Prince Alfred Hospital until 1936, when he returned to England. He became Lord Gifford (the fifth Baron Gifford) in January 1937, having inherited the title from an uncle. In March 1939 he married Margaret Allen, from Sydney, and a son was born to them in 1940. We all met quite often after the war, and he remained the good kind friend that he had been to me when I was a little girl. In 1956 he became chairman and managing director of Theatre Tickets and Messengers Ltd, where no doubt his organising ability and remarkable memory served him well. He died on 16 April 1961.

Isabel Crowdy left Government House and returned to England when my parents went back for their holiday. Her place was taken by Dorothy D'Arcy Irvine, daughter of the Bishop Coadjutor of Sydney. We all used to visit Isabel in London, where she lived with her sisters. She became ill not very long after getting back to England and died just before the war.

Harry Budge retired about the time my father's term of office ended. He had been Official Secretary to the Governor of New South Wales since 1902 and was knighted for his services. Rosemary grew up and married a grazier, Ivan Hain, of Moles station, near Cooma. I shall have more to say about her later.

And then, of course, there was the man who made my father's gov-

Charles Gifford, then managing director of Theatre Tickets and Messengers, introduces Father to one of his company's staff.

ernorship a particularly remarkable one for New South Wales—Jack Lang. I do not know whether my father ever met him again after the dismissal. Lang was never again in power. He published three volumes of reminiscences, including *The Turbulent Years*, which covers the period of my father's governorship, and edited and published his weekly eight-page newspaper, the *Century*, until a few days before he died on 27 September 1975, aged ninety-eight.

He was given an impressive state funeral. After mass, celebrated by the Roman Catholic Archbishop in St Mary's Cathedral, his body was taken along Macquarie Street past Parliament House before being taken to Rookwood Cemetery. The cortege was preceded by the New South Wales Military Band, and the hearse was followed by family mourners, including a car full of solemn-eyed children. Then came the Governor, Sir Roden Cutler, in his grey Rolls-Royce, the Governor-General's representative, a naval dignitary, and lastly the Prime Minister, Gough Whitlam, in his Mercedes. A silent crowd of two thousand people lined the streets to watch. Quite clearly his 'people' had not forgotten Jack Lang.

Few politicians have had such a tempestuous career as Lang. He was hated by some, revered by others. He worked to eliminate poverty, and he lived to see some of the reforms he had pioneered, such as widows' pensions and child endowment, become a normal part of social security. But like many men who are ruled by an overwhelming passion, he was ruthless and determined and seemed only able to see one way, Jack Lang's way.

In November 1975, two months after Lang's death, Gough Whitlam, the Prime Minister, was dismissed from office by the Governor-General, Sir John Kerr. Immediately, parallels were drawn between the two dismissals. 'Sir John Kerr's sacking of Gough Whitlam is not without precedent in Australia,' reported the *Daily Telegraph* on 12 November. 'In 1932 Jack Lang, the Labor Premier of New South Wales, was fired by Sir Philip Game, the Governor.' All the old arguments and controversy over the political rights and wrongs of vice-regal reserve powers were once again news headlines.

In 1973 Nigel retired from teaching. Our two elder children were grown up; only Pommy was with us at home. She was twelve years old and about to change schools. It seemed an ideal time for us to make a trip to Sydney, something we had planned to do for years. Pommy was almost the same age as I had been when I first went to Australia, and I was sure that the experience would be something she would never forget. On 3 September 1973 we

My parents in their later years at Blakenhall, near Sevenoaks in Kent, where they lived in their retirement.

all three set off on our long journey.

Never had my spine tingled with so many vibrations as it did when we flew over Sydney Harbour. There, slipping silently by, were the famous landmarks that I had known in my youth: the Harbour Bridge, Government House, the Botanic Gardens, Farm Cove and, beside them, the new gleaming white Opera House. Soon after, the plane made a steep turn, low over Botany Bay, and we were in, settling gently down on the runway. As I stepped down onto the tarmac and sniffed the warm Australian air, I knew that I had come home.

Sydney had changed greatly since the 1930s. One of the first changes I noticed was the opening up of Martin Place into Macquarie Street—an inspired improvement, I thought. I was amazed at the increase in the traffic. Even the Harbour Bridge with its eight lanes—considered so capacious when it was opened—was now too narrow to take the vast volume of cars that crossed the harbour at peak hours. However, I missed the great liners that used to come into the harbour. No longer did the three- and four-funnel ships steam through the Heads; but the ferries still plied their way back and forth over the sunlit water, and now a hydrofoil sped on its way to Manly and back. So there was always a great sense of life and movement. There were many other changes, and in growing and ageing, the city had become even more beautiful.

But I received a poignant reminder of the old days when I was waiting on the ferry wharf at Neutral Bay one glorious sunny afternoon. A man standing on the wharf spoke to me.

'I'm Alf,' he said.

'I'm Rosemary.'

He pointed to a ficus tree. 'Would you believe me if I told you that I slept under that tree for four months?'

Government House was clearly visible across the water. I thought: Would you believe me if I were to tell you that I slept in that house for four years? The Domain was also clearly visible, and I remembered the unemployed people sleeping there, under the trees and in caves, forty years before.

'What did you do when it rained?' I asked him.

'I had a bit of plastic and rolled myself in that.'

I thought: *Plus ça change* . . .

The ferry came and I said goodbye to Alf. Soon I was crossing the harbour to resume a love affair with Sydney that began when I was eleven years old.

The visit was one of reunions and reacquaintance with things of the past. The first reunion was with Lina at her restaurant. Lina had been to see us in England and we had always kept in touch, but this was an evening of reminiscing and talk of the old days. Then there was a trip to Cooma to visit the Hains. I cannot pretend that Rosemary and I recognised each other as we threw our arms around one another in the Cooma car park. But the clock was soon turned back, and in a very short time we had bridged the gap of those intervening years.

An important event was a visit to Government House. Dorothy D'Arcy Irvine had arranged for us to have tea with Sir Roden and Lady Cutler. It felt odd ringing the bell at one's own front door, and odder still to be ushered in by a footman and then a young aide-de-camp and shown where to go, when it was all so familiar. We had tea in the drawing-room. It was very much the same but had been newly furnished. I had forgotten how beautiful some of the pictures were, particularly the one of the Princess of Wales. Sir Roden told me that as a schoolboy he had found my father very frightening. I found this almost impossible to understand; my father had never seemed in the least frightening to me. I wondered how Jack Lang had felt about him. Had he quaked with fear as he entered the front door? I think not.

I had to stifle a longing to get up and run through the rooms, to visit such objects as the billiard table, under which I had spent many an enthralling evening watching dinner party guests leaving their coats, or dash down the long passage to the kitchen to find Mrs Riach, William and Charlie. Just as the frustration was becoming almost unbearable, Sir Roden said he would take us through the other rooms on the ground floor. We went first to the dining-room, where my old friends in their frames still looked down on us. There was Sir Richard Bourke over the sideboard; young Lord Beauchamp still smiled at us from his place over the door, the one with the crack through which I had often watched the guests at dinner; more piercing than a sword was the still steely eye of Governor Bligh from his place by the window. On we went to the ballroom, where Pommy was invited to sit on the gold throne used for the swearing-in ceremony of governors. I could picture the scene of over forty years ago vividly, and as we stood there I seemed to hear an echo from the past: 'I do swear that I will be faithful and true.' For a moment I had difficulty in keeping back the tears.

Sir Roden then said goodbye to us, leaving Lady Cutler to take us into the garden. It had changed a little, from what I could remember. The shrubs in the long borders had been replaced by annuals; pretty, but lacking the character of former days. The cypresses, whose original slender forms had added an Italian touch, so cleverly planned by Professor Waterhouse, had become large, rotund cylinders. Middle age had caused them to lose their youthful figures. But other trees were still the same, and the bulbuls and Willy wagtails still hopped happily over the lawns.

'The wisteria hedge is still there, planted by your mother,' Lady Cutler said. She took us to see it, and I was able to show her one or two other plants that I remembered and recognised as my mother's. As she led us back over the lawn, we looked up at the house. Each window told a story and brought back a flood of memories. I asked which rooms the Queen was to have when she arrived soon to open the Opera House. Lady Culter pointed to her own bedroom and the one that had been mine. 'We are moving out of those two for her,' she told me.

I then asked about the cruiser in Farm Cove. 'Does she ever lie out there now?'

'She hasn't been there for many years,' Lady Cutler replied.

No bells and bugles, I thought; how said.

As we reached the hall to say goodbye, Lady Cutler showed us one more thing: the portrait of my father hanging to the left of the fireplace. It is an excellent likeness, and his smiling eyes seemed to say, 'Enjoy yourselves.'

On our last day in Sydney, a Sunday, we went to St Andrew's Cathedral. Sailors stood at the door, for it was Missions to Seamen Sunday. Sitting in the fifth pew on the left of the aisle, we were only a few feet behind the pew we had used almost forty years before. There was the pulpit, straight in front of us, from which the canon had so skilfully caught the Bible. I let my eyes linger on the mellow walls, the stained-glass windows, the richly carved marble reredos, and I listened with joy to the melodic strains of the organ. It was all exactly as I had remembered it.

As I ruminated on these things, the congregation rose. A small procession was coming up the aisle: Sir Roden and Lady Cutler, followed by a pretty young secretary and an ADC. They walked with a quiet dignity and took their places in the front pew. The choir and clergy followed, impressive in their modesty. There was a pause and then it came: the clarion call of a bugle or, rather, four bugles: so beautifully co-ordinated that they appeared to be one. As the superb notes of the reveille rang through the arches, the sound reverberated back and forth from wall to wall, echoing throughout the great cathedral. I stood listening, transfixed, but my spirit had returned to my old home and I was at the window of my room. I saw once again the cruiser lying in the shelter of Farm Cove, and listened once more to those notes floating across the water.

I went through the motions of kneeling, standing and sitting automatically. I could not take part in the service. Then the deep organ notes pealed forth the final hymn, 'Praise to the Lord, the Almighty, the King of Creation'. I read the words, and as I did so one line seemed to stand out in bolder type than the rest:

Hast thou not seen how thy heart's wishes have been Granted in what He ordaineth?

Index